Foundations of

Psychological Research

Statistics, Methodology, and Measurement

Foundations of

Psychological Research

Statistics, Methodology, and Measurement

Kenneth H. Kurtz

State University of New York at Buffalo

ALLYN AND BACON, INC.   BOSTON, 1965

To Joan

with deep appreciation for her invaluable help

preface

THIS BOOK UNDERTAKES TO PRESENT AS SIMPLY AS POSSIBLE THE BASIC concepts of statistics, philosophy of science, and measurement theory as applied to research in the field of psychology. Its aim is to provide some of the technical background necessary for an understanding of contemporary psychological theory and research.

In presenting statistical materials, I have tried to convey insight into the general nature of statistical procedures and the purposes they serve, rather than to provide a complete armamentarium of statistical tools that will equip the reader for every type of research problem. It is my impression that the field of statistics has a unity and coherence that is often overlooked and that the most widely used statistical procedures are variations of a small number of basic ideas and principles; I have endeavored to bring out this unity as I see it by emphasizing formal similarities among the various procedures considered. More than usual emphasis has been placed on sources of variation in psychological research. The four general sources distinguished are errors of measurement, individual differences, inconsistency of an individual over repeated testings, and errors arising from variations in experimental conditions. In order to clarify the contribution of individual differences and individual inconsistency to variation in data, I have presented in Chapter 4 a relatively simple model illustrating the joint operation of these two major sources of error. The study that this model requires is well repaid, I think, by the light it sheds on topics considered later in the book.

A principle aim of the chapters on scientific method has been to provide an overview of the general character of scientific knowledge; that is, to convey what it means to understand and explain natural phenomena—in particular, behavior—in a scientific manner. This has, of course, entailed a discussion of the nature and function of empirical laws and theory in science. In addition, the status of private experience and of verbal reports pertaining to private experience have been considered in some detail. The analysis is from a frankly behavioristic point of view—not behaviorism in the narrow sense that denies private experience to be a legitimate concern of psychological research and eschews all concepts having a mentalistic flavor, but in the contemporary tradition that holds that the basic data with which psychologists are concerned are observations of behavior, and that the process of introspection is distinct from the process of observation, although the behavior in which it results (typically verbal) may be a fruitful subject of observation.

In brief, the approach taken to measurement is that numbers may be viewed as an abstract system of mathematical constructs having a variety of empirical interpretations, that any given measurement procedure results in a particular interpretation of the number system, and in different measurement procedures different properties of numbers may have empirical significance.   To illustrate the application of measurement procedures to behavioral problems, several approaches to sensory scaling are examined in some detail.   Here, as in the treatment of statistical concepts, the aim has not been to equip the reader to become a practicing psychometrician, but to acquaint him with the essential ideas underlying various scaling procedures.   In order to bring out the essential ideas as clearly as possible, in the case of several scaling methods the experimental and computational procedures described are somewhat simplified versions of more elaborate procedures typically used in practice.   To lay the necessary groundwork for the discussion of sensory scaling, a chapter on the measurement of stimulus thresholds and of differential sensitivity is included.

The book is written so that no specific training in the field of psychology is essential to an understanding of it.   However, to appreciate the significance of the issues and procedures that are discussed, some familiarity with the field of psychology is desirable.   I believe that a good introductory course in psychology is sufficient for this purpose.   The mathematical requisite is a working knowledge of elementary algebra.

This book is an outgrowth of a recent approach at the State University of New York at Buffalo to the handling of material previously presented in two separate courses, Psychological Statistics and Experimental Psychology. The methodological material previously covered in the experimental psychology course has been combined with elementary statistics in a new, two-semester course, for which this book was written as a text; coverage of the substantive material (learning, sensory processes, perception, and so on) previously presented in the experimental psychology course is now provided by a number of separate, content-oriented courses in the curriculum.   First-hand experience with the collection and analysis of behavioral data is provided by a series of demonstration experiments (not included in this text) performed in weekly laboratory sessions conducted in conjunction with the course in statistics and methodology.   The experiments conducted in the laboratory sessions are of two kinds: sampling experiments designed to illustrate a number of statistical principles through the empirical approximation of various theoretical distributions, and experiments—some of them adaptations of investigations reported in the literature—that are designed to answer psychological questions of a substantive nature. The latter experiments have been selected to serve a dual purpose—to familiarize students with a number of specific techniques used in behavioral research and to illustrate the application of various statistical procedures using actual data obtained by the students themselves.

Although this book covers a broader range of topics than statistics, the statistical portions of the material are arranged in a self-contained section (Part II). It is hoped that this arrangement will make the use of the book convenient for readers primarily interested in statistics.

KENNETH H. KURTZ

acknowledgments

I AM INDEBTED TO THE MANY AUTHORS AND PUBLISHERS WHO HAVE GEN-
erously given their permission to reproduce or adapt published tables and
figures and to my colleagues who furnished unpublished data for illustrative
purposes. Specifically, I wish to thank the following publishers for permission to use published material: the *American Journal of Psychology*; the
American Psychological Association, for material published in *Psychological Review*; the *Annals of Mathematical Statistics*; *Biometrics*; Clark
University Press; the Free Press of Glencoe; the Journal Press, for material
published in the *Journal of General Psychology*; the McGraw-Hill Book
Company; the RAND Corporation; the University of California Press, for
material published in *University of California Publications in Psychology*.
I am indebted to Sir Ronald A. Fisher, F.R.S., Cambridge, and to Dr. Frank
Yates, F.R.S., Rothamsted, also to Messrs. Oliver & Boyd Ltd., Edinburgh,
for permission to reprint Tables III and IV from their book *Statistical Tables
for Biological, Agricultural and Medical Research*.

I am also indebted to many of my friends and professional colleagues
for suggestions, encouragement, and moral support in the course of this
work—in particular to four: to Olive P. Lester, my department chairman,
for arranging an adjustment of my teaching load during critical phases of
the work; to B. Richard Bugelski, for helpful suggestions during the early
planning phases and for continuing encouragement and support throughout
the course of the work; to Walter Cohen, for a number of constructive
criticisms of an early draft of the book; and to Raymond G. Hunt, whose
friendly counsel I frequently sought in trying out many of my evolving ideas.
I also wish to thank Arthur M. Bodin, who made a number of useful suggestions concerning the presentation of material in the chapter on regression
and correlation.

I owe an immeasurable debt to my wife, Joan, who—while raising one
child and pregnant with a second—somehow found time to type major portions of what was, typographically, a truly formidable manuscript. Possibly
of even greater importance, she also read most of the manuscript and

brought to my attention a number of passages that were awkward or unclear. The revisions growing out of her suggestions have, I feel, substantially improved the final result.

I am also very grateful to Mrs. Eleanor Greener, Mrs. Roberta Higbee, and Mrs. Viola Hunt for typing sizable portions of the manuscript. I feel extremely fortunate in having had their skilled assistance.

Finally, I am greatly indebted to Mrs. Alice Cheyer for her meticulous care and seemingly infinite patience in copy-editing the manuscript. Her assiduous attention to innumerable questions of typography, style, and clarity of expression has been extremely helpful and is sincerely appreciated.

K. H. K.

contents

PART I

elements of

experimental design

This book is concerned with methods used in the scientific study of behavior. It describes how the results of empirical investigations are analyzed and how such findings are integrated to form a coherent, organized understanding of behavioral phenomena. As background for this undertaking, Part I examines the structure of simple experiments in the field of psychology and briefly discusses certain logical considerations involved in the formation of general conclusions based upon experimental findings.

the structure and interpretation

of an experiment

THE BASE UPON WHICH SCIENTIFIC KNOWLEDGE RESTS IS OBSERVATION. In some instances, particularly in the initial stages of inquiry, a phenomenon may be observed in a natural setting with little or no intervention on the part of the investigator. For example, an investigator might observe the migration patterns of wild animals, the dating patterns of college students, or the social interactions occurring in small groups without manipulating the conditions under which the behavior occurs except to make the necessary arrangements for collecting the data. However, in most areas of investigation questions eventually arise that can best be answered by obtaining data under conditions created by the investigator specifically for that purpose. The latter type of investigation is called an *experiment*.

In terms of structure, the simplest type of experiment is one in which all the observations are made under the same set of conditions. An illustration of this type of experiment is one by Kendrick (1958) designed to test an implication of a theory proposed by Hull (1943, 1952). It is common knowledge that a hungry animal may be trained to perform a response or sequence of responses, such as running down a straight alley, if that response is regularly rewarded by the presentation of food; similarly, a thirsty animal will learn to perform a response that is regularly rewarded by the presentation of water. According to Hull's theory, however, if the response requires sufficient effort, the animal will eventually cease performing it, even though that response is consistently rewarded whenever it occurs.   To test this prediction Kendrick trained thirsty rats in a 10-ft. runway (longer than is customarily employed), giving them 30 trials per day in close succession in order to make the task as effortful as possible.   Under these conditions all the animals eventually ceased running, despite the fact that they consistently received water at the end of the runway if they reached the goal.   Our present interest in this experiment, however, concerns its structure rather than its results.   It is an example of an experiment in which there is only one group, i.e., where all the subjects are tested under the same conditions and the aim of the investigator is simply to determine the characteristics of behavior under those conditions.[1]

RELATIONSHIPS BETWEEN VARIABLES: THE INDEPENDENT
AND THE DEPENDENT VARIABLE

Any attribute or characteristic that varies or is capable of variation (e.g., intensity of stimulation, color of hair, physical strength) is called a *variable.*   Two types of variable, *quantitative* and *qualitative,* may be distinguished.   Quantitative variables are those recorded in numerical form (e.g., the number of errors made in performing a task or the time taken to complete a task); qualitative variables are those recorded in other than numerical form.   Usually the "values" of a qualitative variable are described by a verbal label—for example, an individual's sex may be described as *male* or *female;* a taste quality, as *sweet, sour, salty,* or *bitter;* performance on an examination, as *satisfactory* or *unsatisfactory.*

In contrast to experiments having the simple structure illustrated by Kendrick's study, i.e., those concerned with performance under a single set of conditions, a more complex class of experiments is concerned with the manner in which one variable (e.g., some aspect of behavior) changes with variations in a second variable (e.g., some aspect of the environment).   In its simplest form, such an investigation involves the comparison of data obtained under two different sets of conditions.   An example is a study by Zeaman (1949) in one portion of which two groups of rats were trained to run down a straight runway for food.   The conditions of training were the same for the two groups except in the amount of food received at the goal: one group received a very small amount of food (.05 gm.) on each trial, while the other group received a much

---

[1] In point of fact, Kendrick's study was somewhat more complicated than indicated in the above summary.   Two groups of rats were employed, one descendent from a pair of "emotional" rats and the other descendent from a pair of "nonemotional" rats.   However, as Kendrick points out, the use of two groups was not germane to his central question.

larger amount (2.4 gm.). The aspect of performance that was of interest was the speed with which the animals of the two groups reached the goal. (In agreement with our intuitive expectation, it was found that, on the average, rats receiving the larger amount of food ran faster than those receiving the smaller amount.) In analyzing an experiment of this kind, we distinguish two variables of major interest—an *independent variable* and a *dependent variable*. The independent variable is the characteristic in which the two groups are made to differ (in the Zeaman study, the amount of food given); the dependent variable is the characteristic observed but not directly manipulated by the experimenter (in the Zeaman study, running speed). The dependent variable is so named because its value depends upon, and varies with, the value of the independent variable.

In further discussions it will be convenient to use a general term to designate the conditions of an experiment between which comparisons are made. While the expression *experimental conditions* is frequently used for this purpose, it is occasionally ambiguous because in some contexts it is used to designate conditions of an experiment that are common to all groups, rather than those that differentiate the groups being compared. Accordingly, the expression *experimental treatments* or, more simply, *treatments* will be used to designate the conditions that are compared, i.e., those specific to different groups. For example, in the Zeaman study cited above there were two experimental treatments—small reward and large reward. In some contexts, instead of referring to the various experimental treatments, it is convenient to refer to the *groups* receiving the various treatments, and this practice will occasionally be followed.

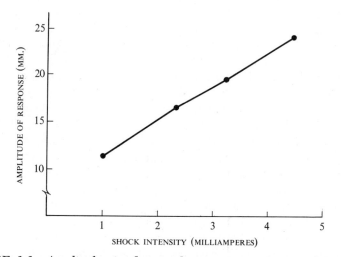

FIGURE 1-1 *Amplitude of reflex circulatory response (measured by change in finger volume) as a function of shock intensity. Adapted from Hovland and Riesen (1940).*

In more elaborate experiments several treatments may be employed, each having a different value of the independent variable. One such study, by Hovland and Riesen (1940), investigated the magnitude of reflex circulatory changes (constriction of peripheral blood vessels, measured by changes in finger volume) produced by electric shocks of varying intensities. Because both the independent variable and the dependent variable of this study are quantitative, it is possible to represent the results in graphic form as shown in Figure 1-1. When manipulation of one variable results in systematic variation of another variable, as illustrated in this figure, the dependent variable is said to vary as a *function* of the independent variable; the relationship between them is called a *functional relationship*.

THE FIXED CONDITIONS OF AN EXPERIMENT

In every experiment the investigator holds certain conditions or variables constant for all the treatments under investigation. Such features of an experimental situation may be termed *fixed conditions*. For example, in the runway study by Zeaman the number of hours of food deprivation at the time of testing was held constant for all animals. Similarly, the number of trials per day and the time intervening between trials was the same for all animals. Such fixed conditions form a constant background against which the variation of the independent variable is studied.

It is important to recognize that the fixed conditions of an investigation may have a significant bearing upon the outcome—the dependent variable may vary as a function of the independent variable in one way under one set of fixed conditions and in a different way under another set of conditions. This is clearly illustrated in a pair of experiments reported by Pechstein (1917). In both experiments the subject's task was to move a stylus through a maze that was shielded from direct vision by a screen. The purpose of the first experiment was to compare the efficacy of two methods of practice—the so-called *whole method* and the so-called *part method*. In employing the whole method, the entire maze was traced from beginning to end on each learning trial; in using the part method, the maze was divided into four sections that were learned separately before the subject attempted the maze as a whole. The dependent variable with which we shall concern ourselves in the present account is the total time devoted to practice before the subject could traverse the entire maze without error. Judged by this measure, the superiority of the whole method of practice was fairly clear-cut—on the average, the time required by subjects using the whole method was about half that required by subjects using the part method. The independent variable (practice method) and dependent variable (total time) of the second experiment were the same as those of the first. In fact, the details of the two experiments were identical except for a difference in one of the fixed conditions. In the first experiment practice was widely distributed (only one trial a day was given during the first four days and two trials a day thereafter); on the other hand, in the second experiment practice was highly massed (each trial followed the preceding one immediately, and learning was completed in one session). Apparently as a result of this change in the spacing of trials, the relationship between the dependent and independent variables in the second experiment was exactly opposite that obtained in the first, i.e., in the second experiment the total time required to master the maze using the whole method was approximately twice as great on the average as the time required using the part method. These results afford striking evidence that the relationship observed between a given dependent variable and a given independent variable may hold only for the particular fixed conditions employed; when these conditions are altered, the results may be quite different.

In many psychological studies the type of subject employed may be regarded as a fixed condition of the experiment. Although a finding obtained with one type of subject, e.g., rats, may hold true for organisms of many kinds, it is not uncommon for the outcome of an experiment to vary depending upon the type of subject employed. Indeed, as is illustrated by the findings of a study by Myers (1959), even different strains of the same species may yield different results. (In this study rats were trained to prevent the occurrence of shock by pressing a bar or turning a wheel in response to a neutral warning stimulus that regularly preceded shock. It was found for rats of the Wistar strain that more rapid learning occurred when the warning stimulus was a somewhat raucous buzzer than when it was a pure tone, while with rats of the Sprague-Dawley strain it made little difference which type of warning stimulus was employed.) Similarly, in finding that one of two learning methods is superior using, say, college students as subjects, we would not be justified in concluding that the same method would be superior for all human beings. It would not be surprising, for example, if the method found to be superior for college students proved to be the poorer method for elementary school children.

In view of the effect that the fixed conditions of an experiment may have upon the outcome, care must be taken not to generalize too broadly the findings of any experiment. That is to say, we cannot safely assume that a relationship found between an independent and a dependent variable under one set of conditions or with one type of subject will necessarily be the same under all possible conditions or with all kinds of subjects. Before we can have confidence in the generality of a finding, it must be demonstrated that the finding holds under a variety of conditions and is not merely an artifact of a fortuitous combination of conditions that prevailed in one particular experiment.

RANDOM SOURCES OF ERROR

In every psychological experiment the dependent variable—usually some measure of behavior—is subject to the influence of certain factors that cannot be held entirely constant from subject to subject or observation to observation. Such influences, when they vary in a chance fashion and do not systematically favor any of the treatments being compared, are called *random sources of error.*

A discussion of random sources of error will be made clearer by reference to the results of an illustrative experiment. In this experiment ten subjects were divided into two equal groups. (A lottery was used to divide the subjects into groups so that the assignment of a given subject to a given group was determined purely by chance.) The experimental task consisted of sorting the cards of an ordinary playing deck (aces and face cards excluded) into four piles on the basis of suit, the time to complete the task being recorded for each subject. Whereas in most experiments employing two groups of subjects the groups are subjected to different experimental treatments in order to determine whether behavior is different under those treatments, in the present experiment both groups received the same treatment. Such an experiment is termed a *dummy experiment* and serves to demonstrate the effects of random sources of error. The card-sorting times of the two groups of subjects are presented in Table 1-1. At the bottom of each column the mean for that group is recorded. (This value, sometimes referred to as the *average,* is computed by summing the numbers in each column and dividing by five, the number of cases summed.)

TABLE 1-1 *Card-sorting times of two groups of subjects tested under the same experimental treatment. (Times are recorded to the nearest whole second.)*

	GROUP I	GROUP II
	45	39
	47	43
	34	35
	44	48
	40	35
	—	—
MEAN	42	40

The effects of random sources of error are evident in the above data in two ways.   First, random errors underlie the variation among subjects in the same group.   For example, the fact that the scores of the five subjects in Group I are all different is a consequence of random sources of error.   Second, because the two groups in the above experiment received identical treatments, the difference between the means of the two groups may be attributed entirely to random sources of error.

A portion of the uncontrolled variation of the dependent variable arises from errors inherent in the measurement process itself, so-called *errors of measurement*.   In timing a subject's performance by means of a stopwatch, for example, the experimenter may not be perfectly consistent in starting and stopping the watch at the beginning and end of the task, with the result that slightly different times may be recorded on two trials even though the actual times are the same.

A second source of uncontrolled variation may be thought of as arising from the inconsistency of individual subjects in repeated performances of the same task under a given set of conditions.   For example, even a well-trained subject exhibits some variation in sorting time from trial to trial in repetitions of the card-sorting task described above.   Thus, even if all the subjects in the experiment summarized in Table 1-1 were of equal ability, i.e., exhibited the same average sorting time over a long series of trials, there would still be variation among their scores in a given experiment because of individual inconsistency.   That is to say, on the trial recorded in the experiment some subjects would score higher than usual and some lower than usual, with the result that the time scores would not all be equal. The causes of individual inconsistency are manifold.   Over a short time span individual variation is caused by lapses of attention, slips of the hand, and other factors that vary depending upon the type of task in question.   Over a longer time span an individual's performance will vary with changes in his state of rest or fatigue, his emotional mood, his health, his preoccupation with personal problems, and similar factors.

Individual differences, i.e., relatively stable differences among individuals in proficiency at a given task, are another important source of variation in psychological research.   In virtually any task in which performance can be evaluated, some subjects will consistently perform better than others.   Such differences arise from several causes, including innate differences in aptitude and differences in the past experiences of individuals.   Because in many experiments the proficiency of subjects in the experimental task is not known beforehand, the subjects are assigned to experimental groups on the basis of a lottery or some equivalent procedure.   When such a procedure is followed it is expected that differences in ability will tend to average out, so that the average ability in the two groups will be approximately the same.   However, the two or more groups of an experiment are rarely matched perfectly, i.e., one group will usually contain more high-scoring individuals than the other. Thus, a difference between the mean scores of two groups (e.g., as obtained in the dummy experiment reported in Table 1-1) may arise in part as a result of individual differences in proficiency at the experimental task.

Other random sources of error result from uncontrolled variations in the conditions of testing. One such variation might be the occurrence of distracting noises originating outside the laboratory; another, variations in temperature or humidity. Still another source of variation in the test conditions arises in experiments employing several experimenters, some subjects being tested by one experimenter and others being tested by another. In such cases, there are frequently variations in the technique of individual experimenters that lead to slightly different results. Certain experimenter-produced variations may arise even when the same experimenter tests all subjects: an investigator's proficiency may improve as he becomes better practiced in administering the experimental procedures or, if the experiment requires the repetition of a monotonous procedure, his proficiency may suffer in later stages of an experiment as a result of boredom.

Many of the sources of error discussed above are amenable to a certain degree of control: variations in temperature, humidity, and noise can be reduced by suitably constructed laboratories; experimenter differences can be reduced by rigorous training; individual differences among subjects can be reduced by careful selection of homogeneous groups; and so on. The degree of control that can be achieved is limited, however, and in every experiment, no matter how well controlled, there occurs a certain degree of uncontrolled variation in the dependent variable.

In experiments involving the comparison of two or more treatments, the difficulty created by random sources of error is that they tend to obscure the effect, if any, of the independent variable upon the dependent variable. On the one hand, we have seen that in a dummy experiment such as described above (or, what amounts to the same thing, in an experiment in which the treatments compared have no differential effect upon the dependent variable), a difference may arise between the means of different groups purely as a consequence of random sources of error. On the other hand, when the different treatments being compared do in fact act to produce a difference in the mean values of the dependent variable, this difference may be offset (i.e., diminished or even entirely wiped out) by the operation of random sources of error. Thus, in evaluating the outcome of an experiment, we must make allowance for the possibility that an observed difference between two treatments may be solely the result of random sources of error or, conversely, that the failure to obtain an appreciable difference may be the result of such errors.

In later chapters procedures will be described for determining whether the difference observed between the means of two experimental treatments is a consequence of the differences in treatment or merely due to random sources of error. Essentially, we evaluate the extent of random sources of error by examining the variation among subjects receiving the same experimental treatment; then on the basis of this variation we determine how large a difference might reasonably be expected to occur between the means of two treatments as a result of such factors. If an observed difference between treatments is greater than might reasonably be expected on the basis of random sources of error, we conclude that manipulation of the independent variable produced it; otherwise we conclude that the difference could simply be the result of chance.

SYSTEMATIC SOURCES OF ERROR

It is essential that the two (or more) treatments of an experiment differ systematically only with respect to the independent variable; other potential influences upon the dependent variable should either be held constant (fixed conditions) or distributed in a chance fashion so that they cannot produce a difference (over and above the unavoidable differences arising from random sources of error) between the treatments being studied. There are various ways—some patently obvious, others more subtle—in which this principle can be violated, with the result that certain sources of error systematically favor one experimental treatment over another. One way in which systematic sources of error may arise is by testing all the subjects in one group at a different time or place than subjects in the other group. In animal experiments, for example, if one treatment group is run during the winter and the other during the spring, the two groups may differ in their general state of health. Similar errors may arise with human subjects when the subjects receiving one treatment are tested at a different time than subjects receiving the other treatment. For example, if all the subjects in one treatment group are tested just prior to school examinations, they are liable to be poorly rested and under an emotional strain. Another kind of error arises when all the students in one college class or section are tested under one treatment and all the students in another class are tested under another treatment. There are various ways, aside from differences in the independent variable, in which two classes may vary in composition, thus invalidating the results of such a study. For example, at one university all the members of the football team are in the same section of the introductory psychology class because all other sections conflict with football practice. If this section should receive one experimental treatment and then be compared with another section receiving a different treatment, it would be unclear whether any difference observed between the performance of the two sections was a consequence of the difference in experimental treatments or of the group composition.

The problem created by systematic sources of error is that the effects of two independent variables—one intentional and the other inadvertent—are confounded, i.e., inseparably intermixed so that it is impossible to know which of these variables is responsible for differences observed in the dependent variable. The solution to this problem is simple in principle, if not in practice: all uncontrolled factors that might effect the outcome of the dependent variable should be prevented from systematically affecting one group of an experiment and not the others, or from affecting one group one way (favorably) and other groups another way (unfavorably).

GENERALIZATION VERSUS INTERPRETATION

It is important to distinguish two types of inference, *empirical* and *theoretical,* that can be made in stating the conclusions of an experiment. Empirical statements are essentially generalized descriptions of what has actually been observed; theoretical statements, on the other hand, involve a conjecture concerning the mechanisms underlying an observed phenomenon. The distinction may be illustrated by referring to an investigation of the recognition thresholds of printed words (McGinnies, 1949). Some of the words employed in this study were emotionally neutral; others were socially taboo, i.e., words that are not ordinarily used in polite conversation. Each word was presented briefly a number of times, the duration of exposure being increased slightly on each presentation, until the subject was able to correctly identify the word. For each of the subjects participating in the study it was found that the average duration of exposure necessary for identification of the neutral words was less than that necessary for identification of the taboo words. On the basis of this finding it might be concluded that, in general, longer exposure times are necessary for identification of taboo words than for identification of neutral words. This conclusion is an empirical generalization—it simply extends the findings of this particular study to a wider range of words and people than were actually observed, i.e., it assumes that the difference observed between the two sets of words used in the experiment would also be obtained with other words of the same kinds and with other subjects than those who actually took part in the experiment. On the other hand, various conjectures may be advanced concerning the mechanisms underlying the above finding. The interpretation suggested by McGinnies is that taboo words arouse unpleasant emotions and that some sort of defensive mechanism interferes with the perception of stimuli that evoke unpleasant emotional reactions. The latter inference is seen to be more than an extension of what was actually observed—it is a theoretical inference, i.e., an interpretation.

While a detailed examination of theoretical interpretation will be deferred until a later chapter, it will be noted here that usually, if not always, a given experimental finding can be interpreted in a variety of different ways and therefore the correctness of any specific interpretation is always open to question. (For example, an alternative interpretation of McGinnies' finding is that subjects are reluctant to report socially taboo words to the experimenter and therefore wait until they are absolutely certain about the identification of a taboo word before reporting it, whereas they are more willing to take a chance and report a neutral word even when they are not certain about its identification.) Whenever a theoretical interpretation is made of an experimental finding, that interpretation is best regarded as provisional and subject to change in the light of new experimental findings.

DESIGNING AN EXPERIMENT SO AS TO RESTRICT THE POSSIBLE INTERPRETATIONS

An ideal experiment would be one in which only one interpretation of the findings is possible. Although this ideal cannot be fully attained in practice, it is often possible to approximate it by designing an experiment so as to restrict the number of interpretations that would seem plausible in the light of our general knowledge concerning the phenomenon under investigation.

For purposes of illustration, let us examine some of the problems involved in designing an experiment to test a hypothesis proposed by Miller and Dollard (1941) concerning the effects of learning upon the discriminability of stimuli. According to this hypothesis, stimuli that are initially difficult to discriminate will become more distinctive (i.e., easier to discriminate) for a given individual if he learns to respond to each stimulus with a different response. (For example, varieties of roses that are almost indistinguishable to an untrained observer may be easily discriminated by a horticulturist who has learned a different name for each variety.) To investigate this phenomenon in the laboratory we might employ the experimental plan represented schematically in Table 1-2.

TABLE 1-2 *Experimental Plan I: the effects of prior learning on the distinctiveness of stimuli*

	TASK *1*	TASK *2*
EXPERIMENTAL GROUP	Learn verbal responses to Stimuli *A, B, C,* ···	Learn motor responses to Stimuli *A, B, C,* ···
CONTROL GROUP	(Omit Task *1*)	Learn motor responses to Stimuli *A, B, C,* ···

In this plan one group of subjects (the *experimental group*) learns two tasks in succession. In the first task the subjects learn a different verbal response to each of a series of similar stimuli. In the second task, using the same set of stimuli, a different motor response is associated with each stimulus (e.g., a vertical lever is tilted away from the subject in response to one stimulus, toward the subject in response to another stimulus, to the left in response to a third stimulus, and so on). A second group of subjects (the *control group*) learns the second task without the benefit of prior experience in the first task. According to Miller and Dollard's hypothesis, the stimuli of Task *2* should, as a result of preliminary training on Task *1*, be more discriminable for subjects of the experimental group than for subjects of the control group, and the experimental subjects should therefore master Task *2* more rapidly than control subjects. However, if we examine the situation more closely we find that there are other factors than the hypothesized increase in discriminability of stimuli that might result in superior learning by experimental subjects. For example, it is known that on tasks of this type, subjects who are given a series of similar tasks in succession show improvement from task to task even though the various tasks have no stimuli or responses in common—a phenomenon that is presumably due in part to the development of more efficient learning techniques. Thus, as a test of Miller and Dollard's hypothesis concerning the increased discriminability of stimuli, the experimental plan described above would be inconclusive, for the pattern of results that their hypothesis predicts could readily be interpreted in other ways.

The difficulty with the experimental plan described above is that practice on Task *1* not only provides the type of experience that, according to Miller and Dollard's hypothesis, results in increased discriminability of stimuli, but also provides, among other things, the opportunity for the development of more efficient learning techniques. One way of improving the experiment would be to give the control group preliminary training on a task that would afford it the same opportunity as the experimental group for developing more efficient learning techniques but would not increase the discriminability of the stimuli encountered in Task *2*. Such an experimental plan, represented schematically in Table 1-3, was employed by Cantor (1955).

TABLE 1-3 *Experimental Plan II: the effects of prior learning on the distinctiveness of stimuli*

	Task *1*	Task *2*
EXPERIMENTAL GROUP	Learn verbal responses to Stimuli *A, B, C,* ⋯	Learn motor responses to Stimuli *A, B, C,* ⋯
CONTROL GROUP	Learn verbal responses to Stimuli *X, Y, Z,* ⋯	Learn motor responses to Stimuli *A, B, C,* ⋯

In Cantor's study the stimuli used in Task 2 (Stimuli *A, B, C,* · · ·) were a series of lights differing slightly in color (reds, oranges, and yellows). The same stimuli were used in the preliminary task (Task *1*) learned by the experimental group; a different series of colors (blues and greens) was used for the preliminary task learned by the control group. Thus, both groups had the same general type of learning experience prior to learning Task 2. The only difference was that in the experimental group the two tasks employed the same stimuli, thus affording experimental subjects the presumed benefits of increased distinctiveness of stimuli in learning Task 2, whereas in the control group the two tasks employed different series of stimuli, thus depriving control subjects of such benefits. Because the two groups presumably had equal opportunities to develop more efficient learning techniques, any difference observed between the performance of the two groups on Task 2 could not be readily interpreted to be a consequence of differential learning techniques.

Unfortunately, no matter how carefully an experiment is designed, the findings can always be interpreted in more than one way; there is no such thing as a "perfect experiment" in the sense that only one interpretation is possible. For example, although the outcome of Cantor's study was in agreement with Miller and Dollard's hypothesis (the experimental subjects learned Task 2 more rapidly than the control subjects), it is possible that the experimental subjects learned more rapidly, not because of increased discriminability of the stimuli involved, but—to mention merely one possibility—because the use of familiar stimuli in Task 2 gave them greater confidence in their ability to learn that task, and the relaxed state generated by their increased confidence was more conducive to efficient learning. Admittedly, the latter interpretation is somewhat farfetched and might be dismissed by many psychologists as too unlikely to merit serious consideration. Nonetheless, it calls attention to the limited goals that may be achieved in designing an experiment: in general, we cannot rule out all possible interpretations but one; at best, we can design an experiment so that certain likely hypotheses are ruled out in interpreting the outcome and only hypotheses that seem unlikely on the basis of our general knowledge remain as alternatives to the hypothesis of major interest.

EX POST FACTO INVESTIGATIONS

Thus far we have considered investigations in which the treatment to which a given subject is assigned is under the direct control of the investigator. For example, in Cantor's study, considered above, whether a given subject was assigned to the experimental group or the control group was determined by the experimenter. In some investigations, however, the "treatments" that are compared are not under the direct control of the investigator, but occur naturally. For example, in a study comparing the life span of married and unmarried individuals, the marital status of any given individual is not under the direct control of the investigator; individuals are merely sorted into two groups on the basis of that characteristic. To distinguish investigations in which the independent variable is directly manipulated by the investigator from those in which subjects are sorted on the basis of some naturally occurring characteristic, we shall refer to investigations of the former type as *experiments,* those of the latter type as *ex post facto investigations.* The designation *ex post facto,* Latin for "from after the fact," serves to indicate that the investigation in question is conducted after variations in the independent variable have already been determined in the natural course of events.

Although, as will be explained below, one variable in an ex post facto investigation cannot with confidence be said to depend upon the other in the same sense as in an experimental study, it is nevertheless customary in an ex post facto investigation to designate one of the variables as independent and the other as dependent. The independent variable is the one on the basis of which the individuals are sorted (in the above example, marital status); the dependent variable is the one observed or measured following sorting (in the above example, life span).

When it is found in an experiment that the dependent variable varies with changes in the independent variable, we have demonstrated our ability to control or manipulate the dependent variable through manipulation of the independent variable. For example, the study by Zeaman cited earlier demonstrates that we may control the speed with which rats traverse a runway by varying the amount of food that they receive at the goal. On the other hand, when it is found in an ex post facto investigation that the dependent variable varies with naturally occurring differences in the independent variable, it does not necessarily follow that direct manipulation of the independent variable will result in similar variations in the dependent variable. Consider, for example, the finding reported by Rogerson and Rogerson (1939) that a group of children that had been breast-fed during infancy subsequently exhibited a higher level of performance in elementary school than a group of children that had been partly or wholly bottle-fed. It cannot be concluded on the basis of such a finding that performance in school may be improved by breast feeding during infancy. (Indeed, in the light of everything that is known concerning the differences between breast and bottle feeding, such a conclusion would appear to be false.) Very likely the relationship observed by Rogerson and Rogerson was an outcome of variations in one or more underlying variables that influenced both the type of feeding received by the children studied and the level of performance they subsequently achieved in school. The investigators point out that their study was conducted at a clinic where breast feeding was encouraged and that failures to breast feed were often the result of poor health of the infant, the mother, or both. Thus (to somewhat oversimplify matters in the interest of clearer exposition), a reasonable interpretation of Rogerson and Rogerson's finding would seem to be that both the type of feeding received by the infants and their subsequent performance in school were influenced by health, good health tending to result more often in successful breast feeding and in superior school performance. Despite the observed association of school performance with type of feeding, it is by no means clear—indeed, it is rather doubtful—that level of school performance was a direct consequence of type of feeding.

It must be emphasized that, while experimental studies permit a type of conclusion that ex post facto studies do not, it does not follow that conclusions based upon experiments are never in error. We have already noted ways that erroneous conclusions may be drawn on the basis of an experimental study: we can make incorrect theoretical interpretations of experimental findings, and we can generalize too broadly, i.e., assume the relationship observed between an independent and dependent variable to hold over a greater variety of conditions than is actually the case. However, when a dependent variable is found to vary with changes produced by the experimenter in an independent variable, then the ability to manipulate that dependent variable, at least under the specific fixed conditions of that experiment, has been demonstrated. On the other hand, as illustrated by the study of infant feeding considered above, the finding that variations in one variable are associated with naturally occurring variations in some other variable does not assure that manipulation of the one variable will produce variation in the other.

REFERENCES

CANTOR, JOAN H. Amount of pretraining as a factor in stimulus predifferentiation and performance set. *J. exp. Psychol.,* 1955, **50,** 180–184.

HOVLAND, C. I. and A. H. RIESEN. Magnitude of galvanic and vasomotor response as a function of stimulus intensity. *J. gen. Psychol.,* 1940, **23,** 103–121.

HULL, C. L. *Principles of behavior.* New York: Appleton-Century-Crofts, 1943.

———— *A behavior system.* New Haven: Yale Univ. Press, 1952.

KENDRICK, D. C. Inhibition with reinforcement (conditioned inhibition). *J. exp. Psychol.* 1958, **56,** 313–318.

MC GINNIES, E. Emotionality and perceptual defense. *Psychol. Rev.,* 1949, **56,** 244–251.

MILLER, N. E. and J. DOLLARD. *Social learning and imitation.* New Haven: Yale Univ. Press, 1941.

MYERS, A. K. Avoidance learning as a function of several training conditions and strain differences in rats. *J. comp. physiol. Psychol.,* 1959, **52,** 381–386.

PECHSTEIN, L. A.   Whole vs. part methods in motor learning.   A comparative study.   *Psychol. Monogr.,* 1917, **23,** No. 2.

ROGERSON, B. C. F. and C. H. ROGERSON.   Feeding in infancy and subsequent psychological difficulties.   *J. ment. Sci.,* 1939, **85,** 1163–1182.

ZEAMAN, D.   Response latency as a function of the amount of reinforcement.   *J. exp. Psychol.,* 1949, **39,** 466–483.

ADDITIONAL READINGS

ANDREAS, B. G.   *Experimental psychology.*   New York: Wiley, 1960. Chap. 2.

FISHER, R. A.   *The design of experiments* (7th ed.).   New York: Hafner, 1960. Chap. 2.

HUFF, D.   *How to lie with statistics.*   New York: W. W. Norton, 1954.   Chap. 8.   An illuminating and entertaining discussion of the interpretation of ex post facto investigations.

MC GUIGAN, F. J.   *Experimental psychology.*   Englewood Cliffs, N. J.: Prentice-Hall, 1960.   Chaps. 6 and 7.

UNDERWOOD, B. J.   *Psychological research.*   New York: Appleton-Century-Crofts, 1957.   Chaps. 4 and 5.   A detailed discussion, with many actual examples, of how systematic errors may occur in psychological research and how they may be avoided.

ZIMNY, G. H.   *Method in experimental psychology.*   New York: Ronald Press, 1961.   Chaps. 2–6.

statistical analysis

The fact that any set of observations exhibits some variation as a consequence of random sources of error gives rise to problems of two kinds. First, it is necessary to summarize in some intelligible fashion the observations obtained under any given experimental treatment. Second, in drawing general conclusions on the basis of a limited number of experimental observations, some allowance must be made for the fact that, were an experiment repeated, the pattern of results would almost certainly be somewhat different because of random sources of error.

Part II describes some of the more commonly used procedures for dealing with the problems arising from the variation of experimental observations. Chapters 2 and 3 are primarily concerned with procedures for describing aggregates of observations, and the remaining chapters of Part II deal with statistical inference, i.e., the concepts and procedures involved in forming general conclusions on the basis of a limited number of observations, making due allowance for the effects of random sources of error.

CHAPTER 2

frequency distributions

IN PSYCHOLOGICAL RESEARCH NUMERICAL OBSERVATIONS ARE TYPICALLY obtained in aggregates—for example, one measure for each of a group of subjects or several measures based upon a single subject.   Usually when data are recorded in the order of their occurrence the overall properties of the entire set of data are not immediately evident.   Under these circumstances the first task of the investigator is to organize and summarize his observations so that the properties of the set of data as a whole are more readily apparent.   In this chapter we will consider the use of tables and graphs for this purpose.

DISCRETE AND CONTINUOUS VARIABLES

Before proceeding to the task at hand, it will be useful to distinguish two kinds of quantitative variable—*discrete* and *continuous*.   Discrete variables are those that vary only in distinct steps, i.e., assume only certain isolated values.   Examples are the number of times a given response occurs in a specified interval of time, the number of errors committed in completing a task, and the number of training trials necessary to achieve a specified level of performance in a given task.   Each of these variables is discrete because only whole-number values are possible.   On the other hand, continuous variables are those that vary continuously rather than in discrete steps, i.e., variables that can have not only whole-number values, but any fractional or decimal value as well.   In contrast to discrete variables, which are usually based on some form of counting, continuous variables are based upon some form of measurement.   One kind of continuous measure commonly used in psychological research is time—for example, the time required by rats to reach the goal of a runway or, more generally, the time required by any subjects to complete a specified task. Another is response amplitude—for example, amount of saliva secreted, the distance a limb is moved in response to a painful stimulus, or the force exerted in pressing a lever.

THE FREQUENCY TABLE

For purposes of illustration, we will first consider two sets of hypothetical data. Let us assume that an investigator interested in the efficiency of two makes of calculator has observed 20 skilled operators perform a standard problem on a calculator made by one manufacturer (Calculator A) and a second group of 20 skilled operators perform the same problem on a calculator made by another manufacturer (Calculator B). The performance of each subject is assessed by recording to the nearest second the time required to complete the problem. We will assume the times on Calculator A, listed in the order of testing, were 65, 63, 62, 64, 63, 65, 63, 63, 66, 64, 67, 64, 64, 62, 63, 66, 62, 60, 63, and 64 sec., and the times on Calculator B were 70, 68, 72, 74, 71, 71, 70, 67, 70, 71, 73, 71, 70, 72, 69, 71, 72, 70, 71, and 68 sec.

Comparison of these two sets of data is greatly facilitated if they are arranged in a frequency table such as Table 2-1.

TABLE 2-1   *Frequency distributions of time scores on two calculators (hypothetical data)*

TIME (SECONDS)	CALCULATOR A Tally	Frequency	CALCULATOR B Tally	Frequency
74		0	/	1
73		0	/	1
72		0	///	3
71		0	ЖЖ /	6
70		0	ЖЖ	5
69		0	/	1
68		0	//	2
67	/	1	/	1
66	//	2		0
65	//	2		0
64	ЖЖ	5		0
63	ЖЖ /	6		0
62	///	3		0
61		0		0
60	/	1		0

The first column of the table lists the times in 1-sec. steps for the range of values obtained. The second column is a tally of the times for Calculator *A*. This tally is obtained simply by entering a mark for each observation in the appropriate space, arranging the marks in groups of five to facilitate counting. (A tally of the observations in this form is a preliminary step in the preparation of a frequency table and is not normally presented in the final table.) The third column is a listing of the frequencies with which the various values occurred using Calculator *A*. The last two columns present a tally and a listing of frequencies of the times obtained using Calculator *B*. A specification of the frequencies with which various values occur in a set of observations is called a *frequency distribution*. Table 2-1 presents two frequency distributions, one for each calculator. It is apparent that the two distributions differ somewhat, the times on Calculator *A* ranging from 60 to 67 sec. with a concentration in the vicinity of 63 and 64 sec., those on Calculator *B* ranging from 67 to 74 sec. with a concentration around 70 and 71 sec.

When values of a continuous variable are rounded to the nearest whole number, as in the case of the observations considered above, each whole number represents a *class* of values, i.e., all values falling within a certain interval on the scale of measurement. For example, following customary rounding practices, the whole number 63 is used to record all values between 62.5 and 63.5. The latter two values, which lie at the extremes of the interval in question, are referred to as *class boundaries;* more specifically, they are designated as the *lower class boundary* and the *upper class boundary,* respectively, of this class. The number of observations falling within a given class is called the *class frequency.*[1]

In some distributions the range of observations encountered is so great that it is inconvenient to employ a separate class for each whole number. In such cases broader classes, each including several whole num-

[1] When a number to be rounded is exactly halfway between two whole numbers, a question arises. How, for example, do we round a value such as 70.5—do we classify it as 70 or 71? Apparently there would be equal justification for either choice, and we solve this problem simply by adopting a convention. The convention usually followed is to round to the next higher number, e.g., 70.5 is rounded to 71. This procedure introduces a slight bias that is negligible for most practical purposes. However, when it is desired to eliminate this bias, numbers halfway between two whole numbers may be rounded to the nearest *even* number. Following the latter practice, 70.5 would be rounded downward to 70, whereas 71.5 would be rounded upward to 72. Following this convention, some numbers are rounded upward and some downward, so that the tendency to raise the average of a set of scores by rounding upward is offset by the opposite tendency to lower the average by rounding downward.

It should be noted that recording measures of a continuous variable always involves some degree of rounding, even when measures are recorded to a greater degree of precision than the nearest whole number. If, for example, measurements are recorded to the nearest tenth of a unit, all values between, say, 60.35 and 60.45 are recorded as 60.4; similarly, if measurements are recorded to the nearest hundredth of a unit, all numbers between 60.035 and 60.045 are recorded as 60.04; and so on.

bers, are used. This manner of grouping data is illustrated in Table 2-2, which presents the frequency distribution of times taken by 59 rats to traverse a 12-in. runway on their first training trial.

TABLE 2-2 *Frequency distribution of runway running times*

TIME (SECONDS)	FREQUENCY
160–169	1
150–159	0
140–149	1
130–139	1
120–129	0
110–119	0
100–109	0
90–99	0
80–89	0
70–79	1
60–69	1
50–59	1
40–49	3
30–39	2
20–29	13
10–19	23
0–9	12

Based on unpublished data provided by Kress (1963).

The original values on which this distribution is based ranged from 3 sec. to 167 sec.; thus, to have employed a separate class for each whole number would have required 165 classes. Not only is such a large number of classes unnecessarily cumbersome, but with so many classes the observations would be so sparsely and irregularly scattered that it would be difficult to gain an overall impression of the form of the distribution. Accordingly, broader intervals have been employed in classifying the data: all times ranging from 0 sec. to 9 sec. have been included in the first class, those from 10 to 19 sec. in the second class, and so on.

In certain of the procedures to be described below it is important to identify accurately the class boundaries employed when data are grouped in this manner. Determination of the class boundaries follows from a consideration of the rounding procedures employed in recording the original data. The data summarized in Table 2-2 were originally recorded to the nearest whole second. Thus, the highest recorded value included in the first class is 9 sec., the lowest recorded value in the next class is 10 sec. Inasmuch as fractional values below 9.5 sec. would have been rounded to 9 sec. and fractional values above 9.5 sec. would have been rounded to

10 sec., it is apparent that the boundary between the first and second classes is 9.5 sec.; similarly, the boundary between the second and third classes is 19.5 sec., and so on.   In general, the boundary between two adjacent classes is the point midway between the highest recorded value in one class and the lowest recorded value in the next (e.g., the boundary between the first and second classes is the point midway between 9 sec. and 10 sec.).   When the point midway between these two values is not obvious from inspection ̄ ̄ ̄ ̄ ̄ay be readily determined by taking the average of the two val ̄ ̄ ̄ ̄ ̄n.

We ha ̄ ̄ ̄ ̄ ̄ ̄ ̄ ̄ ̄ ̄ss boundaries used in classifying measures of a c ̄ ̄ ̄ ̄ ̄ ̄ ̄ ̄ ̄rmined by rounding practices.   However, ̄ ̄ ̄ ̄ ̄ values to be taken as class boundaries he values of which are inherently whole ̄ ̄ ̄ng.   A simple and useful solution to ̄ ̄ discrete variables *as if* a rounding ̄ ̄ ̄hose values.   For example, in deal- ̄ ̄ ̄ber of errors, the value 4 would ̄ ̄ ̄ ̄alues extending from 3.5 to 4.5. ̄ ̄ ̄variable, if one class included ̄ ̄ ̄ded values from 5 to 9, the ̄ ̄ ̄e taken to be 4.5.   It should here does not involve any ̄ ̄ ̄e variables (e.g., that the ̄ ̄ ̄cedure is merely a con- ̄ ̄ ̄les a number of proce- bles.

̄ ̄ ̄d in Chapter 3 it is
nece ̄ ̄ ̄ ̄ ̄ classifying observations, ̄ ̄ ̄ ̄ successive classes.
For exa ̄ ̄ ̄ ̄ ̄undary of the first
class in ̄ ̄ ̄ ̄ ̄ary of the second class)
is 9.5 sec. ̄ ̄ ̄econd class is 19.5 sec.; thus,
the class in ̄ ̄ ̄ ̄vely, the class interval can be determined by no ̄ ̄ ̄ ̄oetween the lowest recorded value in one
class and the l ̄ ̄ ̄ ̄ued value in the next higher class.   For example,
the lowest reco ̄ ̄ ̄ value in the second class is 10 sec. and that in the third class, 20 sec., indicating that the class interval is 10 sec.   Applying similar criteria to the data presented in Table 2-1, we note that a class interval of 1 was used in classifying the times on the two calculators.   More generally, in recording values of a continuous variable to the nearest whole number, we are, in effect, classifying data using a class interval of 1.

It is apparent that the size of the class interval used will determine the number of classes necessary to accommodate a given set of data, and a question arises concerning the number of classes that should be used.

Several considerations have a bearing upon this decision. One is the use that is to be made of the data. If the data are to be presented graphically, using methods described later in this chapter, sufficient classes should be employed to make the shape of the distribution as clear as possible. If the observations are scattered too thinly over a very large number of classes or are lumped together into a very small number of broad classes, the overall shape of the distribution will be obscured. On the other hand, if calculations such as those described in Chapter 3 are to be performed on the data, a decision concerning the number of classes to be used will be guided by considerations of accuracy, the accuracy of the calculations being greater the greater the number of classes employed. Still another consideration in selecting classes is the convenience of the intervals employed. For example, it is more convenient to read tables based upon a class interval of 5—i.e., in which the lowest and highest values of successive classes are 0–4, 5–9, 10–14, etc.—than tables based upon a class interval of, say, 6 or 7. While no hard and fast rules can be laid down for the number of classes to be employed in preparing a frequency table, for most purposes between 10 and 20 classes will prove adequate. In some instances, particularly when the total number of observations in a distribution is small, the optimal number of classes may be even less than ten.

Having considered the technical aspects of frequency tables in some detail, we conclude this section with some general remarks concerning such tables. When the number of observations involved is large, a frequency table makes possible the presentation of data in much less space than would be required to list each observation separately and, as we have seen above, makes it possible to perceive readily certain gross characteristics of a set of observations as a whole. For these reasons, frequency tables are widely used for the organization and presentation of data. Such tables, for example, constitute the primary method of publishing the extensive data compiled in the national census, as well as most other research data of which a detailed description is desired. Even when not used for final publication of data, the frequency table constitutes the first step in organizing data for other methods of description to be discussed in the remainder of this chapter and in Chapter 3.

GRAPHIC REPRESENTATION OF FREQUENCY DISTRIBUTIONS

For many purposes the most effective way of describing a set of observations is a graphic or pictorial representation of the frequency distribution of those observations. In this section several methods of presenting distributions graphically will be described.

THE DOT FREQUENCY DIAGRAM

One of the simplest methods of picturing a set of observations is a dot frequency diagram such as shown in Figure 2-1.

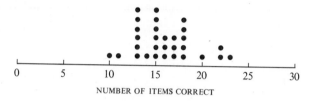

NUMBER OF ITEMS CORRECT

FIGURE 2-1 *Dot frequency diagram of scores on a multiple-choice vocabulary test.*

The data presented in this figure are the number of items answered correctly on a 30-item multiple-choice vocabulary test by each of 30 college students. Each observation (test score) is represented by a dot located at the appropriate point on the scale. Where there are several observations having the same value, the dots corresponding to those observations are arranged in a column above the scale. The dot frequency diagram is a convenient way of tallying a set of observations and examining them in a preliminary manner before performing further calculations. This technique is also useful for the formal presentation of data, especially when the number of observations involved is too small to warrant the use of a histogram, a somewhat more elaborate method of presenting data, described below.

THE HISTOGRAM

Perhaps the most widely used method of describing frequency distributions pictorially is the histogram. Histograms of the distributions of times presented in Table 2-1 are shown in Figure 2-2.

In each histogram the measurement scale is represented along the horizontal axis and the frequency with which each value occurs is represented by the height of a suitably located rectangle. The boundaries of the rectangles are located at points on the scale corresponding to the class boundaries used in classifying the data—for example, the rectangle corresponding to the whole number 63 has its lower boundary at 62.5 and its upper boundary at 63.5. Because the classes are all of the same width, the area of each rectangle, as well as its height, is proportional to the corresponding class frequency. (When the classes are not all of the same width it is customary to construct each rectangle so that its total area, rather than its height, is proportional to the corresponding class frequency.

In such cases, values on the vertical scale do not correspond directly to class frequencies; accordingly, in a histogram prepared in this manner, the values on the vertical scale are usually not stated explicitly—i.e., the units are simply not indicated.)

A histogram, like a dot frequency diagram, conveys at a glance an overall impression of a set of observations. It is immediately apparent from inspection of Figure 2-2, for example, that on the whole the times on

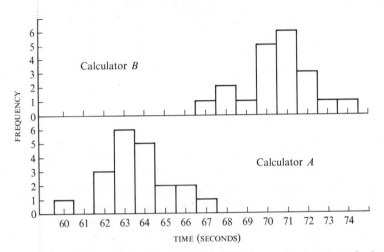

FIGURE 2-2 *Histograms of time distributions obtained with two calculators. Scale markings indicate midpoints of classes. Data are hypothetical.*

Calculator *B* are greater than those on Calculator *A*. Moreover, the points on the scale where the two distributions tend to be concentrated, as well as the range of values in each distribution, are readily seen.

Two alternative methods are commonly used for labeling the horizontal axis of a histogram. One method, illustrated in Figure 2-2, is to indicate the value of the midpoint of each class, i.e., the point midway between the upper and lower boundaries of each class. An alternative method is to list the highest and lowest recorded value in each class. This latter procedure is illustrated in Figure 2-6, which pictures the running times presented in Table 2-2.

THE CUMULATIVE POLYGON

Another method of representing a set of data graphically is the *cumulative polygon*. Using the distributions of times given in Table 2-1, the preliminary calculations required for plotting the corresponding cumulative polygons are presented in Table 2-3.

TABLE 2-3 *Cumulative distributions of time scores on two calculators* (*hypothetical data*)

TIME (SECONDS)	CALCULATOR A Frequency	Cumulative Frequency	Cumulative Proportion	CALCULATOR B Frequency	Cumulative Frequency	Cumulative Proportion
74	0	20	1.00	1	20	1.00
73	0	20	1.00	1	19	.95
72	0	20	1.00	3	18	.90
71	0	20	1.00	6	15	.75
70	0	20	1.00	5	9	.45
69	0	20	1.00	1	4	.20
68	0	20	1.00	2	3	.15
67	1	20	1.00	1	1	.05
66	2	19	.95	0	0	.00
65	2	17	.85	0	0	.00
64	5	15	.75	0	0	.00
63	6	10	.50	0	0	.00
62	3	4	.20	0	0	.00
61	0	1	.05	0	0	.00
60	1	1	.05	0	0	.00
59	0	0	.00	0	0	.00

The first column of Table 2-3 lists the classes (represented by whole numbers) in order of magnitude, and the second column shows the class frequencies for Calculator *A*. The novel feature of Table 2-3 is the listing of cumulative frequencies, presented in the third column. If we imagine progressing along the scale of measurement from the bottom of the table to the top, counting cases as we go, the cumulative frequencies indicate the number of cases included by the time we reach the upper boundary of each succeeding class. To illustrate, the cumulative frequencies in Table 2-3 are obtained as follows: We note first that there are no cases in the bottom class. In other words, if we progress along the scale of measurement as far as the upper boundary of the first class we have not yet encountered any cases. Accordingly, we record 0 as the cumulative frequency for the first class. By the time we reach the upper limit of the next class we have accumulated one case, so we record 1 as the cumulative frequency for the second class. As we progress through the next class we do not accumulate any further cases, so we simply record again the one case accumulated thus far. In the fourth class three more cases are encountered, which, added to the one case accumulated earlier, gives a cumulative frequency of 4. Adding to this total the six cases encountered in the next class gives a cumulative frequency of 10, and so on. The process is continued in this manner until all cases are included. The cumulative frequencies have been converted to cumulative proportions, entered in the fourth column, by dividing each frequency by 20, the total number of cases in the distribution.   The results of similar computations for the distribution of times on Calculator *B* are presented in the last two columns of the table.

Cumulative polygons based upon the cumulative proportions of the two distributions are presented in Figure 2-3.

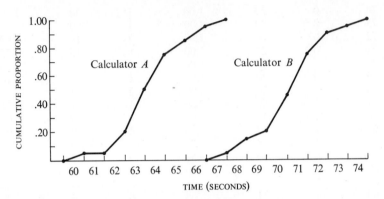

FIGURE 2-3 *Cumulative polygons of distributions of times on two calculators. Scale markings indicate class boundaries. Data are hypothetical.*

These polygons are obtained by plotting a series of points corresponding to the cumulative proportions and then connecting adjacent points with straight lines. (For greater clarity in explaining the construction of cumulative polygons the plotted points have been exaggerated in Figure 2-3. In actual practice, cumulative polygons are usually drawn in such a way that these points are not in evidence. For an example of a polygon so drawn, see Figure 2-4.) The height of each point above the baseline indicates the value of the corresponding cumulative proportion. Each point is plotted directly above the upper limit of the appropriate class, indicating that in moving up the scale, a given cumulative proportion has been attained after passing through the class in question. It will be noted that in the present context the term "polygon" refers to an open figure consisting of several line segments and not, as is usual, to a closed figure such as a pentagon or hexagon.

A comparison of the cumulative polygons plotted in Figure 2-3 with the corresponding histograms in Figure 2-2 shows that each cumulative polygon spans exactly the same portion of the scale (baseline) as does the corresponding histogram. The polygon starts to rise from the baseline at the point corresponding to the extreme left limit of the histogram and reaches the level of 1.00 at the point corresponding to the extreme right limit of the histogram, the increase in the height of the polygon in any given class being directly proportional to the height of the histogram for that class. Thus, the range of values included in a distribution and the value at which the distribution tends to be centered—in short, the location of a set of observations on the scale of measurement—is indicated by the location of the cumulative polygon representing those observations. When cumulative polygons for two distributions are presented on the same set of axes, as in Figure 2-3, the polygon for the distribution containing the higher values is to the right, i.e., higher on the scale; when the values in the two distributions are the same, the two polygons coincide.

The data used above in illustrating the construction of cumulative polygons were measures of a continuous variable. The procedures described are readily extended to data based upon discrete variables if we adopt the convention, described earlier, of treating whole-number values of a discrete variable as if rounding had been employed. Following this convention, the cumulative proportion corresponding to a given whole number is located halfway between that whole number and the next higher whole number—the same as in plotting a cumulative polygon based upon a continuous variable. While other procedures are sometimes employed in plotting cumulative polygons based upon discrete variables, the procedure described here has the advantage of simplicity and consistency with computational procedures to be described in Chapter 3.

Because the histogram is a more familiar method of presenting data than the cumulative polygon, and in view of the fact that these two types of presentation contain essentially the same information, the reader may question the value of the cumulative polygon as a means of describing a set of observations. However, the cumulative polygon has certain applications that make it a useful tool. We have already seen (Figure 2-3) that the cumulative polygon is a convenient device for representing two or more distributions on the same set of axes, thus facilitating their comparison. Although various artifices are available that permit placing two histograms side by side on the same axes, if there is any appreciable overlap between the two distributions such a presentation of the data is usually more difficult to interpret than a presentation in the form of two cumulative polygons. Moreover, as we shall see in the two sections that follow, a cumulative polygon affords a convenient means of determining the proportion of observations below a given value, or the value below which a specified proportion of a distribution lies.

PERCENTILE RANK

In order to appreciate the significance of a given measurement we must have a frame of reference against which to evaluate it. For many types of measurement a rough frame of reference is provided by our background of everyday experience. If we are told that the height of a given individual is 7 ft., we know immediately that this individual is exceptionally tall.   This conclusion is based upon our knowledge that the average height of men is something under 6 ft.   Similarly, we are impressed to learn that some individual lifted a 500-lb. weight, because most of us would have to struggle to lift a weight of 50 or 100 lbs.   Such informal standards, however, are not sufficiently precise for more exacting purposes, and there are many measures for which our everyday experience provides no standard.   If, for example, we are told that on a national examination of college achievement a certain individual answered 70 out of 100 items correctly, we have no way of knowing whether this performance is good or poor—this score may be the best ever attained, or it may be the worst.

There are several ways of providing a frame of reference for evaluating the significance of a measurement or score.   Basically, all such methods provide information concerning the standing of a given individual in relation to some reference group.   At this point we shall consider what is perhaps the simplest and most direct way of providing such information, the *percentile rank* of a score.

The percentile rank of a score relative to a given distribution is the percentage of observations lying below that score.   Percentile ranks for interval boundaries can be read directly from a table of cumulative proportions such as Table 2-3.   From the fourth column of this table we can read directly that 75 per cent of the cases in the distribution of times on

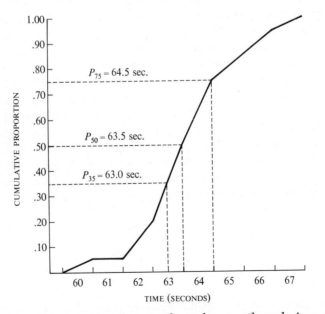

FIGURE 2-4   *Determination of percentiles and percentile ranks from a cumulative polygon. Markings on the time scale indicate class boundaries; numbers on the time scale indicate values of class midpoints. Data are hypothetical.*

Calculator *A* lie below the upper boundary of the 64-sec. class. In other words, a time of 64.5 sec. has a percentile rank of 75 in this distribution. Similarly, a time of 62.5 sec. has a percentile rank of 20.

Alternatively, these values may be determined graphically from a cumulative polygon in the manner shown in Figure 2-4. To find the percentile rank of a time score of 64.5 sec., for example, a vertical line is erected from this point on the scale. From the point where this line intersects the polygon a horizontal line is extended to the vertical axis (ordinate). The level at which this horizontal line intersects the ordinate (75 per cent) gives the percentile rank of the point on the scale from which the process was started. Because the polygon plots the data contained in the table, the two methods agree in the percentile rank assigned to any given value. The same method may also be used to determine the percentile rank of points on the scale other than interval boundaries. For example, as shown in Figure 2-4, the percentile rank of 63 sec. is 35.

It will be noted that the value 63 sec. is the midpoint of a class and the percentile rank of this value is halfway between 20 and 50, the percentile ranks of the lower and upper boundaries, respectively, of this class. In general, the percentile rank assigned to any value by this method will lie the same proportional distance between the percentile ranks of the lower and upper boundaries as the value in question lies between the boundaries: the nearer the value is to a given boundary, the nearer will be the percentile rank of that value to the percentile rank of the boundary. This method of assigning percentile ranks to values between interval boundaries is called *linear interpolation* and is based upon the assumption that the observations within a class are distributed evenly throughout that class. An algebraic method of obtaining the same results will be discussed in the next chapter in connection with the median.

PERCENTILES

It is sometimes desired to reverse the process described above, i.e., to determine the value having a specified percentile rank. It might, for example, be of interest to determine the point on the scale of measurement below which 50 per cent of the observations in the distribution lie. The procedure employed is exactly the reverse of that described above for determining the percentile rank of a value. First, the percentage in question is located on the ordinate and a horizontal line is drawn until it intersects the polygon, then from the point of intersection a vertical line is dropped to the baseline. The point at which this line meets the baseline is the value below which the desired percentage is located. The process is illustrated in Figure 2-4, where the value below which 50 per cent of the observations lie is shown to be 63.5 sec. The values corresponding to various percentages are called *percentiles:* the value below which 50 per cent of the observations lie is the 50th percentile, the value below which 75 per cent of the observations lie is the 75th percentile, etc. A convenient form of notation is to represent the various percentiles by the letter P with an appropriate subscript. For example, the 50th percentile is designated as P_{50}, the 75th percentile as P_{75}, etc. Using this notation, the statement, "The 50th percentile is 63.5 sec.," may be written symbolically as follows: $P_{50} = 63.5$ sec.

Note the distinction between *percentile* and *percentile rank*. A percentile is a numerical value on the measurement scale having a specified proportion of cases below it; percentile rank is a description of the status of a numerical value, namely, the proportion of cases lying below it.

Certain percentiles are used extensively enough to have been given special names. The *quartiles* of a distribution are the points on the scale of measurement dividing the distribution into four equal parts. The first quartile, Q_1, is the value below which one quarter of the observations in a distribution lie; the second quartile, Q_2, is the value below which half the distribution lies; and the third quartile, Q_3, is the value below which three quarters of the distribution lies. Thus, the middle 50 per cent of a distribution is seen to lie between Q_1 and Q_3. It is readily apparent that the first quartile of a distribution is also the 25th percentile, i.e., $Q_1 = P_{25}$. Similarly, $Q_2 = P_{50}$ and $Q_3 = P_{75}$.

The values dividing a distribution into ten equal parts are called *deciles.* The first decile, D_1, is the value below which 10 per cent of the observations lie; the second decile, D_2, is the value below which 20 per cent of the observations lie; and so on. Thus, $D_1 = P_{10}$, $D_2 = P_{20}$, etc.

SKEWED AND SYMMETRICAL DISTRIBUTIONS

A distribution is said to be *symmetrical* if one half is a mirror image of the other. Figure 2-5 shows an idealized symmetrical distribution having the overall contour of a bell. Although experimental data rarely, if ever, conform to this ideal perfectly, many distributions encountered in psychological research constitute a reasonable approximation to it. For example, the distribution of vocabulary scores shown in Figure 2-1 roughly resembles the ideal distribution shown in Figure 2-5, and with a larger number of cases the correspondence would undoubtedly be greater still. On the other hand, the histogram shown in Figure 2-6 is markedly asymmetrical. This histogram, based upon the data given in Table 2-2, shows the distribution of running times of 59 rats in a 12-in. runway. In this distribu-

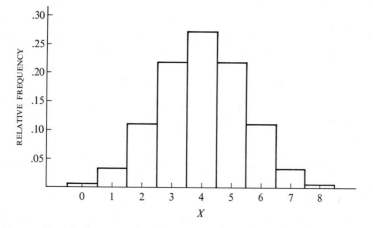

FIGURE 2-5 *Idealized distribution having symmetical, bell-like shape. The distribution shown is the theoretical distribution of the number of heads that would be obtained in a large number of trials on each of which a balanced coin is tossed eight times.*

tion the great majority of observations are concentrated in the first three classes, with a number of extreme observations to the right, i.e., at the high end of the scale; the distribution is asymmetrical because there are no correspondingly extreme observations to the left. A distribution of this type is said to be *skewed*. When the extreme observations are in the upper "tail" of the distribution, as in Figure 2-6, the distribution is *positively* skewed; when in the lower tail, the distribution is *negatively* skewed. It is probably safe to say that positively skewed distributions are encountered

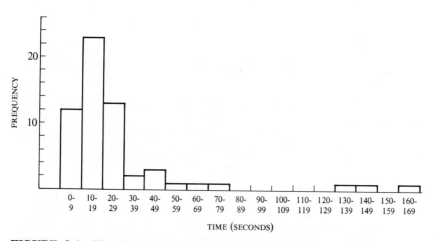

FIGURE 2-6 *Histogram of a positively skewed distribution. Data are running times of 59 rats in a 12-in. runway. Numbers on time scale indicate the lowest and highest recorded value in each class.*

much more frequently in psychological research than are negatively skewed distributions. Besides measures of response times, many of which are positively skewed, distributions of the number of trials required to master a learning task (e.g., to memorize a list of unrelated words in sequence) are often positively skewed.

Information concerning the shape of a distribution—whether it is symmetrical or skewed—is also conveyed by the cumulative polygon of that distribution. Cumulative polygons of symmetrical, bell-shaped distributions have the general appearance of those presented in Figure 2-3. It will be noted that these polygons are roughly S-shaped, the top half (the portion above the 50th percentile) having approximately the same curvature as the lower half. By way of contrast, the cumulative polygon of a positively skewed distribution (the distribution of running times described in Table 2-2 and Figure 2-6) is presented in Figure 2-7.

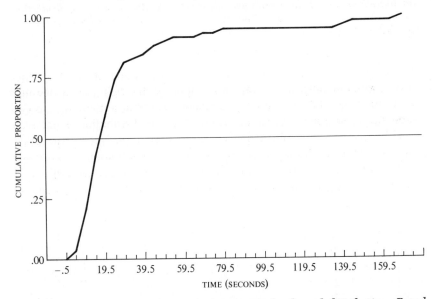

FIGURE 2-7   *Cumulative polygon of a positively skewed distribution. Based upon the same data as Figure 2-6. In order to show certain details of the cumulative polygon more clearly, the data were grouped in narrower classes (0–4 sec., 5–9 sec., and so on) than used in preparing the histogram shown in Figure 2-6. Markings on time scale indicate class boundaries.*

To facilitate comparison of the upper and lower portions of this polygon, a horizontal line has been drawn at the level of 50 per cent. It will be noted that the upper portion of this polygon is markedly elongated relative to the lower portion. In the cumulative polygon of a negatively skewed distribution, this pattern is reversed, i.e., the lower portion of the polygon is elongated relative to the upper portion.

The two general types of distributions described above—(1) symmetrical, bell-shaped distributions and (2) distributions having the form of an asymmetrical bell—include the vast majority of distributions encountered in psychological research. A description of some less common forms of distribution (*J*-shaped and *U*-shaped distributions) will be found in Freund (1960, Chap. 2).

PROBLEMS

1. Characterize each of the following measures as *discrete* or *continuous:* (*a*) number of students graduating from a given school in a given year; (*b*) number of blind alleys entered in traversing a maze; (*c*) force with which a lever is pressed; (*d*) change in blood pressure following the presentation of a painful stimulus; (*e*) number of contests (e.g., boxing matches) won; (*f*) number of pounds lost during a period without eating; (*g*) time taken to complete a puzzle; (*h*) number of items correct on a true-false quiz; (*i*) height gained by a given child during a 6-month period.

2. The times required by ten subjects to complete a standard task, recorded to the nearest tenth of a second and arranged in order of magnitude, were as follows: 7.8, 10.1, 12.2, 14.7, 16.2, 18.5, 21.4, 23.6, 29.6, 37.0 sec. (*a*) Summarize these data in a frequency table using the following classes: 5.0–9.9 sec., 10.0–14.9 sec., · · · , 35.0–39.9 sec.   (*b*) Identify the class boundaries of the above classes.   (*c*) What is the size of the class interval?

3. Assume that the data presented in Problem 2 were rounded to whole-number values.   Summarize the rounded values in a frequency table using the following classes: 5–9 sec., 10–14 sec., · · · , 35–39 sec.   How do the class frequencies compare with those obtained in Problem 2?   Explain any discrepancies observed.

4. The following distribution gives the times, recorded to the nearest second, taken by 32 rats to reach the goal of a straight runway.

Time (seconds):	5	6	7	8	9	10	11	12
Frequency:	4	8	8	4	3	2	2	1

(*a*) Plot a cumulative polygon of the above distribution and determine the 25th and 75th percentiles.   (*b*) Determine the percentile rank of a time of 7 sec. and that of a time of 9.5 sec.

5. Plot a cumulative polygon of the following distribution of test scores of 200 individuals.

X	3–5	6–8	9–11	12–14	15–17	18–20	21–23	24–26	27–29	30–32	33–35
f	20	0	20	40	40	20	10	20	10	10	10

(*a*) Determine the values of the nine deciles of this distribution.   (*b*) Determine the values of the three quartiles.   (*c*) Determine the percentile rank of a test score of 10 and that of a test score of 13.

6. Plot histograms of the distributions described in Problems 2, 3, and 4. Plot dot frequency diagrams of the distributions described in Problems 3 and 4.

REFERENCES

FREUND, J. E. *Modern elementary statistics* (2d ed.). Englewood Cliffs, N. J.: Prentice-Hall, 1960.

KRESS, G. C., JR. The effects of intense aversive stimulation upon subsequent sensitivity to aversive stimuli. Unpublished doctoral dissertation, State Univ. of New York at Buffalo, 1963.

ADDITIONAL READINGS

EDWARDS, A. L. *Statistical methods for the behavioral sciences.* New York: Rinehart, 1954. Chap. 5.

GUILFORD, J. P. *Fundamental statistics in psychology and education* (3d ed.). New York: McGraw-Hill, 1956. Chaps. 2, 3, and 6.

UNDERWOOD, B. J., C. P. DUNCAN, JANET A. TAYLOR, and J. W. COTTON. *Elementary statistics.* New York: Appleton-Century-Crofts, 1954. Chaps. 1–4.

CHAPTER 3

measures of

central tendency and variability

THE GRAPHIC AND TABULAR METHODS DESCRIBED IN CHAPTER 2 ARE especially useful when a detailed description of an entire distribution is desired. However, for many purposes it is useful to summarize a specified characteristic of a distribution in terms of a single numerical measure. The characteristics that are most often of interest are *central tendency* and *variability*. In this chapter we shall examine the most commonly used measures of these two characteristics of distributions.

MEASURES OF CENTRAL TENDENCY

Broadly speaking, the central tendency of a distribution is the point on the scale of measurement at which the observations tend to be centered or around which they are concentrated. For example, casual inspection of Figure 2-2 shows that the distribution of times on Calculator *A* is centered at about 63 or 64 sec.; times on Calculator *B*, at about 70 or 71 sec. Three measures that indicate central tendency in more specific terms are the *mean,* the *median,* and the *mode.* Although in many distributions these three measures have very nearly the same value, they are based upon somewhat different conceptions of central tendency, impart somewhat different information concerning a distribution, and, in some distributions, differ appreciably in value. Accordingly, it is necessary to be familiar with the special meaning of each of these measures and to distinguish the situations in which they are more or less interchangeable from those in which they are not.

THE MEAN

The most familiar of the three measures of central tendency is the *arithmetic mean,* commonly referred to as the *average* of a set of observations. As noted earlier, this measure is simply the sum of a set of observations divided by the number of cases summed.   Thus, the mean of the numbers 4, 6, and 11 is $(4 + 6 + 11)/3 = 21/3 = 7$.

In order to discuss observations and the computations based upon them in general terms it is convenient to employ some general symbols. In statistical work individual observations are generally represented by the letter X with a subscript identifying the particular score being referred to. Applying this system to the numbers used in the preceding paragraph, the first number, X_1, is 4; the remaining numbers, X_2 and X_3, are 6 and 11, respectively.   The operation of summing a series of numbers is represented by the expression ΣX, read "sum of the X."   The first symbol, Σ, is the Greek letter *sigma* and is used to indicate summation; the second part of the expression, X, indicates what is summed.   The meaning of ΣX is expressed succinctly in the equation

$$\Sigma X = X_1 + X_2 + \cdots + X_n$$

The two halves of this equation are interchangeable, both indicating summation of a series of numbers from first to last.   The three dots indicate that a portion of the series has been omitted for brevity.   The last number in the series is represented by X_n.

Two more general symbols will be useful in our present work: the number of observations in a distribution will be represented by the letter n; the mean of a series of observations, by the symbol $\overline{X}$, read "X-bar." Using these symbols we may write the formula for the mean as follows:

$$\overline{X} = \frac{\Sigma X}{n} \tag{3-1}$$

When data are grouped, i.e., arranged in a frequency table, the operation of multiplication may be utilized in obtaining the sum of the observations.   In the distribution of times on Calculator A presented in Table 2-1, for example, there are three observations having the value 62 sec.   The sum of these three observations is $3(62) = 186$ sec.   Similarly, the sum of the six observations of 63 sec. in the next class is $6(63) = 378$ sec. In general, the sum of the observations in any given class is the value of those observations multiplied by the class frequency.   After the sub-total for each class has been obtained in this fashion, the grand total may be obtained by adding together all subtotals. A convenient manner of organizing these computations is shown in Table 3-1.

TABLE 3-1   *Computation of mean using grouped data—Example 1. Times on Calculator A*

X	f	fX
67	1	67
66	2	132
65	2	130
64	5	320
63	6	378
62	3	186
61	0	0
60	1	60
	20	1,273

$$\overline{X} = \frac{\Sigma fX}{\Sigma f} = \frac{1,273}{20} = 63.65$$

The first column lists values of X; the next column lists the frequency with which each value of X occurs; and the third column gives the subtotal for each class, obtained by multiplying the value of X by the corresponding frequency. The grand total, of course, is obtained by adding the subtotals for all classes. We may represent the subtotal for a given class by fX, the product of the frequency and value of X for that class. The grand total for the entire distribution may be written ΣfX, the sum of the products for all classes. The total number of cases is Σf, the sum of the frequencies of all classes. The computation of the mean using grouped data may therefore be summarized as follows:

$$\overline{X} = \frac{\Sigma fX}{\Sigma f} \tag{3-2}$$

Although this formula expresses the computations somewhat differently than Formula (3-1), one should not lose sight of the fact that both formulae express essentially the same thing, namely, that the mean of a set of observations is the grand total of those observations divided by the total number of cases.

The problem considered above illustrates the computation of the mean in the special case in which each class corresponds to a whole number. More generally, the sum of the observations within a given class is approximated by the product of the class frequency and the class midpoint (the point midway between the lower and upper boundaries of the class).   The rationale for this procedure may be explained by considering a hypothetical example.   Suppose one of the classes used in grouping data included values from 5 to 9 and there were five observations in this class. Assuming these five observations to be distributed evenly throughout the class, their values would be 5, 6, 7, 8, and 9, and their sum would be 35. Alternatively, this sum may be computed by multiplying the class midpoint (7) by the number of observations (5).   Of course, in actual practice the observations within any given class are not usually distributed as evenly throughout the class as in our hypothetical example, but the product of the class frequency times the class midpoint usually provides a reasonably good approximation of the actual sum of the observations within a class.

The use of this procedure in computing the mean of grouped data is shown in Table 3-2 using the distribution of times given in Table 2-2.

TABLE 3-2   *Computation of mean using grouped data—Example 2. Runway running times*

TIME (SECONDS)	f	X	fX
160–169	1	164.5	164.5
150–159	0	154.5	0.0
140–149	1	144.5	144.5
130–139	1	134.5	134.5
120–129	0	124.5	0.0
110–119	0	114.5	0.0
100–109	0	104.5	0.0
90–99	0	94.5	0.0
80–89	0	84.5	0.0
70–79	1	74.5	74.5
60–69	1	64.5	64.5
50–59	1	54.5	54.5
40–49	3	44.5	133.5
30–39	2	34.5	69.0
20–29	13	24.5	318.5
10–19	23	14.5	333.5
0–9	12	4.5	54.0
	59		1,545.5

$$\overline{X} = \frac{\Sigma fX}{\Sigma f} = \frac{1,545.5}{59} \approx 26.2 \text{ sec.}$$

The midpoint of a given class may be found in either of two ways: (1) by adding half the class interval to the lower boundary of the class in question or (2) by computing the average of the upper and lower class boundaries. For example, by either of these methods the midpoint of the second class

(10–19 sec.) is computed to be 14.5 sec.   The midpoints of other classes are removed from this one in steps of 10 sec.—the class interval.   Thus, the midpoint of the next higher class is 24.5 sec., obtained by adding 10 sec. to 14.5 sec.   Succeeding midpoints may be obtained by as many repetitions of the above procedure as are required.[1]   The class midpoints obtained in this manner are listed in the third column of Table 3-2.   In the fourth column are listed the products obtained by multiplying each class midpoint by the corresponding class frequency.   The remaining calculations are the same as in the preceding example, presented in Table 3-1. (The symbol $\approx$ at the bottom of Table 3-2 indicates approximate equality of the quantities to the left and right.   In this case an approximation is involved because the value of the fraction 1,545.5/59 has been rounded to the nearest tenth.)

An interesting interpretation of the mean is based upon an analogy between the distribution of a set of observations and a physical model in which a rigid bar is balanced upon a fulcrum (represented in Figure 3-1).

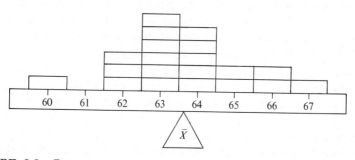

FIGURE 3-1   *Representation of the mean of a distribution as the point of physical balance.*

In this analogy, the individual observations are represented by objects of uniform mass (e.g., coins or poker chips) that can be stacked one on top of another.   If a rigid bar is marked off in equal units to represent the midpoints of successive classes of the distribution and a stack of weights equal in number to the corresponding class frequency is placed at each mark, then the supporting bar will be in balance when a fulcrum is placed at the point on the scale corresponding to the mean of the distribution.   The model pictured in Figure 3-1 is based upon the distribution of times on

---

[1] Following the above procedure, the midpoint of the lowest class is determined to be 4.5 sec., i.e., 10 sec. less than the midpoint of the next higher class. This procedure implicitly assumes that the lower boundary of the lowest class is —.5 sec.—an assumption that in this case is unrealistic. Since the true lower limit of the lowest class is zero seconds, the midpoint of this class is actually 4.75 sec., the point midway between zero and 9.5 sec. However, for most purposes the value obtained by the simpler procedure described above is sufficiently accurate, and the refinement described here is usually not worth the trouble.

Calculator *A,* presented in Table 2-1, and the bar is shown in balance with the fulcrum placed at 63.65, the mean of the distribution. It is readily apparent that if an extreme observation were added at the high end of the scale, the bar would tip and it would be necessary to shift the fulcrum to the right to restore balance, the extent of the shift being greater the more extreme the position of the added score.

THE MEDIAN

The *median* of a distribution is the point on the scale of measurement below which (and above which) 50 per cent of the cases lie. In other words, the median is the 50th percentile, P_{50}. In computing the median of ungrouped data it is convenient first to arrange the observations in order of magnitude. When a distribution includes an odd number of observations, no two of which are alike, the median is the value of the middle observation; when the distribution includes an even number of observations, no two of which are alike, the median is the average of the middle pair of values. Thus, in the distribution consisting of the observations 2, 5, and 8, the median is 5. In the distribution consisting of the observations 3, 5, 7, and 9, the median is 6, the average of 5 and 7.

When data are grouped or, what amounts to the same thing, when several observations have the same value, computation of the median is somewhat more complicated. We first determine what constitutes 50 per cent of the total number of cases, then we determine the point on the scale of measurement below which 50 per cent of the cases lie. The procedure will be illustrated with reference to the distribution of times on Calculator *A* presented in Table 2-3. Inasmuch as the total number of cases is 20, half the total number is 10. We proceed up the scale of measurement (i.e., the time scale), counting cases as we go, until we reach the point on the scale below which ten cases lie. Turning to Table 2-3, we note that there is one case in the 60-sec. class. Since there are no cases in the 61-sec. class, we proceed to the next one, where we encounter three additional cases, giving a total of four cases so far. (This total and those for succeeding classes are recorded in the cumulative frequency column.) In the 63-sec. class we encounter an additional six cases, bringing the total to ten, the required frequency. What point on the scale do we now take as the median? The last six cases, which brought the total to ten, all lie below the upper boundary of the 63-sec. class. Accordingly, this boundary, 63.5 sec., is taken as the median; exactly half the total cases lie below this point and half lie above.

Of course, things do not always work out so nicely as in the above example; the frequencies do not always oblige us by adding up to exactly the number we are seeking. The solution to this problem may be illustrated by reference to the distribution of times on Calculator *B,* also presented in Table 2-3. The cumulative frequency for the 70-sec. class is 9, one short of the ten cases required; the cumulative total for the next class is 15, five more than required. Apparently, the median for this distribution lies somewhere between the lower and upper boundaries of the 71-sec. class, but exactly where is not immediately clear. The following procedure is to some extent arbitrary, but has the merit of involving an assumption that, more often than not, is a reasonable approximation to the true state of affairs. When there is more than one observation in a class, that class is considered to be divided into as many equal parts as there are observations, and it is assumed that one observation is located in each part. In other words, the observations in a class are assumed to be spaced evenly throughout the class. Figure 3-2, in which each class is shown as an in-

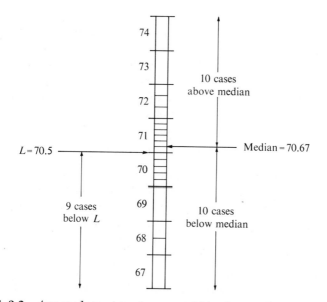

FIGURE 3-2 *Assumed spacing of scores within classes, showing rationale of linear interpolation in computing median.*

terval on the scale of measurement, represents this assumption pictorially. In the lowest interval there is but one observation, located by convention at the center of the interval. In the second interval there are two observations. Accordingly, this interval has been divided into two equal parts and one observation located in the middle of each. The remaining intervals are treated in a similar fashion. The median may now be computed as follows: The interval containing the median is determined by examining the cumulative frequencies. It has already been shown for the present data that the median is located in the 71-sec. class, since the cumulative frequency up to the lower boundary of this class is 9, one short of the required ten cases.   The median is obtained by adding to the lower boundary (70.5 sec.) as much of the interval as is needed to include the required cases.   Since one case is needed from the interval and there are six cases in the interval, one-sixth of the interval must be traversed in order to attain the required cumulative frequency of ten cases.   Thus, the median is obtained by adding one-sixth of the class interval to the lower boundary of the median class.   Since the class interval is 1 sec., the amount to be added to the lower boundary (computed to the nearest hundredth of a second) is .17 sec.   Thus, the median is approximately 70.50 + .17 = 70.67 sec.

The above calculations are summarized in the following formula:

$$P_{50} = L + \left(\frac{f_d}{f_m}\right) c \qquad (3\text{-}3)$$

Stated in words, Formula (3-3) asserts that the median, P_{50}, is equal to the lower boundary, L, of the median class plus a proportion, f_d/f_m, of the class interval, c.   The proportion f_d/f_m is the proportion of cases required from the median class, f_d being the number of cases required from the median class to obtain a cumulative frequency equal to 50 per cent of the total cases, and f_m being the number of cases in the median class.[2]   Substituting the appropriate numbers in Formula (3-3), we have:

$$P_{50} = 70.50 + (1/6)1 \approx 70.67 \text{ sec.}$$

When a distribution is represented by a histogram the median may be interpreted graphically as the point on the scale of measurement dividing the histogram into two equal halves.   That is to say, if a vertical line is erected at the point on the scale of measurement corresponding to the median, half the area of the histogram will be located to the left of the line and half to the right.

The method described above for computing the median is the algebraic equivalent of the graphical method of computing percentiles described in Chapter 2.   Within the limits of accuracy of the graphical method, the two methods give exactly the same results.   The method given for computing the median may be readily adapted to the computation of any percentile—the only difference is that the appropriate percentage is used in computing the number of cases lying below a given percentile.   In computing the 75th percentile of the distribution of times on Calculator B, for example, the number of cases needed is 75 per cent of 20, i.e., 15.   Once the number of cases is established, the remaining computations are the same as in computing the median.

It sometimes occurs that the median is located in a gap, or empty interval, as, for example, in the following distribution: 2, 3, 3, 6, 8, and 9.

---

[2] The subscript d in f_d is chosen to suggest the word "deficit," i.e., the discrepancy between the cumulative frequency at L and 50 per cent of the total cases.

In this distribution the median could be taken as any point between 3.5 and 5.5, for wherever the median is located within this range, 50 per cent of the cases lie below it and 50 per cent above it. It is conventional in such cases to take the midpoint of the gap as the median. The midpoint of the gap may be obtained by taking the average of the midpoints of the classes immediately above and below the gap. According to this convention, the median of the above distribution is $(3 + 6)/2 = 4.5$.

For rough purposes the median is sometimes taken to be the midpoint of the class containing P_{50}. According to this practice, the median of the distribution of times on Calculator *B* would be computed to be 71 sec., the midpoint of the class in which P_{50} is located. To distinguish this conception of the median from the one described above, the median computed in the rough manner will be designated the *crude median*. The crude median may be defined as the midpoint of the interval above which and below which no more than 50 per cent of the cases lie. It will be noted that in the distribution of times on Calculator *B*, nine cases (equal to 45 per cent of the total cases) lie below the median class, and five cases (equal to 25 per cent of the total cases) lie above the median class.

THE MODE

A third measure of central tendency, the *mode,* is the value occurring with the highest frequency. Thus, the mode indicates the value that is typical in the sense of being most common. The modes of the distributions of times on Calculators *A* and *B* (Table 2-1) are seen to be 63 sec. and 71 sec., respectively. When data are not recorded to the nearest whole number, i.e., where classes are formed on the basis of broader or narrower class intervals, the mode is taken to be the midpoint of the class having the

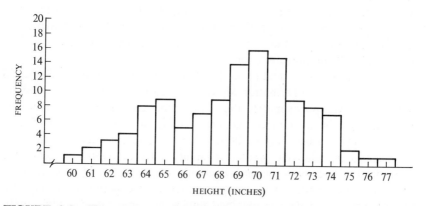

FIGURE 3-3 *Histogram of a bimodal distribution. Data are heights of 122 college students, including 39 women and 83 men. Original data have been slightly modified for clarity of illustration.*

highest frequency.   For example, the modal value in the distribution of running times presented in Table 2-2 is 14.5 sec., the midpoint of the second class.   Sometimes the highest frequency in a distribution is shared by two adjacent classes, i.e., both have the same frequency.   In such cases, the mode may be assigned the numerical value of the boundary separating the two classes.

There are some distributions having the general shape shown in Figure 3-3.   This figure shows the distribution of heights for 122 college students enrolled in a statistics course.   (For clarity of illustration, the distribution has been slightly modified to remove minor irregularities.)   It will be noted that this distribution has two distinct modes, one at 65 in. and the other at 70 in.   A distribution of this kind is said to be *bimodal*.   Very often when a distribution has this shape it is because the observations are based upon individuals of two kinds, whose distributions, if considered separately, would have different central tendencies.   In the case of the distribution shown in Figure 3-3, the group included members of both sexes.   When the distributions of the two sexes were examined separately, each of the distributions was shaped roughly like the idealized, bell-shaped distribution shown in Figure 2-5, the men's distribution having a mode at 70 in., the women's at 64 in.

RELATIVE ADVANTAGES OF THE MEAN, MEDIAN, AND MODE

We have considered three measures of central tendency, and a question naturally arises concerning which measure is most suitable for a given set of observations.   There is no simple answer to this question that is applicable to all situations; the choice of a measure of central tendency depends upon a number of considerations, including the shape of the distribution being summarized, the use that is to be made of the measure of central tendency, and the particular conception of central tendency that is most appropriate to the problem at hand.   Some of these considerations and their bearing upon the choice of a measure of central tendency will be discussed briefly in this subsection.

For measures that tend to be distributed in a symmetrical, bell-shaped form similar to the distribution shown in Figure 2-5, the mean, median, and mode have approximately the same numerical value.   However, the mean has certain advantages that make it the preferred measure of central tendency for distributions of this kind.   One consideration favoring the mean is its relatively greater reliability.   By *reliability* is meant the extent to which a given measure fluctuates over a series of repetitions of the same experiment.   If we imagine a series of experiments in each of which a new set of data is obtained under the same experimental conditions, we would expect any measure of central tendency to exhibit a certain degree of fluctuation from experiment to experiment.   When the raw data tend to be distributed in a symmetrical, bell-shaped fashion, the mean tends to fluctuate least from experiment to experiment, i.e., it is the most stable or reliable measure of central tendency available. Another advantage of the mean is that the most versatile and widely used statistical procedures for drawing general conclusions on the basis of experimental findings make use of this measure of central tendency. (Some of the procedures referred to will be described in detail in the chapters that follow.)

In skewed distributions the values of the mean, median, and mode may differ appreciably. For example, in the distribution of running times presented in Figure 2-6, the mode is 14.5 sec., the median is 17.1 sec., and the mean is 26.2 sec. In a distribution of this kind the value of the mean is greatly affected by the extreme scores, with the result that the mean is shifted, relative to the other measures of central tendency, in the direction of the longer tail of the distribution. The relative position of the mean is readily understood if it is recalled that the mean may be interpreted as the point on the scale of measurement at which a physical representation of the distribution is in balance. Because of the effect on the mean of the extreme scores in a skewed distribution, the mean is often regarded as a poor indication of what value is "typical" in a distribution having this form. For example, in the distribution of running times referred to above, roughly three-fourths of the animals had running times less than the mean and only one-fourth had running times greater. Moreover, the advantages that favor the use of the mean with symmetrical distributions do not necessarily apply when the distribution of data tends to be skewed. For one thing, with data that are distributed in this manner the mean is not necessarily more reliable than the median; for another, many of the statistical procedures that favor the use of the mean with symmetrical distributions are not strictly applicable to data having a skewed distribution. For these reasons, the median is often preferred to the mean for describing the central tendency of skewed distributions.

Another kind of situation in which the median might be preferred to the mean as a measure of central tendency is one in which the data are "contaminated" by the presence of occasional gross errors. Such gross errors might arise, for example, as a result of an undetected and intermittent malfunctioning of a measuring instrument, an undetected illness of an animal subject, or an error of recording on the part of the experimenter. Such gross errors, if few in number, will have a relatively small effect on the median of a distribution; on the other hand, their effect on the mean may be substantial. Consequently, when the presence of such errors is suspected, the median may be preferable to the mean as a measure of central tendency.

The median is also useful in describing the central tendency of distributions in which the value of some of the extreme observations is indeterminate, i.e., unknown.   Such a situation is fairly common in learning experiments in which the measure used is the number of trials required by a subject to attain some specified level of mastery.   In order not to spend an inordinate amount of time with occasional slow learners, an experimenter may set a limit on the number of trials given any subject; if the subject does not master the problem in the number of trials allowed, learning is simply discontinued at that point.   When this procedure is followed, the exact scores of such subjects are unknown—it is known only that their scores exceeded the maximum allowed.   In distributions containing indeterminate observations of this kind it is not possible to compute the mean, but—provided the indeterminate scores constitute less than 50 per cent of the distribution—the median may be computed without difficulty.

The mode, like the median, is affected relatively little by the presence of extreme scores or gross errors of measurement, and its value may be determined even when a number of extreme scores are indeterminate.   However, the mode has certain limitations that make it the least frequently used of the three measures of central tendency we have considered.   One disadvantage of the mode is that its value is affected to a considerable extent by the class boundaries used for purposes of classifying observations.   For example, if a class interval of 5 sec. were used in classifying the running times presented in Figure 2-6, the mode would be 12 sec., whereas with the data grouped as shown in Figure 2-6 we have seen that the mode is 14.5 sec.—a difference of approximately 20 per cent!   Another disadvantage of the mode is that it is highly unreliable, fluctuating considerably in repetitions of a given experiment unless very large numbers of observations are obtained.   Still another limitation of the mode is that it is not amenable to statistical calculations of the sort that are possible with the mean and, to a lesser extent, with the median.   The chief value of the mode lies in the aptness, for certain purposes, of the conception of central tendency upon which it is based.   There are certain problems in which the chief interest of the investigator may be to determine what is the most commonly occurring (modal) value.   For example, an investigator concerned with the family size (number of children) typical of various socioeconomic groups within our society might be chiefly interested in determining the family size occurring most commonly within each group.   The mode, by definition, is the measure that is appropriate under these circumstances.

MEASURES OF VARIABILITY

Thus far we have considered measures of the central tendency of a distribution, i.e., ways of indicating the point on a scale of measurement at which the observations in a distribution are centered. Another important characteristic of a distribution is the variability or dispersion of the observations comprising it, i.e., the extent to which the observations scatter above and below the center of the distribution. On the one hand, the observations in a distribution may tend to be very much alike, all of them having values close to that of the mean; on other hand, the observations in a distribution may be widely scattered, some falling far above the mean and others far below it. In this section we will consider a number of measures that are commonly used for describing the variability of a set of observations.

For purposes of illustration, we will consider the performance of one subject on a mirror-aiming task.

In this task the subject attempted to strike a target (a straight line running from left to right) with the point of a pencil held in his hand. The subject sat opposite a mirror in which he could see a reflection of the target, a direct view of the target being prevented by a suitably placed screen. Deviations from the line were measured to the nearest tenth of an inch. To eliminate negative numbers and decimal values, the following arbitrary system was used to record the subject's performance: a direct hit was scored as 50; if the subject overshot the line by one-tenth of an inch, his score was 51; if he overshot by two-tenths of an inch, his score was 52; if he undershot by one-tenth of an inch, his score was 49; and so on. The subject was given ten preliminary trials to "get the range," followed by a series of 100 test trials.

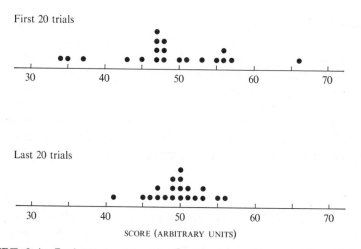

FIGURE 3-4 *Performance of one subject on first 20 test trials and last 20 test trials of mirror-aiming task*

The upper part of Figure 3-4 shows the distribution of scores on the first 20 test trials; the lower portion of the figure shows the distribution on the last 20 trials. (The distributions have been slightly modified to simplify subsequent calculations.)   It is apparent that the two distributions, though similar in central tendency, differ markedly in variability. During the first 20 trials the scores were scattered widely above and below the central value, whereas during the last 20 trials they clustered much more closely about the central value. This difference in variability is also apparent from the cumulative polygons for the two distributions (Figure 3-5).

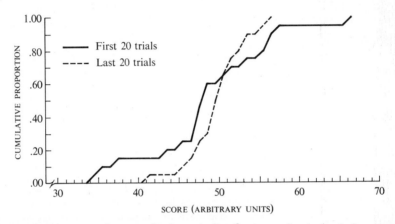

FIGURE 3-5 *Cumulative polygons of distributions of mirror-aiming scores on first 20 test trials and last 20 test trials.*

The cumulative polygon for the first 20 trials rises gradually, indicating a relatively large variability; that for the last 20 trials rises steeply, indicating a smaller variability.   (The relationship between steepness of a cumulative polygon and variability can be remembered easily if it is recalled that the cumulative polygon of a distribution spans exactly the same portion of the scale of measurement as is occupied by the corresponding histogram.)

As in describing central tendency, it is often convenient to express the variability of a distribution in the form of a single numerical value. We next consider several measures commonly used for this purpose.

THE RANGE

One measure of variability that immediately suggests itself is the *range* of values included in a distribution, i.e., the difference in value between the highest and lowest scores.   On the first 20 trials of the mirror-aiming task described above, the highest and lowest scores were 66 and 34, respectively, yielding a range of 32 units.   The corresponding values for the last 20 trials were 56 and 41, a range of 15 units—approximately half the range of values on the first 20 trials.   The conceptual simplicity of the range recommends its use for presenting data to lay audiences, which are usually unacquainted with more sophisticated measures of variability. A shortcoming of the range stems from the fact that it is based upon only two observations in a distribution—the lowest and highest—and may therefore be greatly influenced by any unusual factors affecting these particular observations. Consequently, the range is a highly unreliable measure of variability, i.e., if several sets of observations were collected under identical circumstances, we would expect the range to fluctuate considerably from one set of data to another. We shall therefore consider other methods—which depend upon a greater proportion of the observations in a distribution and which, under most conditions, are more reliable than the range—for describing variability.

THE INTERQUARTILE RANGE

A second measure of variability, the *interquartile range,* is similar to the range in its underlying logic but differs from the range in being determined by a larger proportion of the observations in a distribution. The interquartile range is the distance between the first and third quartiles of a distribution and may be represented symbolically by the difference $Q_3 - Q_1$. By virtue of its definition, the interquartile range is seen to be the interval on the scale of measurement within which the middle 50 per cent of the distribution is located. Extending to the computation of Q_1 and Q_3 the procedures and conventions used in computing the median (Q_2), the values of Q_1 and Q_3 for the first 20 test trials of the mirror-aiming task are found to be 46 and 54, respectively; the interquartile range is $54 - 46 = 8$. By similar computations the first and third quartiles for the last 20 test trials are found to be 47.5 and 51.5, yielding an interquartile range of 4. Thus, the interquartile range of the first distribution is twice that of the second, this ratio being roughly the same as that between the ranges of the two distributions.

A derivative measure sometimes used to describe the dispersion of a distribution is the *semi-interquartile range.* As its name implies, this measure is simply one-half of the interquartile range, i.e., $(Q_3 - Q_1)/2$. Inasmuch as these two measures convey exactly the same information in slightly different form, there is little to choose between them. If anything, the greater simplicity of the interquartile range would seem to recommend that measure.

THE STANDARD DEVIATION AND VARIANCE

A third widely used measure of variability is the *standard deviation* of a distribution, represented by the letter *s*. Because the computations involved in determining the standard deviation are somewhat more elaborate than those connected with the other measures of variability we have considered, and because the need for such an elaborate measure is not immediately clear, it is perhaps well to indicate that this measure has a number of important applications that will be developed in succeeding chapters. For the present, however, emphasis will be placed upon the use of this statistic as a measure of variability.

Before defining the standard deviation it is convenient to define a more basic concept, that of *deviation from the mean,* represented by the lower-case letter x. The deviation x of a given raw score X from the mean is defined as follows:

$$x = (X - \overline{X})$$

To illustrate, consider the following series of numbers: 6, 7, 8, 9, 10. It is apparent from inspection that the mean of this set of numbers is 8. The deviation of the first number, 6, from the mean is $(6 - 8) = -2$, the negative sign indicating that the number in question is below the mean. Similarly, the deviation of the last number, 10, from the mean is $(10 - 8) = 2$.

The standard deviation of a set of observations may be defined as follows:

$$s = \sqrt{\frac{\Sigma x^2}{n - 1}} \qquad (3\text{-}4)$$

Here, as earlier, the symbol n is used to represent the total number of observations in the distribution. According to Formula (3-4), the standard deviation is computed by determining the deviation of each score from the mean, squaring each deviation, summing the squares of deviations, dividing the sum by $n - 1$, and taking the square root of the result. The use of Formula (3-4) in computing the standard deviation is illustrated in Table 3-3 for the first 20 trials of the mirror-aiming task. The original scores are listed in the first column in order of magnitude, the deviations of the scores from the mean are listed in the second column, and the squares of these deviations are listed in the third column. Because of the squaring operation, all of the entries in the third column are positive in sign. The final calculations are shown at the bottom of the table. The numerator, Σx^2, is obtained by adding the squared deviations entered in the third column. (The final step in the calculation of s, taking a square root, is facilitated by using a table of square roots such as Table A-9 of Appendix A. The use of this table is explained in Appendix B.)

It is apparent that the more widely the scores in a distribution are scattered about the mean, the greater will be the deviations of the scores from the mean and the greater will be the squares of these deviations. Hence, the more widely scattered the scores of a distribution, the greater is the standard deviation of the distribution. For example, as shown in

TABLE 3-3 *Computation of standard deviation using definitional formula. First 20 trials of mirror-aiming task*

X	x	x^2
66	17.5	306.25
57	8.5	72.25
56	7.5	56.25
56	7.5	56.25
55	6.5	42.25
53	4.5	20.25
51	2.5	6.25
50	1.5	2.25
48	$-.5$	.25
48	$-.5$	.25
48	$-.5$	.25
47	-1.5	2.25
47	-1.5	2.25
47	-1.5	2.25
47	-1.5	2.25
45	-3.5	12.25
43	-5.5	30.25
37	-11.5	132.25
35	-13.5	182.25
34	-14.5	210.25
970		1,139.00

$$\overline{X} = \frac{970}{20} = 48.5$$

$$s = \sqrt{\frac{\Sigma x^2}{n-1}} = \sqrt{\frac{1,139}{19}} \approx \sqrt{59.9} \approx 7.74$$

Table 3-3, the standard deviation of the first 20 trials of the mirror-aiming task is approximately 7.74 units; that of the last 20 trials is approximately 3.46 units (computations not shown). The ratio of these two standard deviations is roughly 2:1, about the same as the ratio between the ranges of the two distributions and between the interquartile ranges.

The square of the standard deviation (i.e., s^2) occurs sufficiently often in statistical work to have been given a special name—the *variance*. The formula for the variance, obtained by squaring both sides of Formula (3-4), is as follows:

$$s^2 = \frac{\Sigma x^2}{n-1} \tag{3-5}$$

It will be noted that if the denominator of the formula for variance were n, rather than $n-1$, the variance would simply be the mean value of the squared deviations. Because of its formal similarity to a mean, the variance is sometimes called the *mean square*.

It is obvious that s and s^2 are closely related concepts, that both convey essentially the same information concerning a distribution, and that the value of one can be readily determined from the value of the other. Nonetheless, in later chapters we shall find that these two measures have somewhat different properties: for certain purposes we shall be interested in s; for other purposes, in s^2. At certain points in the present chapter we shall refer to s^2 rather than s purely as a matter of notational convenience. For example, in the bottom portion of Table 3-4 repeated use of the square-root radical has been avoided by first computing the variance and then, as a final step in the calculations, obtaining the standard deviation by taking the square root of the variance.

SELECTING A MEASURE OF VARIABILITY THAT IS CONSISTENT WITH A GIVEN MEASURE OF CENTRAL TENDENCY

We have seen that the standard deviation and variance are defined in terms of the deviations of observations from the mean of a distribution. Thus, in a certain sense both these measures of variability presuppose the use of the mean as a measure of central tendency. Accordingly, it is customary to use the standard deviation (or variance) to describe the variability of a distribution when the mean is used to describe central tendency. This practice gains further support from the fact that a number of useful statistical procedures, some of which are described in later chapters, require information concerning both the mean and the standard deviation of a set of observations.

On the other hand, it would seem inconsistent to use the median as a measure of central tendency and the standard deviation—which presupposes use of the mean—as a measure of variability. Indeed, we have seen that the median is often selected as a measure of central tendency because the mean is not deemed appropriate for that purpose with the data in question. Therefore, when the median is used as a measure of central tendency it is customary to use either the range or the interquartile range—neither of which presupposes computation of the mean—as a measure of dispersion. Similar reasoning would suggest the use of one of the latter two measures for describing variability when the mode is used as a measure of central tendency.

A COMPUTATIONAL FORMULA FOR THE VARIANCE

Very often the formula used to define a measure such as the variance or standard deviation is not the most convenient formula to use in actually computing its value. As a case in point, while Formula (3-4) constitutes the definition of the standard deviation, this measure may often be computed more conveniently using the following computational formula:

$$s = \sqrt{\frac{n\Sigma X^2 - (\Sigma X)^2}{n(n-1)}} \qquad (3\text{-}6)$$

Squaring both sides of Formula (3-6), we obtain the following computational formula for the variance:

$$s^2 = \frac{n\Sigma X^2 - (\Sigma X)^2}{n(n-1)} \qquad (3\text{-}7)$$

The term ΣX^2 in Formulae (3-6) and (3-7) represents the sum of the squares of the observations in a distribution. For example, in the distribution consisting of the numbers 2, 3, and 4, the value of ΣX^2 is $2^2 + 3^2 + 4^2 = 29$. The term $n\Sigma X^2$ stands for *n times* ΣX^2, which in the above example is $3(29) = 87$. The term $(\Sigma X)^2$, read "sum of the X, quantity squared," stands for the square of the sum of the observations in the distribution. In other words, to obtain $(\Sigma X)^2$, the observations are first summed and the total is squared. In the above example, $(\Sigma X)^2$ is equal to $(2 + 3 + 4)^2 = 9^2 = 81$.

The use of Formula (3-7) in computing the standard deviation is illustrated in Table 3-4 for the first 20 trials of the mirror-aiming task. The raw scores are listed in the first column of the table; the squares of the raw scores, in the second column. (Lacking a calculator, one may find the latter most conveniently by reference to a table of squares such as Table A-9 of Appendix A.) The two sums, ΣX and ΣX^2, are recorded at the bottom of the first and second columns, respectively. The remaining calculations are shown at the bottom of the table: first, the variance is computed, then the standard deviation is obtained by taking the square root of the variance. It will be noted that the use of the computational formula eliminates the step of subtracting the mean from every value of X, thereby reducing the computational labor. In a later section it will be shown how the labor can be reduced still further by coding the values of X.

The computation of the standard deviation of grouped data is illustrated in Table 3-5. The data presented are the number of learning trials required to memorize a list of 12 unrelated three-letter words by rote.

> The printed words were presented one at a time in succession, each word being exposed for approximately two seconds. Learning was by the anticipation method, i.e., when a given word was presented the subject attempted to anticipate the following word by pronouncing it aloud before it was presented. The measure recorded was the number of presentations of the list required before the subject recited the list correctly twice in succession.

As in computing the mean from grouped data, the data are treated, in effect, as if all the observations in a given class had values equal to the

TABLE 3-4 *Computation of standard deviation using computational formula—ungrouped data. Scores on first 20 trials of mirror-aiming task*

X	X^2
66	4,356
57	3,249
56	3,136
56	3,136
55	3,025
53	2,809
51	2,601
50	2,500
48	2,304
48	2,304
48	2,304
47	2,209
47	2,209
47	2,209
47	2,209
45	2,025
43	1,849
37	1,369
35	1,225
34	1,156
970	48,184

$$s^2 = \frac{n\Sigma X^2 - (\Sigma X)^2}{n(n-1)} = \frac{20(48,184) - (970)^2}{20(19)}$$

$$= \frac{963,680 - 940,900}{380} = \frac{22,780}{380} \approx 59.9$$

$$s \approx \sqrt{59.9} \approx 7.74$$

midpoint of the class.   The first four columns of Table 3-5 are analogous to those of Table 3-2 used in computing the mean of grouped data: the first column lists the lowest and highest observation in each class; the second column lists the frequency within each class; the third column, the midpoint of each class; and the fourth column, an approximation of the total for each class, i.e., the midpoint of each class multiplied by the corresponding class frequency.   The novel feature of Table 3-5 is the last column, headed fX^2.   This column lists an approximation of the sum of the squares of the observations within each class.   These values could be computed by determining X^2 for each class and multiplying each value of X^2 by the corresponding class frequency; however, the value of fX^2 for a given class may be obtained more easily by multiplying the value of X for that class by the corresponding value of fX.   For example,

TABLE 3-5 *Computation of standard deviation using computational formula—grouped data. Number of trials to memorize 12 unrelated words in sequence*

NUMBER OF TRIALS	f	X	fX	fX^2
36–38	1	37	37	1,369
33–35	0	34	0	0
30–32	0	31	0	0
27–29	0	28	0	0
24–26	2	25	50	1,250
21–23	1	22	22	484
18–20	2	19	38	722
15–17	4	16	64	1,024
12–14	4	13	52	676
9–11	12	10	120	1,200
6–8	19	7	133	931
3–5	13	4	52	208
	58		568	7,864

$$s^2 = \frac{n\Sigma fX^2 - (\Sigma fX)^2}{n(n-1)} = \frac{58(7,864) - (568)^2}{58(57)}$$

$$= \frac{456,112 - 322,624}{3,306} = \frac{133,488}{3,306}$$

$$\approx 40.38$$

$$s \approx \sqrt{40.38} \approx 6.35$$

in the bottom class, multiplying 4 (the value of X) by 52 (the value of fX) yields the product 208, the value of fX^2.   (The reader should avoid the common error of squaring fX, an operation that produces f^2X^2 rather than the desired quantity, fX^2.)   The sum of the values in the fourth column, ΣfX, corresponds to ΣX for ungrouped data; the sum of the values in the last column, ΣfX^2, corresponds to ΣX^2 for ungrouped data.   Making these substitutions, Formula (3-7) becomes

$$s^2 = \frac{n\Sigma fX^2 - (\Sigma fX)^2}{n(n-1)} \tag{3-8}$$

The computation of s^2 using Formula (3-8) is shown at the bottom of Table 3-5.   In the final step the standard deviation is obtained by taking the square root of the variance.

DERIVATION OF THE COMPUTATIONAL FORMULA FOR VARIANCE

So that the reader may better appreciate the equivalence between definitional Formulae (3-4) and (3-5) and their computational counterparts,

Formulae (3-6) and (3-7), it will be shown how Formula (3-7) may be derived by simple algebra from Formula (3-5). To simplify matters, we will concern ourselves initially only with the numerator of Formula (3-5). When we have finished our manipulation of the numerator, we will divide the result by $n - 1$, thus obtaining the variance. We start, then, with Σx^2, which we may rewrite as follows:

$$\Sigma x^2 = \Sigma(X - \overline{X})^2$$

We will temporarily dispense with the summation sign (Σ) on the right of the equal sign by writing out the series of terms that it implies, thus:

$$\Sigma x^2 = (X_1 - \overline{X})^2 + (X_2 - \overline{X})^2 + \cdots + (X_n - \overline{X})^2$$

If we expand each of the expressions in parentheses as indicated by the exponents, we obtain

$$\Sigma x^2 = (X_1^2 - 2\overline{X}X_1 + \overline{X}^2) + (X_2^2 - 2\overline{X}X_2 + \overline{X}^2)$$
$$+ \cdots + (X_n^2 - 2\overline{X}X_n + \overline{X}^2)$$

in which there is an expression of the form $(X^2 - 2\overline{X}X + \overline{X}^2)$ corresponding to each observation in the distribution. If the terms in the above series are rearranged with like terms grouped, we obtain

$$\Sigma x^2 = (X_1^2 + X_2^2 + \cdots + X_n^2) - (2\overline{X}X_1 + 2\overline{X}X_2 + \cdots + 2\overline{X}X_n)$$
$$+ (\overline{X}^2 + \overline{X}^2 + \cdots + \overline{X}^2) \quad (3-9)$$

The first series of terms on the right is simply the sum of the squares of all of the observations, i.e., ΣX^2. In the last series of terms $\overline{X}^2$, the mean squared, occurs n times, once for each observation in the distribution; the sum is simply $n\overline{X}^2$. Turning to the middle series of terms, each term is seen to have the common factor $2\overline{X}$. If this quantity is factored out, the middle series becomes $2\overline{X}(X_1 + X_2 + \cdots + X_n)$. Using summation notation, this series may be written simply $2\overline{X}\Sigma X$, i.e., the sum of the observations multiplied by twice the mean. Making the changes indicated, Equation (3-9) for Σx^2 simplifies to

$$\Sigma x^2 = \Sigma X^2 - 2\overline{X}\Sigma X + n\overline{X}^2$$

We eliminate $\overline{X}$ by substituting its equivalent $(\Sigma X)/n$, obtaining

$$\Sigma x^2 = \Sigma X^2 - 2\left(\frac{\Sigma X}{n}\right)\Sigma X + n\left(\frac{\Sigma X}{n}\right)^2$$

which simplifies to

$$\Sigma x^2 = \Sigma X^2 - \frac{2(\Sigma X)^2}{n} + \frac{n(\Sigma X)^2}{n^2}$$

After cancelling n's and combining fractions, we obtain

$$\Sigma x^2 = \Sigma X^2 - \frac{(\Sigma X)^2}{n}$$

Multiplying ΣX^2 by n/n and combining fractions, we obtain the following computational formula for Σx^2, the sum of squares of deviations around $\overline{X}$:

$$\Sigma x^2 = \frac{n\Sigma X^2 - (\Sigma X)^2}{n} \tag{3-10}$$

Dividing both sides of Formula (3-10) by $(n - 1)$ gives the computational formula for variance,

$$s^2 = \frac{\Sigma x^2}{n - 1} = \frac{n\Sigma X^2 - (\Sigma X)^2}{n(n - 1)}$$

The computational formula for variance is thus seen to be a variant of the definition of variance, derivable from the latter by means of elementary algebra.

MODIFYING VALUES BY A CONSTANT

When the value of every observation in a distribution is changed in a uniform manner—for example, when a constant is added to every observation or every observation is multiplied by the same amount—the mean and standard deviation of the distribution are modified in predictable ways. Inasmuch as these operations are frequently used in statistical work, it is useful to examine their effects on the mean and standard deviation, and it is to this problem that we now turn.

ADDITION AND SUBTRACTION OF A CONSTANT

If we add a constant to the value of each observation in a distribution, or if we subtract a constant from each value, we obtain a new set of values that we shall refer to as *transformed values*. For example, if we start with the values 6, 8, and 10, and subtract 5 from each value, we obtain the transformed values 1, 3, and 5. In order to discuss the effects of such an operation in general terms, it is convenient to use a distinctive set of symbols to refer to the two sets of values. We shall use the letters $X_1, X_2, \cdots, X_n$ to designate a set of values prior to modification and the letters $V_1, V_2, \cdots, V_n$ to designate the transformed values obtained by an operation such as addition or subtraction of a constant. The means of the two sets of values will be represented by $\overline{X}$ and $\overline{V}$, respectively; the standard deviations, by s_X and s_V, respectively. The operation of subtracting a constant from each value in a distribution can be represented in general form by the equation $V = (X - a)$, which indicates that each value in the derived distribution is obtained by subtracting a constant, a, from the corresponding value in the original distribution.

If a distribution is represented by a histogram, the effect of subtracting a constant from every observation is to displace the entire distribution to the left without changing its shape. The result is that the mean of the transformed values is less than the mean of the original values, but the standard deviations of the two sets of values are the same. In terms of the notation introduced above, $\overline{V} = \overline{X} - a$ and $s_V = s_X$. To illustrate these general relationships, the reader should verify for the example given above—in which $\overline{X} = 8$, $s_X = 2$, and $a = 5$—that $\overline{V} = 8 - 5 = 3$ and $s_V = s_X = 2$.

The effects of adding a constant to every observation are parallel to those of subtracting a constant: the standard deviation is unaffected, whereas the mean is increased by the amount of the constant. In short, if $V = X + a$, then $s_V = s_X$ and $\overline{V} = \overline{X} + a$.

MULTIPLICATION AND DIVISION BY A CONSTANT

The multiplication of every value in a distribution by a constant affects both the mean and the standard deviation of the distribution. To illustrate, if we start with our original values, 6, 8, and 10, and multiply every value by 3, we obtain the following transformed values: 18, 24, and 30. Here, not only has the central tendency been modified, but the scatter of the observations has been increased. The reader should verify that the transformed values have the following mean and standard deviation: $\overline{V} = 24$, and $s_V = 6$. Both the mean and the standard deviation, like each individual observation, have been increased by a factor of 3. In general, if every value in a distribution is multiplied by a constant ($V = cX$), then the mean and standard deviation are both increased by the same factor, i.e., $\overline{V} = c\overline{X}$ and $s_V = cs_X$.

Division by a constant may be regarded as multiplication by the reciprocal of that constant. For example, dividing every value in a distribution by 2 is the same as multiplying every value by 1/2. Making this transformation, the mean and standard deviation of the transformed values would be $\overline{V} = (1/2)\overline{X} = \overline{X}/2$, and $s_V = (1/2)s_X = s_X/2$. Generalizing this result, we may state the following general rule: If every observation in a distribution is divided by a constant, the mean of the transformed values is equal to the original mean divided by the constant, and the standard deviation of the transformed values is equal to the original standard deviation divided by the constant. Expressed in symbolic form, if a set of values are transformed by the equation $V = X/c$, then $\overline{V} = \overline{X}/c$ and $s_V = s_X/c$.

COMBINING SUBTRACTION AND DIVISION

Of special interest are transformations in which one constant, a, is subtracted from each observation in a distribution and then each remainder is divided by a second constant, c. The complete transformation may be described as follows: $V = (X - a)/c$. For purposes of illustration, let us take as our original set of observations the values 6, 8, and 10 and suppose that $a = 4$ and $c = 2$. The manner in which $\overline{V}$ and s_V are related to $\overline{X}$ and s_X may be determined by considering the transformation in two steps: first, the subtraction of a from each value of X and, second, the division of each of the resulting values by c. The intermediate values obtained by subtracting 4 from each value of X are listed in the second column of Table 3-6.

TABLE 3-6 *Results of transformation by subtraction and division considered in two steps*

	ORIGINAL VALUES X	INTERMEDIATE VALUES $X - 4$	FINAL VALUES $V = \dfrac{X - 4}{2}$
	10	6	3
	8	4	2
	6	2	1
MEAN	8	4	2
STANDARD DEVIATION	2	2	1

Applying the rules given above concerning the effects of subtraction of a constant, it follows that the mean of the intermediate values is $(8 - 4) = 4$ and the standard deviation, which is unaffected by subtraction of a constant, is 2. The values of V, obtained by dividing each of the intermediate values by 2, are listed in the last column of Table 3-6. Applying the rules given above concerning the effects of division by a constant, the value of $\overline{V}$ and s_V may be derived from the mean and standard deviation of the intermediate values as follows: $\overline{V} = 4/2 = 2$ and $s_V = 2/2 = 1$. Generalizing this line of reasoning, the mean and standard deviation of the intermediate values are equal to $(\overline{X} - a)$ and s_X, respectively; the mean of the final set of transformed values is given by the formula

$$\overline{V} = \frac{\overline{X} - a}{c} \tag{3-11}$$

and the standard deviation is given by the formula

$$s_V = \frac{s_X}{c} \tag{3-12}$$

It will be noted that, whereas the mean is affected by both operations (subtraction and division), the standard deviation is affected only by division.

In a later section we shall make use of a transformation in which the constant subtracted is the mean of the original observations and the divisor is the standard deviation of the original observations, i.e., a transformation in which $V = (X - \overline{X})/s_X$. Applying Formula (3-11), we may compute the mean of the derived scores as follows: $\overline{V} = (\overline{X} - \overline{X})/s_X = 0/s_X = 0$. Applying Formula (3-12), the standard deviation of the derived scores is $s_V = s_X/s_X = 1$. In other words, whatever the values of the mean and standard deviation of a distribution, if the mean is subtracted from each observation and the residuals are divided by the standard deviation, the transformed values thus obtained are distributed with a mean of zero and a standard deviation of 1.

SIMPLIFYING COMPUTATION OF THE MEAN
AND STANDARD DEVIATION

By making use of transformations such as described in the preceding section it is possible to greatly reduce the arithmetic labor involved in computing the mean and standard deviation of a set of observations. The general strategy employed is to change the original values to a set of transformed values that are easy to work with; calculate the mean and standard deviation of the transformed values, $\overline{V}$ and s_V; and then from these latter values compute $\overline{X}$ and s_X, the mean and standard deviation of the original distribution. The first step is sometimes referred to as *coding* of the original observations; the last step, as *decoding* of the mean and standard deviation.

The use of coded values in computing the mean and standard deviation of a distribution will be illustrated using the distribution of number of trials to memorize a list of words, originally presented in Table 3-5 and reproduced in Table 3-7.

The novel feature of Table 3-7 is the use of coded values in place of original values of X in performing calculations. The values of V, i.e., the coded values of the class midpoints, are listed in the fourth column of the table. These values are obtained by arbitrarily assigning a value of zero to any convenient class (usually a class near the middle of the distribution), values of 1, 2, 3, $\cdots$ to successive classes above the "zero" class, and values of -1, -2, $\cdots$ to successive classes below the "zero" class. An examination of the values of X and V in Table 3-7 will show that V is related to X as follows: $V = (X - 10)/3$. More generally, whenever scores are coded in the manner shown in Table 3-7, the equation relating V and X has the form $V = (X - a)/c$, in which a is the midpoint of the class in which $V = 0$, and c is the class interval.

TABLE 3-7 *Calculation of mean and standard deviation using coded values. Number of trials to memorize 12 unrelated words in sequence*

NUMBER OF TRIALS	f	X	V	fV	fV^2
36–38	1	37	9	9	81
33–35	0	34	8	0	0
30–32	0	31	7	0	0
27–29	0	28	6	0	0
24–26	2	25	5	10	50
21–23	1	22	4	4	16
18–20	2	19	3	6	18
15–17	4	16	2	8	16
12–14	4	13	1	4	4
9–11	12	10	0	0	0
6–8	19	7	−1	−19	19
3–5	13	4	−2	−26	52
	58			−4	256

$$\bar{V} = \frac{\Sigma fV}{n} = \frac{-4}{58} \approx -.069$$

$$s_V{}^2 = \frac{n\Sigma fV^2 - (\Sigma fV)^2}{n(n-1)} = \frac{58(256) - (-4)^2}{58(57)}$$

$$= \frac{14{,}848 - 16}{3{,}306} = \frac{14{,}832}{3{,}306} \approx 4.486$$

$$s_V \approx \sqrt{4.486} \approx 2.118$$

$$\bar{X} = c\bar{V} + a \approx 3(-.069) + 10 = -.207 + 10 = 9.793$$

$$s_X = cs_V \approx 3(2.118) \approx 6.35$$

The last two columns of Table 3-7 show the preliminary calculations necessary for determining the mean and standard deviation of the coded values and are comparable to the last two columns of Table 3-5; the calculation of $\bar{V}$ and s_V are shown in the middle portion of the table. In comparison with the corresponding calculations shown in Table 3-5, it is seen that the use of coded values affords a very substantial reduction in the size of the numbers that must be handled and, hence, in the arithmetic labor involved.

The final step is the decoding of the mean and standard deviation, i.e., the calculation of $\bar{X}$ and s_X, the mean and standard deviation of the original observations, from $\bar{V}$ and s_V, the mean and standard deviation of the coded observations. The relationship between $\bar{V}$ and $\bar{X}$ is given by Formula

(3-11).   Solving this equation for $\overline{X}$, here the unknown quantity, we obtain

$$\overline{X} = c\overline{V} + a \qquad (3\text{-}13)$$

as the formula for decoding the mean.   Similarly, by solving Formula (3-12) for s_X, we obtain the following formula for decoding the standard deviation:

$$s_X = cs_V \qquad (3\text{-}14)$$

The use of Formulae (3-13) and (3-14) in decoding the mean and standard deviation is illustrated in the bottom portion of Table 3-7.   The value of s_X computed there is seen to be the same as the value obtained by direct calculation in Table 3-5.   Although the calculation of $\overline{X}$ by the direct method (without coding) has not been shown, the value of $\overline{X}$ so computed will be found to be in agreement with the value obtained in Table 3-7.

Although the computation of the mean and standard deviation using coded values involves two steps (coding and decoding) that are not performed when these measures are computed directly from the original observations, the additional labor required by the coding and decoding operations is usually more than offset by a simplification of the arithmetic involved.

STANDARD SCORES (Z SCORES)

It was pointed out in the previous chapter that for certain purposes a frame of reference is necessary in order to evaluate a given measure of performance.   For many types of psychological measurement the required frame of reference is provided by determining the standing of a particular observation in relation to some reference distribution.   One method of providing this information—specifying the percentile rank of the score in question—was described in Chapter 2.   In the present section an alternative method—the use of *standard scores*—will be described.

Standard scores (also known as *Z scores*) are scores obtained by transforming the original observations of a distribution so that the mean and standard deviation take on predetermined, standardized values.   The values selected for the mean and standard deviation of the standard scores are, of course, arbitrary; a fairly common practice in psychological testing is to compute standard scores having a mean of 50 and a standard deviation of 10.   The usefulness of standard scores is this: they have built-in information concerning the location of any given score relative to the mean of the reference distribution.   If it is known that a set of standard scores has been computed with a mean of 50 and a standard deviation of 10, then it is apparent at a glance that a standard score of 60 is one standard deviation above the mean, a score of 55 is half a standard deviation above the mean, a score of 30 is two standard deviations below the mean, etc.

The method of computing standard scores follows directly from the general principles discussed earlier in connection with transformations of values. For purposes of illustration, let us consider how a set of raw scores having any mean and standard deviation may be transformed to Z scores having a mean of 50 and a standard deviation of 10. We may conceive of the process as being performed in three stages. First, each score in the distribution is transformed by computing $V = (X - \overline{X})/s$, i.e., the mean is subtracted from each score and the difference is divided by s. (It has been shown in an earlier section that the transformed scores derived in this manner have a mean of zero and a standard deviation of 1.) Second, each transformed score is multiplied by 10, giving rise to a set of scores having a mean of $10(0) = 0$ and a standard deviation of $10(1) = 10$. Finally, 50 is added to each of the values obtained in the second stage, thus modifying the mean without affecting the standard deviation. The resulting Z scores have the mean and standard deviation specified at the outset—50 and 10, respectively. The steps in computing the standard score, Z, corresponding to any given raw score, X, are summarized in the following formula:

$$Z = 50 + 10 \left(\frac{X - \overline{X}}{s} \right) \tag{3-15}$$

The use of Formula (3-15) in computing Z scores may be illustrated with the following problem:

The raw scores of a group of subjects on a given test were distributed with a mean of 97 and a standard deviation of 8. These scores were converted to standard scores having a mean of 50 and a standard deviation of 10. What is the Z score corresponding to a raw score of 85?

The Z score in question is readily computed by substituting the appropriate quantities in Formula (3-15) as follows:

$$Z = 50 + 10 \left(\frac{85 - 97}{8} \right)$$

Solving this equation, we obtain $Z = 50 + 10(-12)/8 = 35$. It is apparent at a glance that this score is one and one-half standard deviations below the group mean.

Standard scores are especially useful when comparisons among two or more different kinds of measures are of interest. For example, let us suppose that a given school requires its applicants to take three tests of ability—a test of abstract reasoning, a test of verbal fluency, and a test of mathematical ability. As we have noted above, in order to provide a frame of reference for evaluating the significance of a given score on a given test we must have information concerning the standing of that score in relation to some reference distribution. In reporting the scores of a given individual on the three tests described above, the necessary information might be provided by stating, with each of his raw scores, the mean and standard deviation of the corresponding test, as follows: Individual A had a raw score of 64 on the first test, which has a mean of 55 and a standard deviation of 9; a raw score of 58 on the second test, which has a mean of 64 and a standard deviation of 6; and a raw score of 62 on the third test, which has a mean of 42 and a standard deviation of 8. However, the same information can be conveyed much more conveniently —and is much more readily grasped—if it is simply stated that his standard scores on the three tests were 60, 40, and 75, respectively. It is immediately clear from these values that, judged in terms of his standing in the reference group, this individual did best on the third test and worst on the second.

For special purposes standard scores may be computed with any mean and standard deviation desired. The value desired for the mean is substituted for 50 in Formula (3-15), and the value desired for the standard deviation is substituted for 10. For example, if it is desired to compute standard scores with a mean of 100 and a standard deviation of 20, the following formula is used: $Z = 100 + 20(X - \overline{X})/s$. For informal purposes, or where negative values are not inconvenient, some workers prefer simply to use the transformation $Z = (X - \overline{X})/s$. Using the latter transformation, values of Z give directly the distance of raw scores from $\overline{X}$ in standard deviation units.

PROBLEMS

The following are the data for Problems 1–4.

PROBLEM 1		PROBLEM 2		PROBLEM 3		PROBLEM 4	
X	f	Interval	f	Interval	f	Interval	f
11	1	45–47	1	50–54	1	70–79	1
10	1	42–44	0	45–49	0	60–69	0
9	2	39–41	0	40–44	0	50–59	1
8	2	36–38	1	35–39	1	40–49	2
7	4	33–35	1	30–34	0	30–39	3
6	6	30–32	0	25–29	1	20–29	4
5	2	27–29	0	20–24	1	10–19	5
	—	24–26	1	15–19	2	0–9	4
	18	21–23	0	10–14	5		—
		18–20	2	5–9	6		20
		15–17	2	0–4	3		
		12–14	5		—		
		9–11	12		20		
		6–8	18				
		3–5	30				
		0–2	22				
			—				
			95				

1. The data given above for Problem 1 are the scores of 18 students on a short objective quiz. Compute the mean, median, and mode of this distribution.

2. The data for Problem 2 are the number of errors made by 95 subjects on a mirror-drawing task. Compute the mean, median, and mode of this distribution.

3. Twenty subjects each memorized a list of nonsense syllables. The distribution of number of trials required for learning is given above. Compute the mean, median, and mode.

4. Twenty rats were shocked in a white compartment and then given the opportunity to jump from the white compartment to an adjoining black compartment. Testing was continued until each animal failed on ten consecutive trials to jump from the white compartment; the measure of interest was the total number of jumps made by each animal before reaching this criterion. The distribution of this measure (number of jumps) is given above. Compute the mean, median, and mode of this distribution.

5. Determine the interquartile range (*a*) for the data of Problem 3 and (*b*) for the data of Problem 4.

6. Using Formula (3-5), compute the variance and standard deviation of the following set of scores: 8, 6, 1, 5, 7, 3. Repeat your calculations using Formula (3-7).

7. Compute the variance and standard deviation of the following set of scores (*a*) using Formula (3-5) and (*b*) using Formula (3-7): 0, 3, 3, 4, 4, 5, 5, 6, 7, 9.

8. (*a*) Using Formula (3-7), compute the variance of the following set of values: 50, 54, 55, 57, 59, 61. (*b*) Subtract 50 from each of the values given above, and compute the variance of the resulting coded values. How do the results compare with those computed in Part (*a*)? Explain.

9. Compute the variance and standard deviation for the data of Problem 1. Subtract 5 from each value of X and repeat your calculations. How do the two sets of results compare?

10. Using the coding procedures described in this chapter, compute the mean and standard deviation (*a*) for the data of Problem 3 and (*b*) for the data of Problem 4.

11. A set of scores are distributed with a mean of 82 and a standard deviation of 12. (*a*) If 22 is subtracted from every score in the distribution, what are the values of $\overline{V}$ and s_{V}, the mean and standard deviation of the resulting scores? (*b*) If every score is divided by 2, what are the mean and standard deviation of the resulting scores? (*c*) If 22 is subtracted from every score and the results divided by 2, what are the mean and standard deviation of the resulting scores?

12. An instructor gave three one-hour quizzes, on which the means and standard deviations were as follows:

Quiz *1*: $\overline{X} = 74, s = 12$
Quiz *2*: $\overline{X} = 86, s = 8$
Quiz *3*: $\overline{X} = 62, s = 14$

Tom's scores on the three quizzes were 62, 82, and 69, respectively. If raw scores on each of the quizzes are converted to standard scores having a mean of 50 and a standard deviation of 10, what is Tom's standard score on each quiz? Is the trend in his performance, relative to the rest of the class, upward or downward?

13. Suppose that in the situation described in Problem 12 the raw scores on each quiz were converted to standard scores having a mean of 100 and a standard deviation of 20. What would be the value of Tom's Z score on each quiz?

ADDITIONAL READINGS

DIXON, W. J. and F. J. MASSEY, JR. *Introduction to statistical analysis* (2d ed.). New York: McGraw-Hill, 1957. Chap. 3. A mathematically rigorous derivation of the effects of coding on the mean and standard deviation is given.

EDWARDS, A. E. *Statistical methods for the behavioral sciences.* New York: Rinehart, 1954. Chap. 3 (an elementary presentation of measures of central tendency and variability), Chap. 4 (a detailed discussion of coding), and Chap. 6 (a description of the computation and use of standard scores).

FREUND, J. E. *Modern elementary statistics* (2d ed.). Englewood Cliffs, N. J.: Prentice-Hall, 1960. Chaps. 3 and 4.

HUFF, D. *How to lie with statistics.* New York: W. W. Norton, 1954. Chap. 2. An informal yet detailed discussion of how wholly different impressions may be conveyed depending upon the choice of a measure of central tendency.

CHAPTER 4

population and sample

As a general rule, the particular observations obtained in any given experiment are of interest because they are in some sense representative of a wider set of possible observations that could be obtained under similar conditions. For example, an investigator interested in the amount of time necessary to memorize a list of words might observe the performance of 30 subjects. Ordinarily he is interested in these subjects because their performance may be regarded as representative of the performance of a large number of similar subjects who could be tested under similar conditions. The complete set of objects or individuals about which it is desired to draw a conclusion is referred to as a *population;* the particular individuals actually observed constitute a *sample* from the population. Drawing conclusions concerning a population on the basis of observations in a sample is known as *statistical inference.* In this chapter we shall examine some of the basic concepts underlying the theory of statistical inference.

TWO TYPES OF POPULATION: FINITE AND INFINITE

In some investigations the population of interest is actual and finite. That is to say, it consists of a limited (often large) number of individuals or objects that actually exist—or existed—at a given time. For example, in taking a poll of consumer preferences, the population of interest might be all individuals in a certain age range living in a given geographic area at the time of the investigation. Other examples of finite populations are all alumni of one school (as of a specified date), all residents of a given state, and all members of a certain profession.   On the other hand, in contrast to such actual, finite populations, many of the populations of interest in science are hypothetical and infinite.   The latter type of population may be illustrated with reference to a study of the learning performance of rats under some specified set of conditions.   In such a study, we obtain a sample of rats and subject them to the conditions we wish to study.   The population in which we are interested consists of all similar rats that could conceivably be subjected to the conditions of the experiment.   At any given moment such a population does not actually exist; it is conceptual or hypothetical.   Moreover, such a population is infinitely large, for the number of rats that could conceivably be subjected to the conditions of the experiment is without limit.   As a rule, whenever we subject individuals to special conditions created artificially in a laboratory we are interested in generalizing to the hypothetical infinite population consisting of all individuals of a given kind who could be so treated. Another type of hypothetical population of interest in psychological research consists of all possible repeated determinations (measures) of a given kind based upon a given individual.   For example, if we measure the reaction time of the same individual ten times, we may conceive of these ten observations as a sample from the population of all possible repeated determinations that could be made of the reaction time of that individual.   Since the possible number of such determinations is essentially without limit, we may conceive of such a population as being infinite; since the population of observations so conceived are not actually performed, such a population is hypothetical rather than actual.

It is apparent from the above considerations why we must often limit our observations to a sample rather than attempting to observe an entire population.   In dealing with an infinite population it is, of course, impossible to observe every (potential) member of the population.   In dealing with large but finite populations, although observation of every individual in a population is logically possible, such a complete accounting is often unfeasible for practical reasons. Even when feasible, observation of all members of a population is often unnecessary; the information provided by a sample may be sufficient for the purposes at hand.

THE MEAN AND VARIANCE OF A FINITE POPULATION

The various measures of central tendency and variability discussed in the preceding chapter may be computed either from the distribution of values in a sample or, provided it is known, from the distribution of values in a population.   Measures based upon the distribution of values in a sample are called *statistics;* corresponding measures based upon the distribution of values in a population are called *parameters*. In order to maintain a clear distinction between statistics and parameters it is customary to use Roman letters to represent statistics and Greek letters to represent parameters. For example, the mean of a sample is represented by $\overline{X}$; the mean of a population, by μ (the Greek letter *mu*, pronounced "mew," which corresponds to the letter m). Similarly, the standard deviation of a population is represented by the Greek letter σ (*sigma*), the counterpart in the Greek alphabet of the letter s.[1]

If we represent the total number of individuals in a finite population by the letter P, we may write the formula for the population mean as follows:

$$\mu = \frac{\Sigma X}{P} \qquad (4\text{-}1)$$

This formula for μ is seen to be completely analogous to that for $\overline{X}$, the only difference being that μ is based upon the distribution of values for an entire population.

Using the notation introduced above, we may define σ^2, the population variance, as follows:

$$\sigma^2 = \frac{\Sigma(X - \mu)^2}{P} \qquad (4\text{-}2)$$

The numerator of this formula is obtained by taking the deviation of each observation from the population mean, squaring the deviations, and summing them; the denominator is the total number of cases involved. Thus, σ^2 is the mean of the squared deviations around μ. The population standard deviation, σ, is simply the square root of σ^2. (Comparing Formula (4-2) with Formula (3-5), it will be noted that the definition of s^2 is highly similar to that of σ^2, the difference being that in computing s^2 deviations are taken around $\overline{X}$ rather than μ, and the sum of the squared deviations is divided by one less than the total number of cases. As will be explained in detail in Chapter 6, the reason for using $n - 1$ in computing s^2 is to obtain a better estimate of σ^2: if the sample variance is computed by dividing the sum of the squared deviations by n, the resulting estimate of σ^2 is slightly biased; dividing by $n - 1$, the bias is eliminated.)

In order to show the relationship between the definition of the mean of a finite population and the definition, presented in a later section, of the mean of an infinite population, it is useful to manipulate Formula (4-1) algebraically to obtain a different, but equivalent, formula. Let us begin by considering a miniature population in which the values of X

---

[1] It should be noted that there is considerable diversity among texts in the symbols used to represent various statistics and parameters. Accordingly, when referring to other texts the student cannot assume that the symbols used have the same meaning as in this text. The definition of each symbol in any text should be carefully checked.

are as follows: 5, 5, 6, 6, 6, 6, 7, 7.   Since the various values of X occur more than once, we may obtain the sum of the observations by multiplying each value by the frequency with which it occurs and summing the resulting products.   Following this procedure, Formula (4-1) may be written as follows:

$$\mu = \frac{f_1 X_1 + f_2 X_2 + \cdots + f_h X_h}{P} \qquad (4\text{-}3)$$

In this formula X_1 represents the lowest value of X (5 in the illustrative distribution above), X_2 represents the next higher value (6 in the illustrative distribution), and X_h represents the highest value; f_1, f_2, $\cdots$, f_h represent the frequencies with which the respective values of X occur. Substituting in Formula (4-3), we obtain

$$\mu = \frac{2(5) + 4(6) + 2(7)}{8} = \frac{48}{8} = 6$$

The right-hand side of Formula (4-3) is written as a single fraction with P as the denominator.   It may, however, be rewritten as the sum of a series of fractions, all with the common denominator P, as follows:

$$\mu = \frac{f_1 X_1}{P} + \frac{f_2 X_2}{P} + \cdots + \frac{f_h X_h}{P}$$

Finally, each of the terms on the right may be rearranged as follows:

$$\mu = \left(\frac{f_1}{P}\right) X_1 + \left(\frac{f_2}{P}\right) X_2 + \cdots + \left(\frac{f_h}{P}\right) X_h \qquad (4\text{-}4)$$

In terms of the numerical example given above, Formula (4-4) becomes $\mu = (2/8)5 + (4/8)6 + (2/8)7 = 6$.   In this formula, each value of X is multiplied by the *relative frequency* (f/P) with which that value occurs in the distribution.   Inasmuch as Formula (4-4) was derived algebraically from Formula (4-1), the two formulae state essentially the same definition of μ and lead, of course, to the same numerical value.   As we shall see in a later section, the definition of μ for an infinite population closely parallels Formula (4-4).

In order to provide a background for the definition of σ^2 for infinite populations it is useful to develop a formula for σ^2 paralleling Formula (4-4) for μ.   We start with

$$\sigma^2 = \frac{f_1(X_1 - \mu)^2 + f_2(X_2 - \mu)^2 + \cdots + f_h(X_h - \mu)^2}{P}$$

in which each squared deviation, $(X - \mu)^2$, is multiplied by the frequency, f, with which the value in question occurs in the distribution.   Manipulating the above formula as we did Formula (4-3), we obtain

$$\sigma^2 = \left(\frac{f_1}{P}\right)(X_1 - \mu)^2 + \left(\frac{f_2}{P}\right)(X_2 - \mu)^2 + \cdots + \left(\frac{f_h}{P}\right)(X_h - \mu)^2 \qquad (4\text{-}5)$$

Formula (4-5), in which each squared deviation is multiplied by the relative frequency of the corresponding value of X, is seen to be analogous to Formula (4-4) for μ. It will be shown in a later section that the definition of σ^2 for an infinite population closely parallels Formula (4-5).

SOME ELEMENTARY CONCEPTS OF PROBABILITY THEORY

In defining the mean and variance of infinite populations, and in a number of developments to follow, we shall make use of several elementary concepts from the theory of probability. By way of preparation for these topics, the necessary concepts from probability theory will now be presented briefly.

In performing certain simple procedures such as tossing a coin, throwing a die, or cutting a deck of ordinary playing cards, we can enumerate beforehand all possible outcomes that could be obtained. For example, in tossing a coin we may obtain either a head or a tail; in throwing a die, the die may come to rest with either a 1, 2, 3, 4, 5, or 6 uppermost; and in cutting a deck of cards, any of 52 cards may be obtained. In dealing with procedures of this kind, a probability may be assigned to each of the possible outcomes in such a way that the sum of the probabilities of all possible outcomes is equal to unity, i.e., 1. In some situations the probabilities to be assigned to the various possible outcomes are not known. For example, if a die is loaded, certain outcomes are more probable than others, and we have no basis for knowing the exact probability to be assigned to each. On the other hand, under certain circumstances we have good reason to assume that the various possible outcomes are equally probable. For example, if a die is not loaded, then we assume that all six of the possible outcomes are equally probable, and—since the six probabilities must sum to unity—it follows that the value of each is 1/6. Similarly, in tossing a perfectly balanced coin the two possible outcomes are equally probable, the probability of each being 1/2.

The significance of the mathematical concept of probability to practical affairs is this: Over a series of many trials of a procedure such as throwing a die, the relative frequency with which a given outcome occurs will closely approximate the probability of that outcome. For example, we have noted that the probability of each of the possible outcomes of a throw of a die is 1/6; accordingly, we would find in throwing a die, say, 1,000 times that the value 1 would be obtained in approximately one-sixth of the total number of trials, the value 2 would be obtained in approximately one-sixth of the trials, and so on for each of the possible outcomes. Similarly, in tossing a coin 1,000 times we would find that on about half the trials the coin landed heads and on about half it landed tails.   (It should be noted that, despite their close relationship, probability and relative frequency are not synonymous concepts.   On the one hand, relative frequency is something we observe; on the other hand, probability is an abstract mathematical concept and, as such, is not directly observable. When the probability of a given event is specified by theoretical considerations, we may predict approximately the relative frequency with which that event will occur over a long series of trials; on the other hand, if the probability of a given event is unknown, an estimate of this probability is provided by the relative frequency with which the event is observed to occur.)

If each of the possible values of a quantitative characteristic (i.e., a characteristic that can be described in numerical terms) has a certain probability of occurrence, that characteristic is said to be a *random variable*.   For example, the numerical value obtained in throwing a die is a random variable: several values are possible, and each has a specific probability of occurrence.   The possible values of a random variable X will be designated X_1, X_2, $\cdots$, and the probabilities associated with those values will be designated p_1, p_2, $\cdots$, respectively.   Referring again to the outcome of throwing a die, there are six possible values of X: $X_1 = 1, X_2 = 2, \cdots, X_6 = 6$; as we have already noted, the corresponding probabilities, p_1, p_2, $\cdots$, p_6, are all equal to $1/6$ if the die is unbiased.   A specification of the possible values of a random variable X and the probability associated with each value will be referred to as the *probability distribution of X*.   (In the interest of brevity, when it is clear from the context that the distribution under consideration is a probability distribution—as opposed to a frequency distribution—the distribution in question will simply be referred to as the *distribution of X*.)   A convenient way of describing the probability distribution of a random variable is to list the possible values of X and the associated probabilities in a table such as Table 4-1, which describes the probability distribution of X for throws of an ordinary die.

TABLE 4-1   *Probability distribution of X for throws of an ordinary die*

X	1	2	3	4	5	6
PROBABILITY	$\frac{1}{6}$	$\frac{1}{6}$	$\frac{1}{6}$	$\frac{1}{6}$	$\frac{1}{6}$	$\frac{1}{6}$

In tossing a die, each of the six possible values of X can occur in only one way.   However, in the case of some random variables certain values of X may be obtained in more than one way.   For example, let us consider the random variable X defined as the number of heads obtained when a coin is tossed three times in succession.   (In contrast to the previous example, in which each trial consisted of a single throw of a die, here a single trial consists of a sequence of three tosses of a coin.) The possible outcomes of such a procedure are enumerated in Table 4-2.

TABLE 4-2   *Possible outcomes of three tosses of a coin*

OUTCOME	NUMBER OF HEADS X
HHH	3
HHT	2
HTH	2
THH	2
TTH	1
THT	1
HTT	1
TTT	0

In the first outcome described, a head is obtained on each toss; in the second outcome, a head is obtained on the first and second tosses, a tail on the third; and so on.   Since there are eight possible outcomes, all of which are equally probable, the probability of any given outcome is 1/8. In the second column of Table 4-2 the value of X, the total number of heads, is given for each outcome.   It will be noted that in one outcome $X = 0$, in three outcomes $X = 1$, in three outcomes $X = 2$, and in one outcome $X = 3$.   The probability of any given value of X is the sum of the probabilities of all outcomes yielding that value.   Thus, the probability of obtaining the value $X = 0$ is 1/8; the probability of obtaining the value $X = 1$ is $1/8 + 1/8 + 1/8 = 3/8$; and so on.   The complete probability distribution of X is described in Table 4-3.   In contrast to the probability

TABLE 4-3   *Probability distribution.* $X = $ *number of heads in three tosses of a coin*

X	0	1	2	3
PROBABILITY	$\frac{1}{8}$	$\frac{3}{8}$	$\frac{3}{8}$	$\frac{1}{8}$

distribution described in Table 4-1, in which all values of X have the same probability, in the distribution described in Table 4-3 the various possible values of X have unequal probabilities.

In certain problems we may be interested in two different random variables at the same time. For example, in selecting a card from a playing deck by chance we may define the random variable X as the suit of the card (clubs = 1, diamonds = 2, hearts = 3, spades = 4) and the random variable Y as the value of the card, the possible values ranging from 1 (ace) to 13 (king). Or, to take an example of a different kind, employing a procedure in which two dice are thrown, we may define the random variable X as the value showing on the uppermost face of the first die and the random variable Y as the value showing on the uppermost face of the second die.[2]

In problems concerned with two random variables it is sometimes important to distinguish whether the two variables in question are *correlated* or *independent*. Speaking nontechnically, two random variables are said to be *independent* if the value of one is in no manner dependent upon the value of the other and, hence, in the long run, variations in one are not related to variations in the other in any systematic fashion. In both of the examples given above, the random variables X and Y are independent: in selecting a card from a playing deck, the value of the card (Y) in no way depends upon the suit (X), and vice versa, the probability of obtaining any given value being the same in one suit as in another; similarly, in throwing two dice, the value obtained on one die is independent of the value obtained on the other. On the other hand, two variables are said to be *correlated* if there is a systematic tendency for certain values of one to be associated with certain values of the other. For example, if we define the random variable X as the height of an individual selected by chance from a specified group of individuals and the random variable Y as the weight of the same individual, the two random variables so defined would be correlated rather than independent. In this case the two variables are said to be correlated because we would find that in performing the above procedure with a large number of individuals, small values of Y would tend to be associated more often with small values of X than with large values of X, and large values of Y would tend to be associated more often with large values of X.

It should be noted that in the present context the term *independent* is being used in a different sense than in Chapter 1. In the latter context the designation *independent variable* referred to the variable controlled or manipulated by the investigator. As used in the present context, in-

---

[2] Note that in dealing with a given procedure such as throwing two dice we are not constrained to define a random variable X in any fixed manner. For certain purposes it may be convenient to define a random variable X as the value obtained on the first die, for other purposes it may be convenient to define a random variable X as the sum of the values obtained on the two dice, and for other purposes still other definitions may be useful. Within the context of a given problem a given random variable may be defined in any manner that is convenient, subject only to the restriction that we be consistent within that context.

dependence is not a characteristic of a single variable but a relationship (or perhaps we should say lack of relationship) that may or may not exist between two random variables.

THE MEAN AND VARIANCE OF AN INFINITE POPULATION

We have seen that the distribution of values in a finite population may be described by specifying the frequencies with which the various values of X occur. However, this method is not applicable in describing the distribution of values in an infinite population, for the frequencies of the various values of X in such a population are themselves infinite. For example, if one of the possible scores on a given test is 10 and we imagine testing an infinite number of individuals, there is no limit to the number of times this score may be obtained. Instead of describing the distribution of an infinite population in terms of frequencies, such a population may be described by specifying, for each of the possible values of X, the probability that an observation selected by chance will have the value in question. For example, an experiment in which the reaction time of a given individual is measured once is analogous to throwing a die once and recording the value obtained: various values of X are possible, each having a certain probability, and the particular value obtained is determined by chance. Similarly, measuring the reaction time of the same individual five times is analogous to throwing a die five times and recording the five values obtained. The chief difference between the two situations is that in throwing a die we know the probability of each possible value of X, whereas in measuring the reaction time of a given individual the probabilities of the possible values of X are unknown. It will be noted that an observation selected by chance from an infinite population satisfies the definition of a random variable given in the preceding section—a quantity having several possible values each of which has a certain probability of occurrence.

The way in which the mean and variance of an infinite population are defined depends upon whether the variable in question is distributed in a discrete or continuous manner. The mean and variance of the distribution of a discrete random variable may be defined using simple algebra, whereas the concepts of differential calculus must be employed in defining the mean and variance of the distribution of a continuous random variable. The definitions developed in connection with discrete variables are applicable to a wider range of measures than might at first be apparent, because many variables that are theoretically continuous are discrete in practice as a consequence of limitations of the measuring instruments employed. For example, a timer capable of measuring intervals to the nearest thousandth of a second might be employed to measure reaction time. The values of X that could actually be obtained using such a timer are .000, .001, .002, $\cdots$, the instrument being incapable of finer gradations. Still, definitions of μ and σ^2 for continuous random variables are necessary in connection with certain theoretical distributions—for example, the normal distribution, which is considered in the following chapter. For purposes of simplicity, in this text the definitions of μ and σ^2 will be given only for discrete random variables. The reader interested in how these concepts may be extended to continuous random variables will find the subject treated in texts on mathematical statistics (e.g., Mood and Graybill, 1963; Hoel, 1954).

The definition of μ and σ^2 for the distribution of values in an infinite population will be illustrated with reference to the probability distribution of X for throws of an ordinary die. (This probability distribution may be viewed as a description of the distribution of X in the hypothetical population of all possible throws of a die.) Using the notation introduced in the preceding section, we may define μ, the population mean, as follows:

$$\mu = p_1 X_1 + p_2 X_2 + \cdots + p_h X_h \tag{4-6}$$

In this formula each value of X is multiplied by the probability of that value, and the products are added. Formula (4-6) for the mean of an infinite population exactly parallels Formula (4-4) for the mean of a finite population, with the difference that probabilities are substituted for relative frequencies. Substituting the appropriate values in Formula (4-6), the mean of the probability distribution of X for throws of an ordinary die may be computed as follows:

$$\mu = \left(\frac{1}{6}\right)1 + \left(\frac{1}{6}\right)2 + \left(\frac{1}{6}\right)3 + \left(\frac{1}{6}\right)4 + \left(\frac{1}{6}\right)5 + \left(\frac{1}{6}\right)6 = 3.5$$

The value of μ is sometimes referred to as the *mathematical expectation of X,* or the *expected value of X,* and written $E(X)$; in other words, the designations μ and $E(X)$ are synonymous and may be used interchangeably. (Note that in throwing a die the so-called expected value of X, 3.5, is not a value that can actually occur on any given trial.)

The definition of σ^2 for an infinite population parallels Formula (4-5), again with the difference that probabilities are substituted for relative frequencies. Thus, the definition of σ^2 for an infinite population is

$$\sigma^2 = p_1(X_1 - \mu)^2 + p_2(X_2 - \mu)^2 + \cdots + p_h(X_h - \mu)^2 \tag{4-7}$$

In the probability distribution of X for throws of an ordinary die

$$\sigma^2 = \frac{1}{6}(1 - 3.5)^2 + \frac{1}{6}(2 - 3.5)^2 + \cdots + \frac{1}{6}(6 - 3.5)^2 = 2\frac{11}{12}$$

Just as μ may be referred to as the mathematical expectation of X, σ^2

may be referred to as the mathematical expectation of $(X - \mu)^2$ and is sometimes written $E(X - \mu)^2$.

METHODS OF SAMPLING FINITE POPULATIONS

As yet nothing has been said concerning the manner in which a sample is selected from a population. In this section we will consider procedures that may be used for obtaining a sample when the population of interest consists of a finite number of specific individuals—for example, all registered voters eligible to vote in the national election in a given year, or everyone filing a federal income tax for a given year.

Inasmuch as the purpose of drawing a sample from a population is to gain information concerning the distribution of observations in that population, it is important that the individuals included in a sample in some sense constitute a representative cross section of individuals in the population. As we shall see, there are several alternative ways of selecting a sample so that it is representative of the population from which it is drawn. However, before considering competent methods of drawing a sample, let us examine some of the ways that biases can result when improper sampling procedures are employed. As an illustrative problem, let us suppose that the editor of a college newspaper gives a member of his staff the assignment of conducting a survey to determine the average number of hours devoted to studies by students at that college during the week prior to examinations. A convenient way of obtaining a sample of students would be to select as a group all the students enrolled in a particular course such as physics or biology, for example. However, for reasons already discussed in Chapter 1, we would not have much confidence that a sample selected in this manner would be representative of the entire student body. Another approach to drawing a sample would be to wait at a certain location and include in the sample everyone who happened to pass by. Again, we would have little confidence that a sample obtained in this manner would be representative of the entire student body. If, for example, the person taking the survey posted himself outside the student union building, he would obtain one type of sample; if he posted himself outside the library, he might obtain a sample of quite a different type. Similarly, we must rule out selecting the sample from among the personal friends of the individual conducting the poll. In general, it is to be doubted that any individual's personal friends constitute a representative cross section of a population of any appreciable size. (For example, if the individual drawing the sample were majoring in English, it is likely that a sample of his friends would include a disproportionate number of English majors.) Although in many situations we do not know specifically what biasing influences may be operating, sampling procedures such as those described above must be avoided because they make possible the operation of unknown biasing influences.

One method of obtaining a sample that is free of systematic biases such as those considered above is *simple random sampling.* This sampling plan makes use of a procedure having the following characteristics: first, that every individual in the population has an *equal chance* of being included in the sample, and second, that the selection (or nonselection) of any given individual is *independent* of the selection of every other individual, i.e., the inclusion of any particular individual in the sample in no way affects the chances that any other individual will be included. A sample drawn according to a procedure meeting these specifications is called a *random sample.*

One method for obtaining a random sample is a variation of a form of lottery used in distributing prizes. According to this procedure the members of a population are set in one-to-one correspondence with a series of physical objects (e.g., individual slips of paper bearing the names of members of the population), the objects are thoroughly mixed, and a sample of objects is selected "blind," i.e., without regard to the individuals to which they correspond. This procedure may be somewhat simplified by using numbers rather than names to identify the individuals in the population, so that the identification tags may be used for more than one problem. In actual practice an investigator need not perform a lottery himself. Instead, he may refer to a *table of random numbers,* which presents the results of a lottery—or some equivalent procedure—performed by someone else. An example of such a table is Table A-1 of Appendix A.

The use of a table of random numbers in drawing a sample may be illustrated with reference to the problem considered above, obtaining a sample from the population of students attending a given school. First it is necessary to enumerate all of the individuals included in the population. This might be accomplished for the population in our example by obtaining from the registrar a list of all students enrolled in the school in question. We would then assign a number to each individual in the population for purposes of identification. Assuming there were 700 students, we might use the numbers 000, 001, 002, · · · , 699 for this purpose. We would then enter a table of random numbers, using three columns to obtain numbers having three digits each, and record as many three-digit numbers as required.[3] Since each number identifies a particular individual, it is customary to ignore a given number if it occurs a

---

[3] In this context the term *column* refers to a single-digit column. For ease of reading, the columns of Table A-1 are grouped by twos. The sequence of digits in the first column (reading from top to bottom) is 1, 3, 0, · · ·; in the second, 0, 7, 8 · · · · Using the first three columns to obtain three-digit numbers gives the numbers 100, 375, and 084.

second time after once having been included in the sample. Such a procedure is called *sampling without replacement*.

The number of columns used in reading a table of random numbers will depend upon the number of individuals in the population. If the population consists of no more than ten individuals, the numbers from 0 to 9 are sufficient to identify each individual, and only one column of the table need be used; if the number of individuals in the population is between 10 and 100, the numbers from 00 to 99 suffice, and two columns of the table are employed; and so on.

In using a table of random numbers, it is customary to determine by chance the point at which the table is entered. A simple method of entering the table that is satisfactory for most purposes is to touch a page without looking and begin wherever the page is touched. A more elaborate procedure is to select numbers from the table to determine the number of the page, column, and row at which the table is entered.

It is apparent that a sample selected randomly is not subject to the types of biases possible in the nonrandom sampling procedures discussed above. Accordingly, we would expect a random sample to be reasonably representative of the population sampled except for occasional "flukes" of sampling in which an atypical sample is obtained. Unfortunately, the necessity of enumerating all the individuals in a finite population before a random sample can be drawn often presents a serious obstacle to the use of this method in practice.

A form of sampling known as *stratified sampling* may be employed when the population to be sampled consists of a number of subgroups or *strata* that differ in the characteristic being observed. For example, in planning a public opinion poll designed to assess opinions concerning a given political issue, it may be suspected that opinions will tend to differ systematically among various occupational groups. Stratified sampling consists in identifying the strata of interest and then drawing a specified number of individuals from each stratum. Either simple random sampling or systematic sampling (described below) may be employed in selecting the individuals to be included in the sample from each stratum. When sampling a population in which various strata can be distinguished, the use of stratified sampling is optional; the strata may be disregarded and simple random sampling employed. The advantage of stratified sampling is that each stratum in the population is represented in the sample to an extent determined by the experimenter—usually in proportion to its representation in the population—whereas, using simple random sampling, certain strata may be over- or under-represented in the sample, depending upon chance; consequently, the value of the sample mean is likely to be closer to the value of μ if stratified sampling is employed when applicable than if simple random sampling is used.

Another useful sampling plan is *sampling in two stages*. To illustrate this procedure, let us consider the problem of obtaining a sample of all registered voters in the United States.   Using a two-stage sampling plan, we might first draw a random sample of counties and then draw a sample of voters from each of the counties selected.   In general, two-stage sampling consists in selecting a number of units (e.g., counties) from each of which a number of sub-units (e.g., individuals) are selected in turn. When the units selected in the first stage of sampling are relatively small geographic areas, as in the above example, sampling in two stages considerably reduces the practical problems involved in contacting the individuals included in the sample.   For example, it would be considerably more expensive and time-consuming to contact a sample of individuals scattered throughout the nation than to contact samples of individuals in a small number of selected counties.   A further advantage of sampling in two stages is that it is not necessary, as it is in simple random sampling, to have a complete list of all individuals in the population; rather, it is necessary only to enumerate those individuals included in the units (e.g., counties) selected in the first stage of sampling.

Still another form of sampling is so-called *systematic sampling*. Examples of systematic sampling are the selection of every tenth item on a production line, every fifth house on a street, or the first name on each page of a city directory.   Although in some situations systematic sampling may give a better cross section than simple random sampling, there are certain hazards in the use of systematic sampling if the items in a population vary in a periodic fashion.   For example, if there are ten houses in each city block and we draw a systematic sample by selecting every tenth house (or some multiple of 10), our sample will either contain no corner houses or will consist entirely of corner houses, depending upon the first house selected.   If it should be the case that corner houses tend to be more expensive than others and the variable in which we are interested is related to economic factors, then a systematic sample in this situation might be quite misleading.   Accordingly, it is important in using systematic sampling to be sure that the sampling interval does not coincide with any periodic variation among the items in the population.

SOME PROBLEMS IN DEFINING AND SAMPLING POPULATIONS
OF INTEREST IN PSYCHOLOGICAL RESEARCH

Many psychological investigations, particularly those concerned with what might be called basic behavioral processes, are not concerned with such a highly specific population as, say, all registered voters eligible to vote in a specified election, but with a broader population that might be roughly characterized as "people in general."   It is somewhat ironic that in many such investigations the population actually sampled is, if anything, narrower than that sampled in a typical election survey.   One common practice for obtaining subjects in such investigations is to enlist college students enrolled in psychology courses. Depending upon the policy of the school in question, participation in the experiment may be either optional or compulsory. For purposes of illustration, let us consider a hypothetical investigation in which ten volunteers from an introductory psychology class serve as subjects. Of what population may these subjects be regarded as a representative sample? It is questionable whether there is any entirely satisfactory way of characterizing the population represented by such a sample, but let us attempt to delimit it at least roughly. As a first step, we note explicitly certain populations of which the sample described is *not* representative. It is to be doubted that such a sample is representative of college students in general, for, as we noted earlier, the students enrolled in any given course may have special interests or other characteristics that distinguish them from other students. Moreover, if the subjects are volunteers, it is doubtful whether they are even representative of the population consisting all students taking the same course. At best, such a sample might be regarded as representative of all subjects who could be obtained in a similar way under similar circumstances, i.e., volunteers enrolled in this particular course meeting at this particular time of day taught by this particular instructor at this particular school, and so on. To conceptualize such a population we might imagine coming back to the same course each year and making the same appeal for subjects. Assuming there is nothing about this year's class that distinguishes it in any systematic fashion from classes of the same course taught in other years—and such an assumption is always questionable—we might regard the students obtained this year (those who participated in the experiment) as representative of potential volunteers who could be obtained from similar classes in future years as well as those who could have been obtained from classes in the past. Such a specification is somewhat vague at best, for it is open to question exactly what details of the class from which the sample was obtained should be specified in characterizing the population; in other words, it is not entirely clear what is meant by "similar" classes. However, to attempt a more precise description of this hypothetical population would be a profitless exercise, for as a rule an investigator employing a sample such as we have described is not specifically interested in the population which, strictly speaking, his sample represents. Usually the tacit assumption is made that the results would be much the same for subjects drawn from other sources. Of course it is recognized that there are limits to the generality of findings based upon students enrolled in psychology courses—such findings might not be expected to apply to very young children, mentally retarded individuals, and so on—but usually those limits, the precise range of individuals to which such results apply, are not exactly known and can only be guessed.

Just as there are difficulties in defining the population of "all possible individuals of a given type" tested under a given set of circumstances, there are problems in defining the population of repeated determinations based upon the same individual. For one thing, the characteristics of such a population will differ depending upon the time span over which we conceive the measurements to be taken. Typically, if repeated measurements of the same subject are taken over a short time span like a period of several minutes, they will tend to vary less than if they are taken over a long time span like several months. The reason for the greater variability of measures taken over a long time span is that more factors come into play to produce variation of performance. For example, an individual's state of health and general mood are less likely to change appreciably within a period of a few minutes than over a period of several days.

Another complicating factor in defining a population of repeated measures of a given individual arises from the fact that frequently the process of measuring a subject's performance modifies that subject in such a way that subsequent measurements are different. For example, when a subject's reaction time is measured he may benefit from the practice thus obtained and subsequently may exhibit shorter reaction times. On the other hand, in certain types of task the novelty may wear off after the first few trials so that the subject loses interest in the task and his performance deteriorates. In order to take into account such changes in level of performance we may conceptualize a distinct probability distribution of X corresponding to each stage of practice. The situation might be likened to a die that changes its values each time it is tossed. For example, the values on the six faces of the die, initially 1, 2, $\cdots$, 6, might change to 2, 3, $\cdots$, 7 after the first toss, to 3, 4, $\cdots$, 8 after the second toss, and so on. In a situation of this kind each successive observation must be regarded as a sample drawn at random from a different population (probability distribution), it being impossible to obtain from any given population a sample of more than one observation.

In certain tasks the subject's performance may at first show some improvement with practice and then stabilize as the subject attains his maximum performance level. In such instances, after an initial period of practice, successive measures of the subject's performance may be regarded as having been drawn at random from the population of all possible measures of that subject at that stage of training. Under these conditions it is possible to obtain as large a sample as desired from the population of all possible measurements of a given subject.

A MORE COMPLEX MODEL: A POPULATION OF INDIVIDUALS, EACH HAVING A DIFFERENT PROBABILITY DISTRIBUTION OF X

We have already noted that in many psychological investigations we are interested in a population of individuals, i.e., all possible individuals of a given kind who could be tested under a given set of circumstances. In certain studies of this type, the observation obtained from each individual may be regarded as a fixed value, i.e., a value that is constant for that particular individual. For example, the total number of children borne by a woman during her lifetime is a fixed value for any given woman; similarly, the number of teeth a person possesses on his 65th birthday is a fixed number. On the other hand, we have seen that in many psychological investigations the variable measured is not constant for a given individual but varies from determination to determination. For example, consider an investigation in which several individuals are tested on a standard task, the observation of interest being the number of seconds required by each individual to complete that task. Although we may make but a single determination of the time required by each individual, we know that if any given individual were tested more than once the time taken by that individual would vary from trial to trial. In other words, whatever number of observations are obtained from each subject—whether one or several—those observations may be regarded as a sample from the population of all possible measurements of that particular individual. The conceptualization of this type of situation is somewhat more complex than those we have considered thus far: not only do we conceive a population of individuals, but also a separate probability distribution of X for each individual. In such a situation, sampling is performed in two stages. First a sample of individuals is obtained, then a sample is taken of the performance of each individual.

The general characteristics of the situation described above may be illustrated by an analogy in which each individual is represented by a die, the possible values (markings on the face of the dice) varying from die to die. A specific example of such a model is presented in Table 4-4, which describes 20 dice—each representing a different individual—numbered from *1* to *20* for purposes of identification.

Die *1* is an ordinary die, its six faces having the values 1, 2, · · · , 6. Die *2* is specially constructed, its faces bearing the values 7, 8, · · · , 12. The remaining dice are also specially constructed, the values borne by each being indicated in the right-hand portion of Table 4-4. (The values of τ listed in the second column of the table will be explained below.) In our analogy the probability distribution of X for a given individual is represented by the probability distribution of X for the corresponding die. (Because of their equivalence, we shall speak of dice and individuals interchangeably. In terms of this analogy, Individual *1* is the lowest scoring subject, measures of his performance ranging from 1 to 6; Individual *2* is a somewhat higher scoring subject, measures of his performance ranging from 7 to 12; and so on.) Although our illustrative model contains a finite number of dice, we may simulate drawing a sample from an infinite population of dice (individuals) as follows: We place the 20 dice in an

TABLE 4-4 *Model population representing possible values of* X *for 20 individuals.* $\sigma^2 = 1{,}199\frac{11}{12}$; $\sigma_\tau^2 = 1{,}197$; $\sigma_\epsilon^2 = 2\frac{11}{12}$

INDIVIDUAL	τ	POSSIBLE VALUES OF X
1	3.5	1, 2, 3, 4, 5, 6
2	9.5	7, 8, 9, 10, 11, 12
3	15.5	13, 14, 15, 16, 17, 18
4	21.5	19, 20, 21, 22, 23, 24
5	27.5	25, 26, 27, 28, 29, 30
6	33.5	31, 32, 33, 34, 35, 36
7	39.5	37, 38, 39, 40, 41, 42
8	45.5	43, 44, 45, 46, 47, 48
9	51.5	49, 50, 51, 52, 53, 54
10	57.5	55, 56, 57, 58, 59, 60
11	63.5	61, 62, 63, 64, 65, 66
12	69.5	67, 68, 69, 70, 71, 72
13	75.5	73, 74, 75, 76, 77, 78
14	81.5	79, 80, 81, 82, 83, 84
15	87.5	85, 86, 87, 88, 89, 90
16	93.5	91, 92, 93, 94, 95, 96
17	99.5	97, 98, 99, 100, 101, 102
18	105.5	103, 104, 105, 106, 107, 108
19	111.5	109, 110, 111, 112, 113, 114
20	117.5	115, 116, 117, 118, 119, 120

urn, mix them up, and draw one blindfolded.   Having selected a given die, we obtain as many repeated observations as we wish for that die by throwing it the required number of times and recording the result of each throw. We then *return that die to the urn,* mix the dice, draw a second die, and toss it the required number of times, and so on.   By returning each die to the population after sampling it, we have, in effect, created an infinite population, for the population will never be exhausted and we may draw from it as large a sample of dice as we wish.

Before proceeding further with our analysis of the model described above, some general comments concerning the aims of this analysis may be helpful in orienting the reader.   To make our model as concrete as possible a set of specific values have been assumed for purposes of illustration.   Certain characteristics of this set of numbers are purely arbitrary and might readily have been altered without changing the general characteristics of the model that are of interest.   For example, there is no overlap between the potential scores of two different individuals.   This is not an essential characteristic of the model—we could, for example, have included one individual (die) having the values 4, 5, · · · , 9, another having the values 6, 7, · · · , 11.   (The latter values are seen to overlap with the former.)   To have constructed the model in this way would have somewhat complicated the analyses that we shall perform below, but would not have changed the general characteristics in which we are interested. Moreover, it should be emphasized that the computations performed below using the numerical values of the model described in Table 4-4 are not typically performed in an actual research situation. In actual research situations the necessary information—the possible values of X and the probability of each—are simply not available. The purpose of the computations presented below is to illustrate in a concrete manner the meaning of the concepts developed in the accompanying discussion—in particular, σ^2, σ_ϵ^2, and σ_τ^2. We shall find that these concepts are of value in analyzing a variety of research situations even though their specific values in a given research situation typically are not known.

To proceed with our analysis, let us imagine an experiment in which we select a sample of five individuals (college students, let us say) and determine the time it takes each to complete a standard task. An analogy to this experiment in terms of the model described in Table 4-4 would be to draw a sample of five dice, rolling each die once and returning it to the urn before drawing the next. For example, the five dice selected might be those representing Individuals *2, 6, 9, 13,* and *17,* the observed values of X obtained by throwing these dice once each being 8, 35, 49, 76, and 98, respectively.

Thus far we have conceptualized a probability distribution of X for each of the dice considered separately. Let us now consider the overall distribution of X, i.e., the distribution of all possible values that could be obtained by drawing dice one at a time, throwing each die once and recording the result. We shall refer to this distribution as the *composite probability distribution of X* or, more briefly, as the *composite distribution of X.* It is from this distribution that, using a two-stage sampling procedure, we have drawn a sample of five observations in the hypothetical experiment described above. As shown in Table 4-5, the values of X in this

TABLE 4-5 *Composite probability distribution of X*

X	1	2	$\cdots$	120
PROBABILITY	$\dfrac{1}{120}$	$\dfrac{1}{120}$	$\cdots$	$\dfrac{1}{120}$

$$\mu = 60.5; \; \sigma^2 = 1{,}199\frac{11}{12}$$

distribution are 1, 2, $\cdots$, 120, all of which have an equal probability of being included in the sample. In other words, $p_1 = p_2 = \cdots = p_{120} = 1/120$.

As a first step in analyzing the properties of our illustrative model let us determine the mean and variance of the composite distribution of X. The mean of this distribution, computed by Formula (4-6), is

$$\mu = \left(\frac{1}{120}\right) 1 + \left(\frac{1}{120}\right) 2 + \cdots + \left(\frac{1}{120}\right) 120$$

$$= 60.5$$

The variance, computed by Formula (4-7), is

$$\sigma^2 = \left(\frac{1}{120}\right)(1 - 60.5)^2 + \left(\frac{1}{120}\right)(2 - 60.5)^2 + \cdots + \left(\frac{1}{120}\right)(120 - 60.5)^2$$

$$= 1,199 \frac{11}{12}$$

The variation in X arises from two sources: (1) variation "within" individuals, i.e., variation of repeated determinations based upon the same individual, and (2) variation among individuals, i.e., individual differences. It is instructive to evaluate these two sources of variation separately, and it is to this task that we now turn.

To assess variation of repeated determinations based upon the same individual, we must consider separately the probability distribution of X for each individual in the population. For purposes of illustration, the probability distribution of X for Individual 1 is described in Table 4-6.

TABLE 4-6 *Probability distribution of X for Individual 1 (one of 20 individual probability distributions)*

X	1	2	3	4	5	6
PROBABILITY	$\frac{1}{6}$	$\frac{1}{6}$	$\frac{1}{6}$	$\frac{1}{6}$	$\frac{1}{6}$	$\frac{1}{6}$

$$\tau_1 = 3.5; \; \sigma_{\epsilon_1}^2 = 2\frac{11}{12}$$

This distribution describes the relative frequency with which each value of X occurs in the hypothetical population of all possible repeated determinations based upon Individual 1. To draw a sample of n observations from this hypothetical population we would measure Individual 1 (simulated by throwing Die 1) n times. It will be noted that, because we are here considering a single individual, the only values possible are 1, 2, $\cdots$, 6, the probability of each being $1/6$. Since we have already used the symbol μ to represent the mean of the composite distribution of X, it will help avoid confusion if we use τ, the Greek letter *tau*, to designate the mean for a given individual.   To identify the individual to which a particular value of τ corresponds we shall affix a numerical subscript.   For example, τ_1 denotes the mean of the probability distribution of X for Individual *1*; τ_2 denotes the mean of the probability distribution of X for Individual *2*; and so on.   Using Formula (4-6), τ_1 may be computed as follows:

$$\tau_1 = \left(\frac{1}{6}\right)1 + \left(\frac{1}{6}\right)2 + \cdots + \left(\frac{1}{6}\right)6 = 3.5$$

We shall denote the variance of the probability distribution of X for Individual *1* by $\sigma_{\epsilon_1}^2$, that for Individual *2* by $\sigma_{\epsilon_2}^2$, and so on.   (The subscript ϵ, the Greek letter *epsilon*, serves to distinguish the variance of X for a particular individual from σ^2, the variance of the composite distribution of X; the sub-subscripts 1, 2, $\cdots$, 20 serve to identify the particular individual in question.)   Using Formula (4-7), the variance of the probability distribution of X for Individual *1* may be computed as follows:

$$\sigma_{\epsilon_1}^2 = \left(\frac{1}{6}\right)(1 - 3.5)^2 + \left(\frac{1}{6}\right)(2 - 3.5)^2 + \cdots + \left(\frac{1}{6}\right)(6 - 3.5)^2 = 2\frac{11}{12}$$

By means of similar calculations it may be shown that for each of the 20 individuals $\sigma_\epsilon^2 = 2^{11}/_{12}$.   (Since $\sigma_{\epsilon_1}^2 = \sigma_{\epsilon_2}^2 = \cdots = \sigma_{\epsilon_{20}}^2$, there is no need to make a distinction among the values of σ_ϵ^2 for the various individuals, and this quantity will hereafter be written without a numerical sub-subscript.)   It has been noted in Chapter 1 that in actual psychological research the variation among repeated determinations based upon the same individual arises from a number of factors, including errors of measurement, individual inconsistency, and uncontrolled variations in the conditions of testing.   In an actual research situation σ_ϵ^2 would constitute a measure of the total variation arising from the combined effect of these three factors acting together.

We turn now to the second source of variation in our model, that associated with individual differences.   As a first step in assessing individual differences we compute τ for each of the 20 individuals in the population.   Making appropriate substitutions in Formula (4-6), the value of τ has been computed for each individual and the resulting values of τ have been recorded in the second column of Table 4-4.   Let us now imagine a hypothetical experiment in which we mix the 20 dice in an urn, draw a die at random, record the value of τ, and repeat the process for as many values of τ as desired, returning each die to the urn before drawing the next.   (It should be noted that an experiment such as described above would not be possible in actual practice, because the values of τ would be unknown.)   With reference to the sampling procedure described above we may treat the quantity τ as a random variable having the probability distribution summarized in Table 4-7.   We shall denote the mean and variance of the probability distribution of τ by μ_τ and σ_τ^2, respectively.

TABLE 4-7   *Probability distribution of* τ

τ	3.5	9.5	$\cdots$	117.5
PROBABILITY	$\dfrac{1}{20}$	$\dfrac{1}{20}$	$\cdots$	$\dfrac{1}{20}$

$$\mu_\tau = 60.5; \; \sigma_\tau{}^2 = 1,197$$

The amount of variation due to individual differences is indicated by the value of $\sigma_\tau{}^2$. If individual differences are small, i.e., if all individuals exhibit approximately the same level of performance, $\sigma_\tau{}^2$ will be small; on the other hand, large differences among individuals will result in a large value of $\sigma_\tau{}^2$. In order to compute the value of $\sigma_\tau{}^2$ we must first determine the value of μ_τ. Using Formula (4-6), the value of μ_τ is found to be 60.5, which is seen to be the same as the value of μ, the mean of the composite distribution of X. Substituting in Formula (4-7), the value of $\sigma_\tau{}^2$ for our illustrative model is computed as follows:

$$\sigma_\tau{}^2 = \left(\frac{1}{20}\right)(3.5 - 60.5)^2 + \left(\frac{1}{20}\right)(9.5 - 60.5)^2 + \cdots + \left(\frac{1}{20}\right)(117.5 - 60.5)^2$$

$$= 1,197$$

It might be well at this time to summarize the main points of the analysis so far. In a typical psychological experiment we might draw a sample of, say, five subjects and obtain a single observation from each under a specified set of circumstances. Using our model of 20 specially constructed dice, such an experiment can be simulated by selecting five dice (the analogues of individual subjects) one at a time, throwing each die once, and recording the values observed. A sample drawn in this fashion is a sample of five observations from the composite distribution of X summarized in Table 4-5. The mean of this probability distribution, designated μ, was computed to be 60.5; the variance, designated σ^2, was computed to be $1,199\,^{11}\!/_{12}$. The variation among the values of X in this distribution were seen to arise from two sources of variation—variation "within" dice (i.e., variation of repeated determinations based upon any given die) and differences among dice. These two sources of variation were evaluated numerically by computing $\sigma_\epsilon{}^2$ and $\sigma_\tau{}^2$, respectively. The first of these quantities, $\sigma_\epsilon{}^2$, is the variance of the probability distribution of X for a given die. Although this quantity could conceivably vary from die to die, depending upon the manner in which the faces of the various dice were numbered, in our particular model $\sigma_\epsilon{}^2$ has the same value for every die, namely, $2\,^{11}\!/_{12}$. The second of the above quantities, $\sigma_\tau{}^2$, is the variance among the individual means ($\tau_1, \tau_2, \cdots, \tau_{20}$) of the

20 dice and in our illustrative model was found to have a value of 1,197.

Finally, let us turn our attention to an important relationship among the values of σ^2, σ_τ^2, and σ_ϵ^2. An examination of the values of these three parameters in our illustrative model—$1,199\frac{11}{12}$, $1,197$, and $2\frac{11}{12}$, respectively—indicates that the following relationship holds:

$$\sigma^2 = \sigma_\tau^2 + \sigma_\epsilon^2 \tag{4-8}$$

In other words, the variance of X in the composite distribution of X is the sum of the variance associated with individual differences and the variance of repeated determinations based upon the same individual. This relationship will hold true in any model in which σ_ϵ^2 is the same for all individuals.

The concepts developed above in connection with our hypothetical model are useful in interpreting the variation that occurs among the observations obtained in certain kinds of psychological investigation. If the variable measured is of the kind that varies with repeated determinations based upon the same individual, and if each observation in a sample is based upon a different individual, then the total variation exhibited by the observations in the sample is a composite of variation due to individual differences and variation of repeated determinations, i.e., of the variation identified in our model as σ_τ^2 and σ_ϵ^2, respectively. In Chapter 8 we shall see how these two components of variation contribute to discrepancies that almost invariably occur between values of $\overline{X}$ based upon different samples drawn from the same population, or, what amounts to the same thing, samples drawn from two different populations in which the distributions of X are the same.[4]

PROBLEMS

1. Tom offers Jack the following bet: Jack is to toss a coin twice in succession. If the coin lands heads both times, Tom will pay Jack one dollar; if the coin does not land heads both times, Jack is to pay Tom one dollar. List all possible outcomes of such a procedure (tossing a coin twice in succession) and specify the probability of each outcome.

2. Let the random variable X be defined as the number of heads obtained when a coin is tossed twice in succession. The possible values of X are $X = 0$, $X = 1$, and $X = 2$. On the basis of your answer to Problem 1, specify the probability of each of these outcomes.

[4] At this point the reader might find it of value to re-examine the discussion of random sources of error in Chapter 1 and relate the remarks in that section to the concepts presented here.

3. On the basis of your answer to Problem 2, compute the mean and variance of the probability distribution of X.

4. Suppose that Tom and Jack repeat the procedure described in Problem 1 (tossing a coin twice in succession) 100 times. Approximately how many times would Jack win the bet, i.e., how many times would the coin land heads on both tosses? Approximately how many times would Tom win?

5. In the game of craps, two dice are rolled at the same time, and the outcome of the game depends upon the sum of the values on the two dice. (In actual practice, this game is usually played using two dice of the same color. However, for purposes of identifying the two dice, let us assume in the present problem that two distinctively colored dice—one red, one white—are used.) (a) List all possible outcomes that could be obtained when two such dice are rolled. (b) What is the probability of each of the possible outcomes? (c) Let the random variable S be defined as the sum of the values on the two dice. What are the possible values of S? How many outcomes give rise to each of the possible values of S; in other words, in how many different ways can each value of S occur? (d) Prepare a table summarizing the probability distribution of S. (e) Compute the mean and variance of the probability distribution of S.

6. An apartment building has 20 floors, each with ten apartments, with one family residing in each apartment. Identify the sampling plan described in each of the following procedures: (a) Three apartments (families) are selected from each of the 20 floors by means of a lottery. (b) The 200 apartments are identified by number, and 60 apartments are selected from the list by means of a lottery, disregarding the floor on which each apartment is located. (c) Three apartments—those nearest the elevator—are selected from each floor. (d) Ten floors are selected by means of a lottery, and from each of these floors six apartments are selected by means of a further lottery, a separate lottery being performed on each of the ten floors in question.

7. On a given test of perceptual-motor skill, the measure obtained is the time required to sort 200 objects into six bins on the basis of shape. For well-practiced subjects the variance of repeated determinations, i.e., the variance of the probability distribution of X for a given individual, is 25. The variance associated with individual differences, i.e., the variance among the means of the probability distributions of different individuals, is 100. (a) Identify the value of σ_ϵ^2, σ_τ^2, and σ^2 for this situation. (b) Let X represent a random variable the value of which is determined by selecting one individual randomly and testing him once. What is the variance of the probability distribution of X; in other words, if an indefinitely large number of values of X were obtained in this manner (selecting a new individual for each observation), what would be the value of the variance of X? (c) If any given individual were tested 20 times in succession, what value would the sample variance based upon these 20 observations approximate? (d) If each of 20 individuals were tested once each, what value would the sample variance based upon these 20 observations approximate?

REFERENCES

HOEL, P. G. *Introduction to mathematical statistics* (2d ed.). New York: Wiley, 1954.

MOOD, A. M. and F. A. GRAYBILL. *Introduction to the theory of statistics* (2d ed.). New York: McGraw-Hill, 1963.

ADDITIONAL READINGS

COCHRAN, W. G. Design and analysis of sampling. In G. W. Snedecor, *Statistical methods applied to experiments in agriculture and biology* (5th ed.). Ames, Iowa: Iowa State College Press, 1956. Pp. 489–523. A discussion of several commonly used sampling procedures.

HUFF, D. *How to lie with statistics.* New York: W. W. Norton, 1954. Chap. 1. An entertaining discussion of some practical problems encountered in sampling and of how inadequate sampling may produce misleading results.

KEMPTHORNE, O. The design and analysis of experiments with some reference to educational research. In R. O. Collier, Jr., and S. M. Elam (eds.), *Research design and analysis: second annual Phi Delta Kappa symposium on educational research.* Bloomington, Ind.: Phi Delta Kappa, 1961. Pp. 97–126. A lucid discussion of the problems encountered in defining and sampling the populations of interest in behavioral and biological research. Although portions of this article are of a technical nature, many of the basic ideas are presented in a nontechnical fashion.

LACEY, O. L. *Statistical methods in experimentation.* New York: Macmillan, 1953. Chaps. 3 and 4. Presents the basic concepts of probability theory and shows in an elementary manner how the concepts are extended to the distribution of continuous variables.

MC CARTHY, P. J. *Introduction to statistical reasoning.* New York: McGraw-Hill, 1957. Chap. 6 (a detailed discussion of simple random sampling) and Chap. 10 (an introduction to more complex methods of sampling).

MOSTELLER, F., R. E. K. ROURKE, and G. B. THOMAS, JR. *Probability and statistics.* Reading, Mass.: Addison-Wesley, 1961. Chaps. 3–5. A systematic presentation of the basic concepts of probability theory.

STEPHAN, F. F. and P. J. MC CARTHY. *Sampling opinions.* New York: Wiley, 1958. A comprehensive treatment of the concepts and methods of sampling written at a level that is suited to the reader without extensive mathematical background.

WALKER, HELEN M. and J. LEV. *Statistical inference.* New York: Holt, 1953. Chap. 2 (elementary probability theory) and Chap. 12 (individual differences and variation of repeated determinations).

WILKS, S. S. *Elementary statistical analysis.* Princeton: Princeton Univ. Press, 1949. Chaps. 4 and 5. An introduction to the basic concepts of probability theory.

YATES, F. *Sampling methods for censuses and surveys* (3d ed.). New York: Hafner, 1960.

CHAPTER 5

the normal distribution

IN THIS CHAPTER WE SHALL DIGRESS BRIEFLY FROM OUR DEVELOPMENT of the theory of statistical inference to consider the basic properties of the normal distribution. The digression will be more apparent than real, however, because in the chapters that follow we shall find that the concepts and procedures developed in connection with the normal distribution have important applications to the topic of statistical inference.

GENERAL CHARACTERISTICS OF THE NORMAL DISTRIBUTION

The normal distribution is one of a number of theoretical distributions that can be described by a smooth curve. As shown in Figure 5-1, representation of a distribution by a smooth curve is similar in concept to representation by a histogram. Part *A* of Figure 5-1 shows a histogram of an idealized distribution in which a relatively wide class interval is employed. In Part *B* the same distribution is represented in a second histogram differing from the first in that a narrower class interval has been employed. To compensate for the fact that each class is narrower and therefore contains fewer cases, the vertical scale has been expanded so that the total areas of the two histograms are the same. The class interval is reduced still further in Part *C*, with the necessary adjustment in the vertical scale again being made. A comparison of the histograms in Parts *A*, *B*, and *C* shows that as narrower and narrower class intervals are employed, the steps in the enclosing outline become finer and finer. If the process is continued to the limiting case in which the class interval is zero, the enclosing outline of the histogram becomes a smooth curve such as depicted in Part *D*.

The curve describing the normal distribution is a symmetrical, bell-shaped curve like that shown in Part *D* of Figure 5-1.   The normal curve

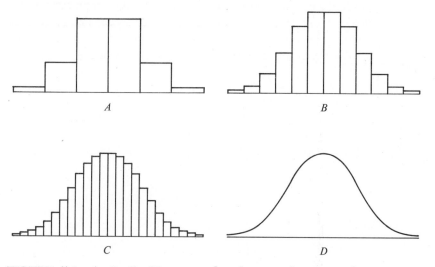

FIGURE 5-1   *A, B, C: Histograms based upon class intervals of varying widths. D: Smooth curve.*

is asymptotic to the baseline on either side of the mean; that is, with increasing distance from the mean the curve approaches the baseline more and more closely but never quite reaches it.   Thus, no matter how far from the mean a point on the scale is located, a portion of the distribution is still more extreme, i.e., located further out.   However, as we shall see, beyond a certain point the proportion of the normal distribution located in the tails of the distribution is so small as to be negligible.

It is emphasized that the normal distribution is a mathematical ideal and, as such, does not actually occur in nature.   However, a number of naturally occurring distributions very closely resemble the mathematical ideal, and the normal distribution provides a useful approximation in such cases.   For example, it was observed by Galton (1889) that the distribution of men's heights is closely approximated by the normal distribution. Similarly, the distributions of scores on many psychological tests—for example, IQ tests and tests of school achievement—are well approximated by the normal distribution.   Not only is the normal distribution useful as an approximation of certain natural distributions, but, as we have noted, it also has a number of important applications in the theory of statistical inference, some of which we shall consider in later chapters.

AREAS OF THE NORMAL DISTRIBUTION

The probability that a value of X drawn at random from a normal distribution will lie below some fixed value is given by the proportion of the total area under the normal curve to the left of a vertical line erected at the fixed value. This statement may be illustrated with reference to Figure 5-2, which pictures a normal distribution in which $\mu = 100$ and

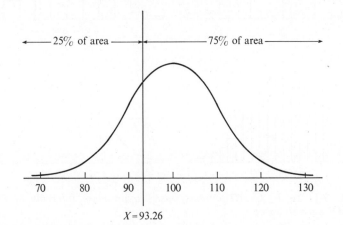

FIGURE 5-2 *Normal distribution in which* $\mu = 100$ *and* $\sigma = 10$. *Twenty-five per cent of the total area lies to the left of the vertical line at* X = 93.26; *75 per cent of the area lies to the right of the line.*

$\sigma = 10$.   (To make the illustration concrete, we may think of this figure as representing the distribution of scores of a population of college students on a test of academic achievement.[1])   Twenty-five per cent of the total area of this distribution lies to the left of the vertical line at $X = 93.26$; accordingly, the probability is .25 that the value of X for an individual drawn at random from the population in question will lie below $X = 93.26$. Conversely, the probability is .75 that a randomly drawn value of X will lie above this value.

It is readily apparent that if the distribution shown in Figure 5-2 had a different location (μ) or a different dispersion (σ), then the proportion of the distribution below $X = 93.26$ would be changed. In general, in order to specify the proportion of the area of a normal distribution below a given value of X we must know the distance—measured in

---

[1] In actual practice, test scores are usually discrete variables, i.e., are recorded as whole-number values. However, in examples involving test scores, we shall make the simplifying assumption that the scores are distributed continuously.

standard deviation units—of that value from μ. For example, in any normal distribution, whatever the value of μ and σ, 84.13 per cent of the total area is located below the value of X that is one standard deviation above μ. Thus, in a normal distribution in which $\mu = 100$ and $\sigma = 10$, 84.13 per cent of the total area is located below $X = 110$; in a normal distribution in which $\mu = 20$ and $\sigma = 5$, 84.13 per cent of the total area is located below $X = 25$; and so on. Approximate proportions of the total area between points one standard deviation above and below μ, between points two standard deviations above and below μ, and between

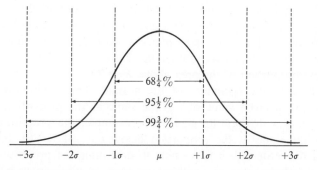

FIGURE 5-3 *Proportions of the area of the normal distribution between values one standard deviation above and below μ, between values two standard deviations above and below μ, and between values three standard deviations above and below μ.*

points three standard deviations above and below μ are given in Figure 5-3. The figure indicates that approximately 68¼ per cent (roughly two-thirds) of the total area lies between the value located one standard deviation below μ and the value located one standard deviation above μ, approximately 95½ per cent lies between the values located -2σ and $+2\sigma$ from μ, and virtually all of the distribution (99¾ per cent) lies between the values located -3σ and $+3\sigma$ from μ.

More detailed information concerning areas of the normal distribution is given in Tables A-2 and A-3 of Appendix A. The use of these tables is explained below in connection with four basic types of problem involving areas of the normal distribution.

1. *Given a value of X, determine the proportion of the area of the normal distribution below that value.* An example of this type of problem is the following: In a normal distribution with $\mu = 60$ and $\sigma = 8$, what proportion of the total area lies below $X = 72$? The first step in solving this problem is to determine the distance from μ in σ units of the value in question. This distance, symbolized by z, may be computed as follows:

$$z = \frac{X - \mu}{\sigma} \qquad (5\text{-}1)$$

It will be noted that the numerator of this fraction is the distance between X and μ in raw score units; dividing by σ gives the distance in σ units. Solving for z in the illustrative problem, we obtain $z = (72 - 60)/8 = 12/8 = 1.5$. In other words, a score of 72 is located one and one-half standard deviations above the mean in the distribution described above. The proportion of the area below this value of z may be determined by reference to Table A-2, which gives the proportions of the total area located below selected values of z, varying in steps of .05 from $z = -3.25$ to $z = 3.25$. We find in Table A-2 that the proportion of the area below $z = 1.5$ is .9332—roughly 93 per cent. If, instead, we wished to determine the proportion of the area *above* a score of 72, the required proportion could be obtained by subtracting .9332 from 1, i.e., $1 - .9332 = .0668$ is the proportion of the area above $X = 72$.

(Because of the symmetry of the normal curve, the proportion of the area above a given value of z is the same as the proportion below a like value of z with opposite sign. For example, the proportion above $z = 1.5$ is the same as the proportion below $z = -1.5$. By taking advantage of this property, it is possible to determine the proportion of the area above a given value of z without resorting to subtraction; it is necessary only to read from Table A-2 the proportion below a like value of z of opposite sign. For example, to determine the proportion above $z = 1.5$, simply take the proportion given in the table for $z = -1.5$, which is seen to be .0668. Conversely, the proportion above $z = -1.5$ is .9332, the same as the proportion below $z = 1.5$.)

2. *Given a certain proportion of the total area of the normal distribution, determine the value of X below which that proportion lies.* Example: A nationally used college entrance examination has $\mu = 500$ and $\sigma = 100$. What is the 90th percentile of this distribution? In this problem we are given a certain proportion of the area and must find first the corresponding value of z and then the corresponding value of X. We could use Table A-2 for this purpose; however, Table A-3, which is organized in terms of selected areas of special interest, is more accurate in this case. From this table we read that the value of z having 90 per cent of the area below it is 1.282. Substituting all of the available information in Formula (5-1), we obtain

$$1.282 = \frac{X - 500}{100}$$

It is a matter of elementary algebra to solve the above equation for X, obtaining $X = 628.2$.

3. *Given two values of X, find the proportion of the area of the normal distribution lying between those values.* Example: In the distri-

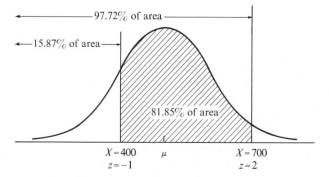

FIGURE 5-4 *Computation of the proportion of the area of the normal distribution lying between two specified values of X.*

bution of examination scores described above $(\mu = 500, \sigma = 100)$, what proportion of the cases lies between $X = 400$ and $X = 700$? The basic approach to solving this type of problem is straightforward: determine the proportion of the area below each of the scores in question; the difference is the proportion of the area between those scores. We first compute z corresponding to $X = 400$ as follows: $z = (400 - 500)/100 = -1$. Similarly, for $X = 700$ we compute $z = 2$. From Table A-2 we find that the proportions of the area lying below these two values of z are .1587 and .9772, respectively. The computations thus far are summarized in Figure 5-4. The proportion of the area between the two scores in question is represented by the shaded portion of the curve. By subtracting the smaller from the larger proportion, the shaded portion is computed to be .8185.

4. *Given a certain proportion of the area of the normal distribution, determine two points, equidistant above and below μ, between which that proportion is located.* Example: In the distribution of examination scores

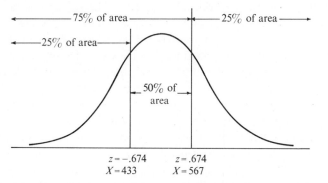

FIGURE 5-5 *Determination of two symmetrically located values of X between which a specified proportion of the area of the normal distribution is located.*

described above ($\mu = 500$, $\sigma = 100$), what two scores include the middle 50 per cent of the distribution? This problem may be solved as follows: Subtracting .50, the proportion of the area between the two unknown scores, from 1.00 (the total area), it is determined that .50 of the area is located in the tails of the distribution. Dividing by 2, we find that .25 of the distribution is located in each tail. Thus, as shown in Figure 5-5, 25 per cent of the total area lies below the lower of the two scores, and 75 per cent lies below the higher of the two scores. According to Table A-3, the values of z corresponding to these percentages are $-.674$ and $+.674$, respectively. Substituting the first of these values of z in Formula (5-1), we obtain $-.674 = (X - 500)/100$. Solving for X, we obtain $X \approx 433$ as the lower of the two scores. By similar computations we may determine the higher of the two scores, $X \approx 567$. Thus, the middle 50 per cent of the distribution is located between $X \approx 433$ and $X \approx 567$.

NORMALIZED STANDARD SCORES (T SCORES)

In earlier chapters we considered the problem of providing a frame of reference against which to evaluate individual observations. One solution to this problem was the conversion of all raw scores in a distribution to standard scores (Z scores) having a known mean and standard deviation, thus obtaining scores with built-in information concerning their standing in the reference distribution. In this section an alternative method of encoding information about a reference distribution will be described.

According to this method, each raw score is converted to a so-called *normalized standard score* or *T score*. The method consists of two steps: we first determine the percentile rank of each score in the original distribution, and then assign each score a new value, namely, the value that would have the same percentile rank in a normal distribution having a mean of 50 and a standard deviation of 10. The use of this method will be illustrated using the distribution of vocabulary test scores originally presented in Figure 2-1 and reproduced in tabular form in Table 5-1. Following a convention described earlier, the data, though discrete, will be treated for purposes of determining percentile ranks as if each class represents an interval throughout which the corresponding observations are evenly distributed; accordingly, the observations in a given class will be treated as if half of them were located below the midpoint of that class and half above. Thus, when we speak of the frequency or proportion of cases below a given whole-number value, we shall understand this frequency to include half the cases having the value in question, plus all cases having lower values. For example, in determining the percentile rank of the raw score 15, we add three cases (half the total number of cases in the 15-item class) to the nine cases included in the four lower

TABLE 5-1   *Computation of T scores*

RAW SCORE (ITEMS CORRECT)	FREQUENCY	CUMULATIVE FREQUENCY TO MIDPOINT	CUMULATIVE PROPORTION TO MIDPOINT	z	T SCORE 50 + 10z
23	1	29.5	.9833	2.1	71
22	2	28.0	.9333	1.5	65
20	1	26.5	.8833	1.2	62
18	5	23.5	.7833	.8	58
17	3	19.5	.6500	.4	54
16	3	16.5	.5500	.1	51
15	6	12.0	.4000	−.3	47
14	1	8.5	.2833	−.6	44
13	6	5.0	.1667	−1.0	40
11	1	1.5	.0500	−1.6	34
10	1	.5	.0167	−2.1	29

classes, obtaining a total of 12 cases below the value 15. Dividing by 30, the total number of cases in the distribution, we obtain .40 as the proportion of cases below $X = 15$. We now ask this question: If a hypothetical variable, T, were normally distributed with a mean of 50 and a standard deviation of 10, what value of T would have the same percentile rank as the raw score 15, i.e., below what value of T would 40 per cent of the distribution be located? Our problem is one of the second type considered in the previous section. Beginning with the equation $z = (T - \mu)/\sigma = (T - 50)/10$ and solving for T, we obtain

$$T = 50 + 10z \qquad (5\text{-}2)$$

Referring to Table A-3, we find that the value of z below which 40 per cent of the area is located is $z = -.253$. Substituting in Formula (5-2), we obtain $T = 50 - 2.53 = 47.47$. Normally, values of T are determined to the nearest whole number and our result would be recorded as $T = 47$.

If it is desired to express the results of a test in the form of T scores, a T score is usually computed for each raw score in the original distribution, as illustrated in Table 5-1 for the distribution of scores on a vocabulary test. The computations summarized in the table are similar to those discussed above for a raw score of 15. Because the final values of T are rounded to the nearest whole number, values of z, obtained by interpolation in Table A-2, are recorded to the first decimal only. The end result of these computations is that each raw score listed in the first column has been converted to the corresponding T score listed in the last column, the latter score being the value that in a normal distribution with $\mu = 50$ and $\sigma = 10$ has the same percentile rank as the corresponding raw score has in the distribution of raw scores.

Superficially, T scores may seem similar to Z scores having a mean of 50 and a standard deviation of 10 (Chapter 3). However, certain distinctions between the two types of scores should be noted. First, a T score of 50 indicates that the corresponding raw score is the median of the original distribution, whereas a Z score of 50 indicates that the corresponding raw score is the mean of the original distribution. (It will be recalled that the median and mean coincide in symmetrical distributions but not in skewed ones.) Second, except when the original distribution is normal, the percentile ranks of Z scores do not conform to those of a normal distribution. Third, except when the original distribution is normal, conversion to T scores alters the relative distances between scores; in effect, the scale is "stretched" at some points and "compressed" at others to make the percentile ranks of the scores conform to those of a normal distribution. For example, the T scores corresponding to raw scores of 10 and 11 in Table 5-1 are 29 and 34, respectively—a difference of 5 points. On the other hand, the T scores corresponding to raw scores of 16 and 17 are 51 and 54, respectively—a difference of only 3 points. In contrast, when raw scores are converted to Z scores the change is uniform throughout the scale, i.e., the relative distances among scores remain fixed.

It should be noted that the normal distribution is not the only theoretical distribution that could be used for encoding information concerning the percentile rank of raw scores; any of a wide variety of theoretical distributions could be employed for the same purpose. The chief advantages of the normal curve for this purpose are (1) that tables specifying proportions of the area of the normal distribution are readily available and (2) workers in the field of testing are familiar with the properties of the normal distribution through long experience, so a system based on the normal curve takes advantage of well-established habits of interpretation.

PROBLEMS

1. A nationally used test of high-school achievement is constructed so that, for the national population of high-school graduates, scores on this test are distributed approximately normally with $\mu = 100$ and $\sigma = 20$. (a) What proportion of high-school graduates achieve a score of 100 or better on this test? (b) What proportion achieve a score of 130 or better? (c) What proportion achieve a score between 100 and 130? (d) In a random sample of 1,000 high-school graduates, approximately how many individuals would have scores in the range between 100 and 130?

2. The scores of a given test are distributed normally with $\mu = 80$ and $\sigma^2 = 36$. (a) What proportion of the population has scores of 71 or better?

(*b*) What is the 30th percentile of this distribution? (*c*) What two scores include the middle 60 per cent of the distribution? (*d*) What proportion of the population has scores between $X = 68$ and $X = 86$?

3. The scores of a given test are distributed with $\mu = 100$ and $\sigma = 10$. (*a*) Determine the two values of X between which the middle 95 per cent of the test scores are located. (*b*) What is the probability that the score of a randomly selected individual will lie outside these limits? (*c*) Determine the two values of X between which the middle 99 per cent of the test scores are located. (*d*) What is the probability that the score of a randomly selected individual will lie outside these limits?

4. The scores of 50 students on a short objective quiz were distributed as follows:

X	3	4	5	6	7	8	9	10
Frequency	1	1	2	8	11	13	10	4

Compute to the nearest whole-number value the normalized standard score (*T* score) corresponding to each value of X.

REFERENCE

GALTON, F. *Natural inheritance.* London: 1889. Cited by Helen Walker, *Studies in the history of statistical method.* Baltimore: Williams & Wilkins, 1929.

ADDITIONAL READINGS

DIXON, W. J. and F. J. MASSEY, JR. *Introduction to statistical analysis* (2d ed.). New York: McGraw-Hill, 1957. Chap. 5.

EDWARDS, A. L. *Statistical methods for the behavioral sciences.* New York: Rinehart, 1954. Chap. 6. A discussion of *T* scores.

GUILFORD, J. P. *Fundamental statistics in psychology and education* (3d ed.). New York: McGraw-Hill, 1956. Chap. 7 (a general discussion of the normal distribution) and Chap. 19 (a detailed discussion of *T* scores).

UNDERWOOD, B. J., C. P. DUNCAN, JANET A. TAYLOR, and J. W. COTTON. *Elementary statistics.* New York: Appleton-Century-Crofts, 1954. Chap. 7.

CHAPTER 6

sampling distributions

THE REASON FOR DRAWING A SAMPLE FROM A POPULATION IS, OF COURSE, to obtain information concerning the distribution of values in the population. Usually, when we compute a statistic on the basis of the observations in a sample, we are interested in that statistic not only as a description of the sample but also as an estimate of the corresponding parameter of the population. For example, we regard $\overline{X}$, the sample mean, as an estimate of μ, the population mean; similarly, we regard s^2, the sample variance, as an estimate of σ^2, the population variance. However, intuition tells us that the use of a statistic to estimate a parameter is likely to involve a certain degree of error, i.e., we cannot as a rule expect a statistic based on any given sample to have exactly the same value as the corresponding parameter. In this chapter we will examine the extent of the errors involved in using $\overline{X}$ as an estimate of μ and will consider the factors that influence the magnitude of such errors. A similar, though less extensive, examination will be made of s^2 as an estimate of σ^2.

Before proceeding with our analysis it is necessary to specify certain characteristics of the sampling procedure on which the analysis is based, because different sampling procedures lead to somewhat different results. First, it should be noted that the details of the theoretical analysis vary depending upon which of the major types of sampling procedure discussed in Chapter 4—simple random sampling, stratified sampling, sampling in two stages, or systematic sampling—is employed. We shall confine our attention here to simple random sampling, the sampling procedure for which the theoretical analysis is least complicated. A similar analysis of more complex sampling procedures will be found in Cochran (1953), Deming (1950), and Sukhatme (1954). A further distinction must be made between sampling procedures in which the probability distribution of X remains unchanged throughout sampling and those in which the probability distribution is altered in the course of sampling. Consider, for example, the problem of drawing a sample of cards from an ordinary playing deck, and assume we are interested in the value obtained (ace, deuce, · · · , queen, king), disregarding suit. If we sample with replacement, i.e., return each card to the deck before drawing the next, the probability distribution of X will be the same for each card drawn. On the other hand, if we sample without replacement, i.e., if we do not return each card to the deck before drawing the next, the probability distribution of X changes with each card drawn. On the first draw the probability of each of the possible values of X is the same, namely 4/52. However, if the first card drawn should happen to be an ace, of the 51 cards remaining in the deck only three will be aces; consequently, on the second draw the probability of obtaining an ace will be only 3/51, whereas the probability associated with each of the other possible values of X will be 4/51. In the discussion that follows we shall confine our attention to sampling procedures in which the probability distribution of X remains the same throughout sampling. This general case includes not only sampling with replacement from a finite population, considered above, but sampling from infinite populations as well (e.g., obtaining a sample of all possible throws of a die). Strictly speaking, the results of our analysis will not be applicable to situations in which a finite population is sampled without replacement. However, it is of interest to note that for situations in which the number of individuals included in the sample is but a small proportion of the total number of individuals in a finite population, as is often the case in practice, the results are very nearly the same whether sampling is with or without replacement. Under these conditions, the theory applicable to sampling with replacement affords a very good approximation of the results obtained when sampling is without replacement.

THE SAMPLING DISTRIBUTION OF $\overline{X}$

The reader is reminded that in actual practice an experimenter typically has no information concerning a population other than that provided by the sample he observes. However, in order to gain an appreciation of how good an estimate of μ is provided by $\overline{X}$, it is useful to study values of $\overline{X}$ based upon samples drawn from a model population the characteristics of which are fully known. In such a situation it is possible, as it is not in practice, to compare values of $\overline{X}$ with the value of μ to determine the size of the errors involved.

Let us take as our illustrative population all possible throws of a specially constructed die. To simplify the arithmetic involved we will consider a die made in the form of a tetrahedron—a pyramid-shaped object having four triangular faces—the values assigned to the four faces being 1, 5, 7, and 11. (Using a die of this type, we would take as the value of X on a given trial the value of the side on which the die comes to rest. In order to relate this model to a population of the type encountered in psychological research, we may, as in previous examples, think of all possible throws of such a die as corresponding to all possible measures of the performance of a given individual on a specified task.) The probability distribution of X for this population is described in Table 6-1.

TABLE 6-1 *Model population. Probability distribution of X for throws of a four-sided die*

X	1	5	7	11
PROBABILITY	$\frac{1}{4}$	$\frac{1}{4}$	$\frac{1}{4}$	$\frac{1}{4}$

$$\mu = 6, \sigma^2 = 13$$

Using Formulae (4-6) and (4-7), the reader may verify that for this population $\mu = 6$ and $\sigma^2 = 13$.

The errors that occur when parameters are estimated on the basis of data in a sample are called *sampling errors*. To illustrate this type of error let us estimate μ for the population described above by computing $\overline{X}$ for a sample drawn at random from that population. In one sample of five throws the values obtained were 1, 5, 1, 5, and 7; the mean of this sample is 3.8, the error in estimating μ being -2.2. Of course, in another sample the values obtained and the error involved might have been different. For example, the values in a second sample of five throws were 11, 11, 7, 1, and 7; in this case, the sample mean is 7.4, which deviates from μ by $+1.4$.

In order to evaluate $\overline{X}$ as an estimate of μ we require information concerning the probability distribution of $\overline{X}$ for samples of a given size, i.e., we need to know the probability of each of the possible values of $\overline{X}$ for a sample of the size in question. This theoretical distribution is called the *sampling distribution of* $\overline{X}$ or the *sampling distribution of the mean*. In order to keep the computations within reasonable bounds we shall investigate the sampling distribution of $\overline{X}$ for an experiment in which the sample includes only two observations. We first enumerate all possible outcomes of such an experiment (i.e., all possible samples that could be obtained), as shown in Table 6-2.

TABLE 6-2 *All possible samples of two observations from model population*

1, 1	1, 5	1, 7	1, 11
5, 1	5, 5	5, 7	5, 11
7, 1	7, 5	7, 7	7, 11
11, 1	11, 5	11, 7	11, 11

In the sample in the upper left cell, the value 1 occurs on both throws of the die; in the sample described in the next cell to the right, the value 1 is obtained on the first throw, the value 5 on the second; and so on. The reader should study Table 6-2 to satisfy himself that it lists all possible outcomes of the experiment described and that all outcomes listed are different. (A question might be raised as to whether the outcome (1, 5) is really different from the outcome (5, 1). Although for certain purposes the difference might be regarded as unimportant, these two outcomes are differentiated by the order in which the two values occur and, for present purposes, must be regarded as distinct.) Inasmuch as the 16 outcomes listed in Table 6-2 are all equally probable, the probability of each is 1/16. The values of $\overline{X}$ for the 16 possible samples are shown in Table 6-3 in an array corresponding to the listing of samples in Table 6-2.

TABLE 6-3 *Values of $\overline{X}$ for all possible samples of two observations*

1	3	4	6
3	5	6	8
4	6	7	9
6	8	9	11

We note that not all 16 samples give rise to a distinctive value of $\overline{X}$. Let us therefore determine how many different values of $\overline{X}$ are possible and the probability of each. We note that the value 1 occurs in only one of the 16 outcomes; hence, the probability of this value of $\overline{X}$ is 1/16. On the other hand, the value 3 occurs in two of the 16 outcomes; thus the probability is 1/16 + 1/16 = 2/16 that $\overline{X}$ will equal 3 in the experiment described. Continuing in this manner, we can determine the probability of each of the possible values of $\overline{X}$. The results of such an analysis are summarized in Table 6-4 and represented in graphic form in Figure 6-1. The information given—a listing of all possible values of $\overline{X}$ and the probability of each—constitutes a description of the sampling distribution of $\overline{X}$ for an experiment in which the sample includes two observations drawn at random from the model population described in Table 6-1.

TABLE 6-4 *Sampling distribution of* $\overline{X}$. *Probability of all possible values of* $\overline{X}$ *for a sample of two observations*

$\overline{X}$	1	2	3	4	5	6	7	8	9	10	11
PROBABILITY	$\frac{1}{16}$	0	$\frac{2}{16}$	$\frac{2}{16}$	$\frac{1}{16}$	$\frac{4}{16}$	$\frac{1}{16}$	$\frac{2}{16}$	$\frac{2}{16}$	0	$\frac{1}{16}$

The sampling distribution of $\overline{X}$ may be viewed as a theoretical distribution describing the manner in which $\overline{X}$ would be distributed if a large number of samples of a given size were drawn at random from a given population and $\overline{X}$ computed separately for each sample. For example, if 1,000 random samples were drawn from the illustrative population de-

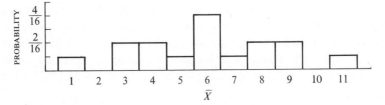

FIGURE 6-1 *Sampling distribution of* $\overline{X}$. *The area of each rectangle represents the probability of the corresponding value of* $\overline{X}$.

scribed in Table 6-1 (each sample consisting of two observations obtained by throwing the pyramidal die twice), each of the possible values of $\overline{X}$ would occur with a relative frequency approximating the probability specified for that value in Table 6-4. It is emphasized that the hypothetical procedure of drawing a large number of samples from the same population is described merely as an aid in conceptualizing the meaning of the sampling distribution of $\overline{X}$ and that such a procedure is not typically employed in actual research. In practice an investigator typically draws but one sample from a given population and computes $\overline{X}$ for that sample. The sampling distribution of $\overline{X}$ is a theoretical distribution, not one that is observed in practice.

The mean of the sampling distribution of $\overline{X}$ will be represented by the symbol $\mu_{\overline{X}}$ (μ with the subscript $\overline{X}$) in order to distinguish it from μ, the mean of the population sampled. Substituting in Formula (4-6) the values given in Table 6-4, $\mu_{\overline{X}}$ may be computed as follows: $\mu_{\overline{X}} = (1/16)1 + (2/16)3 + \cdots + (1/16)\,11 = 6$. It will be noted that $\mu_{\overline{X}}$ has the same value as μ, the mean of the original population. This finding illustrates a general principle of major importance, one which holds true for any population: *The mean of the sampling distribution of $\overline{X}$ is equal to the mean of the population sampled, i.e.,*

$$\mu_{\overline{X}} = \mu \tag{6-1}$$

Because on the average $\overline{X}$ is equal to μ, $\overline{X}$ is said to be an *unbiased estimate* of μ. More generally, a given statistic is said to be an unbiased estimate of a given parameter if the mean of the sampling distribution of that statistic is equal to the parameter in question. It is emphasized that, although the statistic $\overline{X}$, considered abstractly, is an unbiased estimate of μ, the particular value of $\overline{X}$ computed on the basis of data in a particular sample may not be equal to μ. Indeed, although $\overline{X}$ usually provides a reasonable approximation of μ, more often than not $\overline{X}$ deviates from μ to some extent. When we say that a statistic is an unbiased estimate of a parameter, we are not making a statement concerning the value of that statistic for a particular sample but a statement concerning the theoretical sampling distribution of that statistic.

The variance of the sampling distribution of $\overline{X}$—or, as it is also called, the *variance of the mean*—is represented by the symbol $\sigma_{\overline{X}}^2$ (σ^2 with the subscript $\overline{X}$). Using the values given in Table 6-4, this quantity may be computed by means of Formula (4-7) as follows: $\sigma_{\overline{X}}^2 = (1/16)\ (1 - \mu_{\overline{X}})^2 + (2/16)\ (3 - \mu_{\overline{X}})^2 + \cdots + (1/16)\ (11 - \mu_{\overline{X}})^2 = 13/2$. The value $13/2$ may, of course, be reduced to 6.5. It has been presented in unreduced form in order to illustrate more clearly a second principle of major importance: *The variance of the sampling distribution of $\overline{X}$ is equal to the variance of the population divided by the sample size, i.e.,*

$$\sigma_{\overline{X}}^2 = \frac{\sigma^2}{n} \tag{6-2}$$

This relationship, like that described in Formula (6-1), holds true for any population. According to Formula (6-2), the variance of the sampling distribution of $\overline{X}$ depends upon the sample size considered. In the limiting case in which $n = 1$, the variance of the sampling distribution of $\overline{X}$ is equal to that of the population sampled; for all larger samples the variance of the sampling distribution of $\overline{X}$ is less than that of the population.

The *precision* of a statistic refers to the dispersion of the sampling distribution of that statistic, i.e., the extent of variation about the mean of the sampling distribution. When values remote from the mean of the sampling distribution have an appreciable probability of occurrence, the statistic in question is said to be low in precision; when values remote from the mean have only a small probability of occurrence, the precision is high. When a statistic is an unbiased estimate of a parameter, i.e., when the mean of the sampling distribution of the statistic is equal to the parameter estimated, then the precision of the statistic is an indication of how closely the possible values of the statistic conform to the value of that parameter. One measure of the precision of $\overline{X}$ as an estimate of μ is $\sigma_{\overline{X}}$, the square root of the variance of the mean. This quantity, the standard deviation of the sampling distribution of $\overline{X}$, is called the *standard error of the mean*. Taking the square root of both sides of Formula (6-2), we obtain the following formula for the standard error of the mean:

$$\sigma_{\overline{X}} = \frac{\sigma}{\sqrt{n}} \tag{6-3}$$

According to Formula (6-3), the standard error of the mean is inversely proportional to the square root of n, i.e., $\sigma_{\overline{X}}$ decreases as n increases, approaching zero as n approaches infinity. Thus, an investigator who employs a small sample risks a sizable discrepancy between his value of $\overline{X}$ and the actual value of μ, whereas the investigator who employs a larger sample increases the probability that his value of $\overline{X}$ will lie reasonably close to μ. The manner in which $\sigma_{\overline{X}}$ varies with changes in n is shown graphically in Figure 6-2.

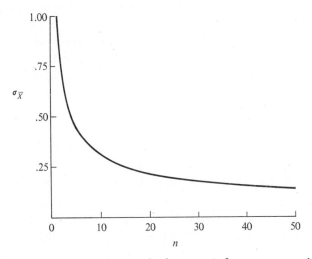

FIGURE 6-2 *Variation in the standard error of the mean as a function of sample size* (n). *For illustrative purposes values of* $\sigma_{\overline{X}}$ *have been computed for samples from a population in which* $\sigma = 1$.

It is apparent from the figure that, in terms of the reduction in $\sigma_{\overline{X}}$, successive increments in sample size result in diminishing returns. For example, increasing sample size from 1 to 10 results in a fairly substantial reduction in $\sigma_{\overline{X}}$ (increase in precision), whereas increasing sample size from 41 to 50 results in a much smaller reduction of $\sigma_{\overline{X}}$.

EXPERIMENTAL ERROR

In Chapter 1 it was noted that when several observations are obtained under a given set of experimental conditions—for example, when several subjects are tested under the same experimental treatment—a certain amount of variation attributable to random sources of error occurs among the values of the observations obtained. The variation among observations obtained under the same experimental treatment is referred to as *experimental error* and may be identified with σ^2, the variance of the hypothetical population of all possible observations that could conceivably be obtained under the conditions in question.

It follows from Formula (6-3) that the precision of $\overline{X}$ may be increased ($\sigma_{\overline{X}}$ reduced) by decreasing experimental error. One way of reducing experimental error is to reduce individual differences among subjects. This aim is perhaps most readily accomplished in research with animal subjects, where it is often possible to employ genetically pure strains and to carefully control the past experience of the subjects, but it may also be accomplished to a limited extent in research with human subjects. For example, in some tasks it is possible to decrease individual differences in performance by giving all subjects preliminary practice on a task of the kind on which they are to be tested. Another way of reducing experimental error is to increase the uniformity of the experimental conditions under which observations are obtained. For example, in testing animal subjects it is often possible to reduce experimental error by such means as carefully controlling the time between feeding and testing, shielding the test apparatus against extraneous noises that are likely to disrupt performance, and holding temperature and humidity within narrow limits.

Skinner (1956) has argued that too often investigators have been satisfied to increase the precision of $\overline{X}$ by using large samples when more is to be gained by reducing experimental error. He points out that in order to reduce experimental error we must discover and learn to control the many factors that affect performance, and that in accomplishing this aim we increase our understanding of behavior and our ability to control it. That is to say, once we have refined our experimental techniques to the point where there is a high degree of consistency (low σ^2) among the observations obtained under a given set of conditions, we are much closer to having achieved control over behavior to a degree that is useful in practice.[1]

THE SHAPE OF THE SAMPLING DISTRIBUTION OF $\overline{X}$

Thus far we have seen how the mean and variance of the sampling distribution of $\overline{X}$ are related to those of the population sampled, but nothing

[1] Some of the ways in which the causes of variability in behavioral research may be discovered and controlled are discussed in detail by Sidman (1960, Part III).

has been said concerning the shape of the sampling distribution of $\overline{X}$. In general, the shape of this distribution varies with two factors: (1) the shape of the population sampled and (2) the size of the sample considered. At one extreme—for samples of one case only—the sampling distribution of $\overline{X}$ is identical in shape to the population sampled; at the other extreme—for infinitely large samples—the sampling distribution of $\overline{X}$ is normal (provided only that the variance of the population sampled is not infinite); for samples of intermediate size the sampling distribution of $\overline{X}$ is intermediate in shape between the population sampled and a normal distribution.

It follows from the above considerations that if the values in the original population are distributed normally, the sampling distribution of the mean is also normal, regardless of sample size. Consequently, when the original population is normal, it is possible, using the methods described in Chapter 5, to solve problems concerning areas of the sampling distribution of the mean. Particularly important is the fact that it is possible to determine the proportion of the area of the distribution located between any two values of $\overline{X}$, or, what amounts to the same thing, the probability that $\overline{X}$ will lie between two specified values.

The determination of areas of the sampling distribution of $\overline{X}$ may be illustrated by means of the following problem:

> The scores on a given IQ test are distributed normally with $\mu = 100$ and $\sigma = 16$. If a sample of four individuals is drawn at random, what is the probability that the mean IQ of the individuals in the sample will lie within 10 points of μ, i.e., that $\overline{X}$ will lie between 90 and 110?

Drawing a random sample of four individuals from a population of individuals and computing $\overline{X}$ may be conceptualized alternatively as drawing a single, randomly selected value of $\overline{X}$ from the sampling distribution of $\overline{X}$. The question posed in the above problem may therefore be rephrased as follows: What proportion of the area of the sampling distribution of $\overline{X}$ (for samples of four cases) lies between $\overline{X} = 90$ and $\overline{X} = 110$? The properties of the sampling distribution may be derived from the facts given concerning the population sampled: from the fact that $\mu = 100$, we deduce that $\mu_{\overline{X}} = 100$; from the fact that $\sigma = 16$ and $n = 4$, we compute $\sigma_{\overline{X}} = 16/\sqrt{4} = 16/2 = 8$. Moreover, because the original population is normally distributed, the sampling distribution of $\overline{X}$ is also normally distributed. Thus, the sampling distribution is normal with a known mean and variance, so we may readily compute the proportion of this distribution located between $\overline{X} = 90$ and $\overline{X} = 110$. We proceed by computing the value of z corresponding to each of these values of $\overline{X}$ and determining the proportion of the distribution below each value; finally, we obtain the proportion of the area between $\overline{X} = 90$ and $\overline{X} = 110$ by subtracting the smaller proportion from the larger.

Because we are dealing with a sampling distribution, the formula for
z presented earlier is somewhat modified in the present problem.   Corresponding to X, the value of an individual observation in Formula (5-1),
we have $\overline{X}$, the value of a sample mean, in the present problem.   Similarly, corresponding to μ in Formula (5-1), we have $\mu_{\overline{X}}$ in the present
problem, and in place of σ in Formula (5-1), we now have $\sigma_{\overline{X}}$.   Making
these changes, the formula for z becomes

$$z = \frac{\overline{X} - \mu_{\overline{X}}}{\sigma_{\overline{X}}} \tag{6-4}$$

For $\overline{X} = 90$, we compute $z = (90 - 100)/8 = -1.25$; for $\overline{X} = 110$, we
compute $z = (110 - 100)/8 = 1.25$.   The proportions of the total area
below these two values of z, .1056 and .8944, respectively, are represented schematically in Figure 6-3.

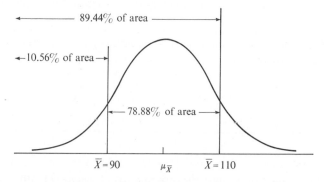

FIGURE 6-3   *Proportion of the sampling distribution of $\overline{X}$ between $\overline{X} = 90$
and $\overline{X} = 110$. Based upon a sample of four cases from a population in which
$\mu = 100$ and $\sigma = 16$.*

The proportion of the area between $\overline{X} = 90$ and $\overline{X} = 110$ is .7888,
roughly 79 per cent.   In other words, the probability is approximately .79
that the mean IQ of a random sample of four individuals will lie between
the values $\overline{X} = 90$ and $\overline{X} = 110$.

Even when the distribution of observations in the population from
which a sample is drawn is not normal, the sampling distribution of $\overline{X}$ is
closely approximated by a normal distribution if the sample is sufficiently
large.   In such cases, the closeness of the approximation will depend not
only upon sample size, but also on the shape of the population distribution.
As a rule of thumb, it has been suggested that for most purposes the sampling distribution of $\overline{X}$ may be treated as a normal distribution whenever
a sample of 30 cases or more is employed.

THE SAMPLING DISTRIBUTION OF s^2

Just as a variety of values of $\overline{X}$ are possible when a sample is drawn from a population, in computing any statistic a variety of different values of that statistic are possible, depending upon the particular values included in the sample. In other words, whenever we compute any statistic, we may conceive a sampling distribution of that statistic. In this section we will examine the sampling distribution of the sample variance, s^2.

For purposes of illustration, we will consider samples drawn from the model population described earlier in this chapter—all possible throws of a four-sided die having the values 1, 5, 7, and 11 on its faces. As in studying the sampling distribution of $\overline{X}$, we shall investigate the sampling distribution of s^2 for an experiment in which the sample includes two observations. We begin by computing s^2 for each of the 16 possible outcomes listed in Table 6-2. These values of s^2 are listed in Table 6-5 in an

TABLE 6-5   *Values of s^2 for all possible samples of two observations*

0	8	18	50
8	0	2	18
18	2	0	8
50	18	8	0

array corresponding to the array of outcomes in Table 6-2. A listing of the possible values of s^2 and the probability of each—in other words, a description of the sampling distribution of s^2—is presented in Table 6-6.

TABLE 6-6   *Sampling distribution of s^2. Probability of all possible values of s^2 for a sample of two observations*

s^2	0	2	8	18	50
PROBABILITY	$\frac{4}{16}$	$\frac{2}{16}$	$\frac{4}{16}$	$\frac{4}{16}$	$\frac{2}{16}$

The mean of the theoretical sampling distribution of s^2 will be represented by the symbol μ_{s^2}. (Alternatively, the mean value of s^2 may be written $E(s^2)$, the expected value of s^2.) Using Formula (4-6), μ_{s^2} may be computed for the distribution represented in Table 6-6 as follows: $\mu_{s^2} = (4/16)0 + (2/16)2 + \cdots + (2/16)50 = 13$. We note that the value of μ_{s^2} is equal to σ^2, the variance of the population sampled. This relationship is a general one and may be stated as follows: *The sample variance, s^2, is an unbiased estimate of σ^2, the population variance.* Stated symbolically,

$$\mu_{s^2} = \sigma^2 \tag{6-5}$$

The reason for defining s^2 with a denominator of $n - 1$, rather than n, is now apparent: when computed as defined, s^2 is an unbiased estimate of σ^2. If computed with a denominator of n, all values of s^2 would be slightly decreased, decreasing the mean of the sampling distribution, thus providing a biased estimate of σ^2.

The shape of the sampling distribution of s^2 depends upon the shape of the population sampled and the sample size in question. For samples drawn from a normal population, the sampling distribution of s^2 is positively skewed, the extent of skewness being greater, the smaller the sample size.

We shall not be concerned with the variance of the sampling distribution of s^2 except to note that for samples drawn from a normal population, the precision of s^2 increases as n increases. In other words, a value of s^2 based upon a large sample is more likely to be close to the value of σ^2, the parameter estimated, than is a value of s^2 based upon a small sample.

SUMMARY

When a sample is drawn from a population and a statistic computed on the basis of the observations in the sample, that statistic may take any of several possible values, depending upon the particular observations included in the sample. An enumeration, for a given sample size, of all possible values of a given statistic and the probability of each value constitutes a description of the sampling distribution of that statistic for the sample size in question.

Because the sampling distribution of a given statistic depends upon the characteristics of the sampling procedure employed, an analysis of the sampling distribution of a statistic is specific to a particular kind of sampling procedure. In this chapter the sampling distribution of $\overline{X}$ and the sampling distribution of s^2 were examined for situations in which the probability distribution of X is the same throughout sampling, a type of sampling that is exemplified by throwing a die n times or by random sampling with replacement from a finite population. The mean and variance of the sampling distribution of $\overline{X}$ were found to be related to the parameters of the population sampled as follows: $\mu_{\overline{X}} = \mu$ and $\sigma_{\overline{X}} = \sigma^2/n$. Concerning the sampling distribution of s^2, it was found that $\mu_{s^2} = \sigma^2$. Although an exact formula for the variance of the sampling distribution of s^2 was not given, it was noted that for samples from a normally distributed population the variance of the sampling distribution of s^2, like that of the sampling distribution of $\overline{X}$, is smaller for large samples than for small samples.

It is emphasized that the sampling distribution of any given statistic is a theoretical distribution and is not observed in practice. The sampling distribution of a statistic may be conceptualized as a description of the manner in which values of that statistic would be distributed if computed for each of a large number of samples of a given size all drawn from the same population. In practice, however, an investigator typically draws but a single sample from a given population and computes but a single value of a given statistic. Although the details—i.e., the actual mean and variance—of the sampling distribution of the statistic in question are usually not known by the investigator, a knowledge of the general principles relating the characteristics of the sampling distribution to the characteristics of the population sampled is of value in enabling the investigator to make allowance for potential sampling errors. The manner in which such knowledge is put to use is the subject of several of the chapters that follow.

PROBLEMS

1. Two ordinary dice—one red and one white—are rolled at the same time, and $\overline{X}$, the mean of the two values obtained, is computed. For example, if the values obtained are 4 on one die and 6 on the other, $\overline{X}$ is equal to $(4 + 6)/2 = 5$. (a) Determine each of the possible values of $\overline{X}$ and the probability of each; in other words, describe the sampling distribution of $\overline{X}$. (Note: The results obtained in Problem 5, Chapter 4, will be useful in arriving at the answer to the present problem.) (b) What is the probability that $\overline{X}$ will be equal to 5.0 or more? (c) Compute $\mu_{\overline{X}}$ and $\sigma_{\overline{X}}^2$ directly from the sampling distribution of $\overline{X}$ obtained above. (d) From calculations presented in Chapter 4, it is known that the random variable X, the outcome of the roll of one die, is distributed with $\mu = 3.5$ and $\sigma^2 = 2\,{}^{11}\!/_{12}$. Making use of this information, determine the value of $\mu_{\overline{X}}$ and the value of $\sigma_{\overline{X}}^2$—for $\overline{X}$ based on two random values of X—using Formulae (6-1) and (6-2), respectively. How do these values compare with those computed directly from the sampling distribution of $\overline{X}$?

2. An investigator wishes to estimate μ, the mean running speed in a runway, using a particular food reward. For a given investment of time and money, he estimates that he can either test 36 animals, using standard procedures and existing facilities, for which experimental error is $\sigma^2 = 36$, or he can test 25 animals, using an improved (but more time-consuming) procedure,

for which experimental error is $\sigma^2 = 16$. For which alternative is the precision of $\overline{X}$ greater?

3. An investigator draws a sample of nine cases from a population that is approximately normally distributed with $\mu = 80$ and $\sigma^2 = 36$. (*a*) What is the probability that $\overline{X}$ will lie within three units of μ, i.e., between 77 and 83? (*b*) What two values include the middle 95 per cent of the sampling distribution of $\overline{X}$?

4. Answer Parts (*a*) and (*b*) of Problem 3, assuming that a sample of 36 cases is employed. Compare these results with those based on a sample of nine cases (Problem 3).

5. A population is distributed normally with $\mu = 100$ and $\sigma^2 = 250$. Assuming that a random sample of ten cases is drawn from this population, what is the probability that $\overline{X}$ will lie within 5 units of μ, i.e., between 95 and 105?

6. Suppose that, in the situation described in Problem 5, the value of σ^2 is 160 (rather than 250). Under these conditions, what is the probability that $\overline{X}$ will lie within 5 units of μ? How does this result compare with that obtained in Problem 5?

7. Two hundred members of a statistics class each draw a random sample of ten cases from a model population in which $\mu = 30$ and $\sigma^2 = 50$. Each student computes $\overline{X}$, the sample mean based upon his ten observations, and the 200 values of $\overline{X}$ obtained by the class are summarized in a frequency distribution. (*a*) What theoretical distribution does the resulting distribution approximate? (*b*) What theoretical value will be approximated by the mean of the class distribution? (*c*) What theoretical value will be approximated by the variance of the class distribution?

8. Two hundred members of a statistics class each draw a random sample of ten cases from a model population in which $\mu = 30$ and $\sigma^2 = 50$. Each student computes s^2, the sample variance based upon his ten observations, and the 200 values of s^2 obtained by the class are summarized in a frequency distribution. (*a*) What theoretical distribution does the resulting distribution approximate? (*b*) What theoretical value will be approximated by the mean of the class distribution?

REFERENCES

COCHRAN, W. G. *Sampling techniques.* New York: Wiley, 1953.
DEMING, W. E. *Some theory of sampling.* New York: Wiley, 1950.
SIDMAN, M. *Tactics of scientific research.* New York: Basic Books, 1960.
SKINNER, B. F. A case history in scientific method. *Amer. Psychologist,* 1956, **11,** 221–233.
SUKHATME, P. V. *Sampling theory of surveys with applications.* Ames, Iowa: Iowa State College Press, 1954.

ADDITIONAL READINGS

EDWARDS, A. E.   *Statistical analysis* (rev. ed.).   New York: Rinehart, 1958.
Chap. 9.   An elementary discussion of the sampling distribution of the
mean.

FREUND, J. E.   *Modern elementary statistics* (2d ed.).   Englewood Cliffs,
N. J.: Prentice-Hall, 1960.   Chap. 9.   An elementary discussion of
sampling distributions.

MOSTELLER, F., R. E. K. ROURKE, and G. B. THOMAS, JR.   *Probability and statistics.*   Reading, Mass.: Addison-Wesley, 1961.   Chap. 9.   Gives a mathematical derivation of the properties of the sampling distribution of the
mean.

WILKS, S. S.   *Elementary statistical analysis.*   Princeton: Princeton Univ. Press,
1949.   Chap. 9.   An elementary discussion of sampling distributions with
a mathematical derivation of the properties of the sampling distribution of
the mean.

CHAPTER 7

statistical inference (1):

inferences concerning a single population

EQUIPPED WITH THE CONCEPT OF SAMPLING DISTRIBUTION, WE ARE PRE-pared to consider the basic procedures of statistical inference, the process of drawing conclusions concerning a population on the basis of information provided by a sample. In this chapter two types of inference will be considered: (1) testing a hypothesis concerning the mean of a population and (2) specifying limits—so-called *confidence limits*—within which the mean of a population is asserted, with a specified degree of confidence, to lie.

TESTING A HYPOTHESIS CONCERNING μ

In certain situations we may wish to determine whether the mean of a population has a particular value. The possibility that the population mean has this value constitutes a hypothesis that can be tested by an ex-periment. Broadly speaking, the procedure employed in testing such a hypothesis is as follows: A sample is drawn from the population in ques-tion, the mean of the sample is determined, and, depending upon the value of the sample mean, a decision is made either to accept the hypothesis or reject it. If the sample mean is reasonably close to the value of μ specified by the hypothesis, the hypothesis is accepted as tenable; on the other hand, if the sample mean departs widely from the hypothetical value of μ—more widely than might reasonably be expected on the basis of sampling error—then the hypothesis is rejected as untenable in the light of the information provided by the sample.

The computations employed in testing a hypothesis vary somewhat, depending upon whether the variance of the population sampled is known or unknown; these two cases will be considered separately.   In actual practice the population variance is usually not known, so a presentation of the latter method would suffice for most practical purposes.   However, because the basic theory involved can be presented more simply for the case in which the population variance is known, this method will be considered first.

PROBLEMS IN WHICH σ^2 IS KNOWN

To illustrate the procedure involved let us consider the following hypothetical problem:

A marksman wishes to determine whether the horizontal (left-right) setting of his gunsight is accurate.   To test the setting he fires a sample of ten shots at a vertical line target.   As illustrated in Figure 7-1, the shots are scattered, some to the left of the line and some to the right of the line.

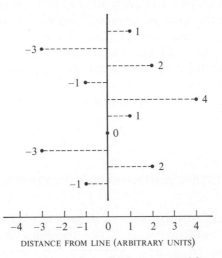

DISTANCE FROM LINE (ARBITRARY UNITS)

FIGURE 7-1   *Location of ten shots fired at vertical-line target.*

A number is assigned to each shot according to its distance from the line, measured along the scale at the bottom.   In this problem the population of interest is the hypothetical population of all possible shots that could be fired at the target with the existing setting of the sight.   Let us assume that on the basis of extensive experience with this type of rifle it is known that σ^2, the variance of the population of shots, is 4.9 and that the population distribution is normal. If the sight is adjusted correctly, the shots will be grouped about the line used as a target, and the average value of all shots in the population will be zero. Thus, the hypothesis that the sight is correctly adjusted may be stated in terms of μ as follows: $\mu = 0$. The alternative to this hypothesis is that the population mean is not equal to zero; it may be written $\mu \neq 0$. The latter statement includes all possibilities other than $\mu = 0$—for example, $\mu = -4$, $\mu = -1$, $\mu = 5$, and so on.

The ten shots actually fired in the test may be regarded as a random sample drawn from the population of all possible shots. The mean of the sample is .20, and we must decide on the basis of this mean whether to accept or reject the hypothesis that $\mu = 0$. Because of sampling error, we expect some discrepancy between the mean of a sample and the hypothesized mean of the population, but just how great a discrepancy should we tolerate before rejecting the hypothesis? Before answering this question in detail, let us examine the logic of the situation in broad terms.

On the one hand, it is possible that the hypothesis $\mu = 0$ is true. Since we have assumed in our illustration that the population of all possible shots is normally distributed, it follows that the sampling distribution of $\overline{X}$ is also normal; consequently, extreme deviations of $\overline{X}$ from zero, although not very likely, are possible. Therefore, no matter how large a discrepancy we require between $\overline{X}$ and zero in order to reject the hypothesis that $\mu = 0$, we must recognize the possibility that such an extreme deviation could occur as a consequence of sampling error, resulting in rejection of this hypothesis even though it is true. An error of this type is called an *error of the first kind* or a *Type I error*.

On the other hand, it is possible that the hypothesis $\mu = 0$ is false. It may be, for example, that μ is actually equal to 1. If this is the case, the sampling distribution of $\overline{X}$ will be centered at the actual value of μ rather than the hypothetical value, and we are more likely to obtain a value of $\overline{X}$ leading us to reject the hypothesis that $\mu = 0$ than if that hypothesis were true. However, even under these conditions (i.e., that $\mu = 1$) it is possible to obtain a value of $\overline{X}$ close to zero, causing us to accept the false hypothesis that $\mu = 0$. An error of this type is called an *error of the second kind* or a *Type II error*.

In general, we must accept as a limitation of the procedures involved that we cannot rule out entirely the possibility of making an error of one kind or the other: when the hypothesis we are testing is true, we cannot avoid some risk of rejecting it, thereby committing a Type I error; when the hypothesis we are testing is false, we cannot rule out altogether the possibility of accepting it, thereby committing a Type II error. (The experimenter, of course, never knows which type of situation prevails—if he did, a test would be unnecessary—and he therefore does not know which of the two types of error he is liable to make.) In the light of these limitations, the goals of our test procedure may be put as follows: first, to incur only a slight risk of rejecting a true hypothesis, and second, insofar as possible, to maximize the chances of rejecting a false hypothesis. As will be demonstrated in detail in a later subsection, the probability of rejecting a false hypothesis depends upon the true state of affairs, i.e., the actual value of μ. The procedure described below for testing a hypothesis concerning μ has the very reasonable characteristic that when the hypothesis being tested is false, the greater the discrepancy between (a) the value of μ according to the hypothesis being tested and (b) the actual value of μ, the greater is the probability that the (false) hypothesis will be rejected.

The procedure for testing a hypothesis concerning μ is based upon the sampling distribution of $\overline{X}$ *under the conditions stated by the hypothesis.* In the gunsight problem presented above, we are told that the population from which the sample was drawn has a variance of 4.9. Being concerned with the sampling distribution for samples of ten cases, we compute the variance of the mean as follows: $\sigma_{\overline{X}}^2 = 4.9/10 = .49$, from which it follows that $\sigma_{\overline{X}} = .7$. According to the hypothesis being tested, the mean of the population of shots is zero. If this hypothesis is true, then $\mu_{\overline{X}}$, the mean of the sampling distribution of $\overline{X}$, is also zero. Knowing the variance of the sampling distribution and the mean implied by the hypothesis, we may select two values of $\overline{X}$, one above $\mu_{\overline{X}}$ and one the same distance below, such that values of $\overline{X}$ equal to or more extreme than the selected values will have only a small probability of occurring—say, 5 chances in 100—if the hypothesis tested is true. The values of $\overline{X}$ setting off the extreme 5 per cent (or other proportion of the sampling distribution of $\overline{X}$), when computed for purposes of testing a hypothesis, are called *critical values.* In Figure 7-2, which pictures the sampling distribution of $\overline{X}$ implied by the hypothesis that $\mu = 0$, the locations of the two critical values are indicated by vertical lines, each setting off one tail of the dis-

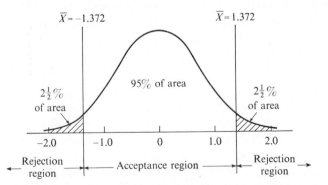

FIGURE 7-2 *Sampling distribution of $\overline{X}$, showing critical values for testing the hypothesis that $\mu = 0$. Based upon $\sigma^2 = 4.9$, $n = 10$, and $\alpha = .05$.*

tribution.   The range of values between the two critical values is called the *acceptance region;* if the obtained value of $\overline{X}$ lies within this range, the hypothesis being tested is accepted.   Values of $\overline{X}$ equal to or more extreme than the critical values are referred to collectively as the *rejection region;* if the observed value of $\overline{X}$ lies in this region, i.e., in either tail of the distribution, the hypothesis is rejected.   Loosely speaking, the critical values delimit a range of values of $\overline{X}$ that might reasonably be expected to occur when the hypothesis is true; because values of $\overline{X}$ more extreme than the critical values, i.e., values of $\overline{X}$ lying in the rejection region, are unlikely to occur if the hypothesis is true, such values are taken as evidence that the hypothesis is false.

The computation of critical values of $\overline{X}$ is a problem of the fourth type considered in connection with the normal distribution in Chapter 5. We note that, with a total of 5 per cent of the area of the sampling distribution of $\overline{X}$ in the two tails, each tail includes 2.5 per cent of the area. Accordingly, the two values of $\overline{X}$ that we seek are the values below which 2.5 per cent and 97.5 per cent of the sampling distribution of $\overline{X}$ are located.   Following the procedures described in Chapter 6, we begin with the formula for z, written as follows: $z = (\overline{X} - \mu_0)/\sigma_{\overline{X}}$, in which μ_0 represents the value of $\mu_{\overline{X}}$ implied by the hypothesis being tested.   Starting with the higher value of z—the value below which 97.5 per cent of the normal distribution lies—and substituting in the above equation, we obtain $1.960 = (\overline{X} - 0)/.7$.   Solving for $\overline{X}$, we obtain $\overline{X} = 1.372$ as the point below which 97.5 per cent of the sampling distribution of the mean is located.   By similar calculations the point below which 2.5 per cent of the distribution of $\overline{X}$ is located is found to be $\overline{X} = -1.372$.   The value of $\overline{X}$ in the sample observed was found to be .20.   Since this value lies between -1.372 and 1.372, i.e., in the acceptance region, the hypothesis that $\mu = 0$ is accepted; the discrepancy between the observed value of $\overline{X}$ and the hypothetical value of μ is not sufficiently great to cause us to reject the hypothesis that the sight is adjusted correctly.

In the above problem the critical values were selected so that the proportion of the area of the sampling distribution in the rejection region —hence, the risk of rejecting a true hypothesis—was .05.   This level of risk was, of course, an arbitrary one, and any other value desired by the investigator could have been selected.   The levels of risk employed most often in practice are .05 and .01—five chances in 100 and one chance in 100, respectively—of rejecting a true hypothesis.   The reader may wonder why even these levels of risk are tolerated in testing a hypothesis.   Why, he may ask, do we not reduce the probability of a Type I error to a level that is really negligible, say, .000001?   The answer to this question is that to do so would require setting the critical values of $\overline{X}$ so far apart, i.e., including such a broad range of values in the acceptance region, that it would be virtually impossible to reject a hypothesis even when it is seriously in error.   Our aim in performing a test is not only to accept a hypothesis when it is true, but to reject it when it is false.   Therefore, in selecting critical values, we must allow a reasonable possibility of rejecting a hypothesis when it is false, and this requires that we incur some risk of rejecting it when it is true.   (The connection between the risk of rejecting a true hypothesis, i.e., a Type I error, and the probability of rejecting a false hypothesis will be examined in greater detail later in the chapter.)

The reader should become familiar with the notation and terminology commonly used in connection with the level of risk of a Type I error.   The symbol α (the Greek letter *alpha*) is commonly used to designate the proportion of the area of the sampling distribution located in the rejection region, i.e., the probability of a Type I error.   If an observed value of $\overline{X}$ lies in the rejection region, it is said to be *statistically significant* or, more simply, *significant*—it signifies that the hypothesis being tested is to be rejected.   The value of α is referred to as the *level of significance*.   If, for example, α is taken as .05, an observed value of $\overline{X}$ in the rejection region is said to be *significant at the .05 level,* and the hypothesis being tested is said to be rejected at the *.05 level of significance*.   In the gunsight problem presented above, the obtained value of $\overline{X}$ lay in the acceptance region and therefore was not statistically significant at the .05 level; that is to say, it did not deviate widely enough from the hypothetical mean to cause us to reject the hypothesis that $\mu = 0$.

The steps in testing a hypothesis concerning μ may be summarized as follows:

1. Decide the size of sample to be employed and the risk to be taken of a Type I error (α).

2. Determine the sampling distribution of $\overline{X}$ implied by the hypothesis, and on the basis of this information compute critical values such that the probability of a Type I error is limited to the value of α decided upon. The critical values are selected so that the proportion of the sampling distribution of $\overline{X}$ in each tail of the distribution beyond the critical values is equal to one-half α.

3. Draw a random sample and compute $\overline{X}$. If $\overline{X}$ lies in the acceptance region, accept the hypothesis; otherwise, reject it.

It should be emphasized that, just as rejecting a hypothesis does not guarantee it is false, accepting a hypothesis does not assure that it is true. To demonstrate this point, let us return to the gunsight problem discussed above and test the hypothesis that $\mu = 1$, i.e., that the gunsight is out of adjustment by a specified amount. Under this hypothesis, the critical values of $\overline{X}$ are $-.372$ and 2.372. The obtained value of $\overline{X}$, .20, is seen to lie in this region, *leading to acceptance of the hypothesis that* $\mu = 1$. But we have already accepted the hypothesis that $\mu = 0$. How can both of these hypotheses be true? The answer, of course, is that they cannot. Both of them have been accepted as *tenable* in the light of the data available, but neither has been proven true. In general, acceptance of a hypothesis is not to be regarded as proof that the hypothesis is true; an accepted hypothesis is but one of several alternatives that are tenable.

We have seen that it is inherent in the nature of the procedures used for testing statistical hypotheses that sometimes the conclusions reached will be false—either a true hypothesis may be rejected or a false hypothesis may be accepted. What, then, becomes of these inescapable errors? Do they become a permanent part of the conclusions of science? Although such false conclusions are unavoidably held for a time, the error is usually discovered sooner or later if the conclusions are important. One way an error may come to light is in the attempt of a second investigator to repeat the observations of a first. Another way such errors may be discovered is in testing predictions based upon an erroneous conclusion. If the predictions are not borne out, the premise upon which they are based becomes suspect, and the earlier experiment, upon which the erroneous conclusion was based, may be repeated.

THE POWER OF A TEST[1]

We have noted that in testing a hypothesis we wish to limit the probability of rejecting it if it is true and at the same time to maximize the probability of rejecting it if it is false. Up to this point we have been chiefly concerned with the situation in which the hypothesis being tested is true. We now turn our attention to the situation in which the hypothesis being tested is false.

The concepts to be considered may be illustrated with reference to the following problem.

> An investigator knows that in a given population the scores on a certain test are normally distributed with a variance of 200; he does not, however, know the exact mean of the population. He draws a sample of eight cases and on the basis of $\overline{X}$ tests the hypothesis that $\mu = 100$. Contrary to his hypothesis, the mean of the population is actually 105. Assuming the investigator adopts the .05 level of significance, what is the probability that he will reject the false hypothesis he is testing?

In dealing with a problem of this type, two sampling distributions must be distinguished: (1) the sampling distribution of $\overline{X}$ *according to the*

[1] The ideas concerning power presented in this and the following three subsections derive from a general theory of hypothesis testing developed by Neyman and Pearson (1933) and described somewhat less technically by Neyman (1950).

hypothesis and (2) the *actual* sampling distribution of $\overline{X}$. It is on the basis of the first of these distributions that critical values are determined—the second distribution is unknown to the investigator. On the basis of his information concerning the population variance, the investigator in the above problem would compute the standard error of the sampling distribution of $\overline{X}$ as follows: $\sigma_{\overline{X}}^2 = \sigma^2/n = 200/8 = 25$; $\sigma_{\overline{X}} = \sqrt{25} = 5$. On the basis of the hypothesis that $\mu = 100$, the critical values for a test at the .05 level of significance are $\overline{X} = 90.2$ and $\overline{X} = 109.8$. The situation is represented in Figure 7-3. The upper distribution is the sampling

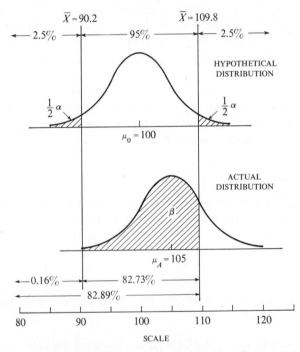

FIGURE 7-3 *Hypothetical and actual sampling distributions of $\overline{X}$ in testing a false hypothesis. Based upon $\sigma^2 = 200$, $n = 8$, and $\alpha = .05$.*

distribution of $\overline{X}$ according to the hypothesis. Critical values, indicated by vertical lines, have been computed so that 95 per cent of the area of this distribution lies in the acceptance region. The lower distribution is the actual sampling distribution of $\overline{X}$, the mean of which is designated μ_A. The problem is to determine the proportion of the area of the latter distribution lying between the critical values, i.e., in the acceptance region. This proportion, designated β (the Greek letter *beta*), is the probability of accepting the hypothesis that $\mu = 100$ even though it is false.   In other words, β is the probability of a Type II error.

The first step in computing β is to determine the distance, in standard-error units, of each critical value from μ_A, the mean of the actual sampling distribution—i.e., to compute, relative to μ_A, a value of z corresponding to each of the two critical values.   For the higher of the two critical values, $z = (109.8 - 105)/5 = .96$; for the lower, $z = (90.2 - 105)/5 = -2.96$.   Reading Table A-2 to the nearest tabled value of z, the proportion of the area lying below the upper critical value is .8289; the proportion below the lower critical value is .0016.   By subtraction, β (the area between these two values) is found to be .8273; under the conditions described, there are roughly 83 chances in 100 of committing a Type II error.

The *power* of a statistical test is the probability of rejecting a false hypothesis using the test in question.   Power may be defined in terms of β as follows:

$$\text{Power} = 1 - \beta$$

In the problem discussed above, for example, the power of the test is $1 - .83 = .17$.   Thus, while the probability of rejecting the hypothesis that $\mu = 100$ would be .05 if that hypothesis were true, the probability of rejection increases to .17 in a situation in which the actual value of μ is 105.   This probability is represented by the unshaded area of the lower (actual) distribution pictured in Figure 7-3.

The value of a statistical test lies in its power to reject a hypothesis that is false; because a statistical test is undertaken with the express purpose of rejecting a hypothesis if it is false, the greater the power of a test, the better.

FACTORS AFFECTING POWER: THE ACTUAL VALUE OF μ

The power of a statistical test is not a fixed value, but varies with a number of factors.   We consider first how power varies depending upon the value of μ_A, the actual mean of the population sampled.   It is apparent from inspection of Figure 7-3 that the greater the distance between μ_0 (the hypothetical value of μ) and μ_A (the actual value of μ), the greater will be the proportion of the area of the actual sampling distribution lying outside the acceptance region, i.e., the greater will be the power of the test to reject the hypothesis being tested.   This important principle will be illustrated by examining the power associated with several values of μ_A.   Assuming $\sigma^2 = 200$, $n = 8$, $\alpha = .05$, and the hypothesis to be tested is $\mu = 100$, the value of the actual mean will be assumed in turn to be 105, 110, 115, and 120, and in each case power will be computed.   The sampling distributions involved are depicted in Figure 7-4.

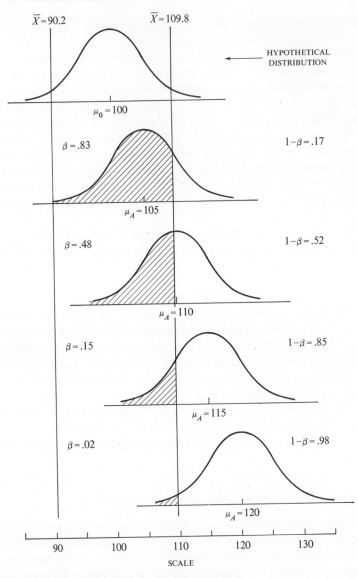

FIGURE 7-4 *Power for various alternatives to μ_0.*

The top distribution is the hypothetical one, on the basis of which
critical values are computed; the remaining distributions are alternatives
having the means listed above.   (It should be noted that in any given
problem there is only one actual sampling distribution of $\overline{X}$; what is being
done here is to determine what the power would be *if* the actual mean
were 105, *if* it were 110, and so on.)   The values of β and of power for
the several distributions are summarized in Table 7-1.

TABLE 7-1 *Probability of rejecting hypothesis* $\mu = 100$ *for several values of actual mean*

ACTUAL MEAN	PROBABILITY OF ACCEPTING HYPOTHESIS	PROBABILITY OF REJECTING HYPOTHESIS
100	.95	.05
105	.83	.17
110	.48	.52
115	.15	.85
120	.02	.98

Because of the symmetry of the distributions involved, it can be seen that the same values of power would be obtained for distributions located equal distances below the hypothetical distribution, i.e., for distributions having means equal to 95, 90, 85, $\cdots$, respectively. The values of power for the various alternative values of μ_A have been plotted in Figure 7-5 and connected with a smooth curve.

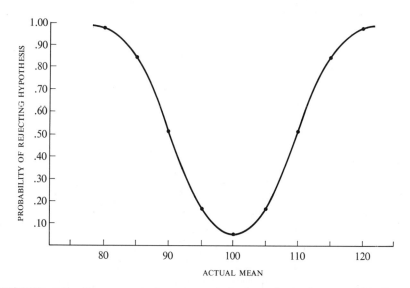

FIGURE 7-5 *Power curve for a test of the hypothesis that* $\mu = 100$. *Based upon the following values:* $\sigma^2 = 200$, $n = 8$, *and* $\alpha = .05$.

This curve is called the *power curve* of the test. It shows that power approaches a minimum of α as the actual mean approaches the hypothetical one, and a maximum of 1.00 as the distance between the actual mean and the hypothetical mean increases. This curve graphically demonstrates a highly important characteristic of the test procedure under consideration—that the chance of rejecting a hypothesis is greater, the greater the discrepancy between the hypothesis tested and the actual state of affairs, and that beyond a certain point, rejection of a false hypothesis is virtually certain.

FACTORS AFFECTING POWER: PRECISION OF $\overline{X}$

We consider next the effect upon the power of a test of increasing the precision of $\overline{X}$, i.e., reducing the value of $\sigma_{\overline{X}}$. We have seen that precision can be increased in either of two ways—by decreasing experimental error (the variance of the population sampled) or by increasing sample size. Each of these operations has the effect of reducing the standard error of both the hypothetical and actual sampling distributions so that there is less overlap between these two distributions, thus reducing β (the proportion of the area of the actual distribution lying in the acceptance region) and increasing the power of the test.

To illustrate the effect upon power of increasing the precision of $\overline{X}$, power will be computed for the conditions described in the illustrative problem given on page 127, assuming a larger sample is employed. Using

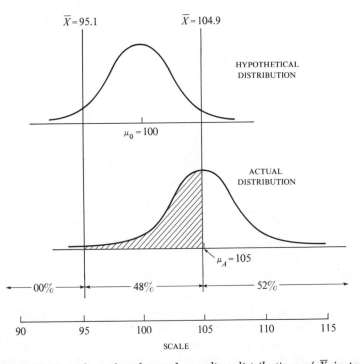

FIGURE 7-6 *Hypothetical and actual sampling distributions of $\overline{X}$ in testing a false hypothesis. Based upon the same conditions as Figure 7-3, except that a larger sample ($n = 32$) is employed.*

a sample of 32 cases, for example, the investigator would compute the standard error of the mean as follows: $\sigma_{\overline{X}}^2 = \sigma^2/n = 200/32 = 6.25$; $\sigma_{\overline{X}} = \sqrt{6.25} = 2.5$. With this value of $\sigma_{\overline{X}}$, and taking $\alpha = .05$, the critical values for testing the hypothesis that $\mu = 100$ are $\overline{X} = 95.1$ and $\overline{X} = 104.9$. (See hypothetical and actual sampling distributions in Figure 7-6.) Relative to the mean of the actual sampling distribution of $\overline{X}$, the values of z corresponding to these critical values are $z \approx (95.1 - 105)/2.5 = -3.96$ and $z \approx (104.9 - 105)/2.5 = -.04$. Although the first of these two values of z is beyond the range given in Table A-2, it is apparent from the table that to two decimal places the proportion of the area below this value of z is .00; the proportion below the second value of z, read to two decimal places, is .48. Thus, $\beta \approx .48 - .00 = .48$, and the power of the test is approximately .52. The power in this case is seen to be substantially greater than .17, the value obtained under identical circumstances with a sample of only eight observations.

In the above example we have computed the power of a test based upon a sample of 32 cases to reject the hypothesis that $\mu = 100$ when, in fact, the actual value of μ is 105. By performing similar calculations for each of the possible values of μ_A we obtain the power curve shown in Figure 7-7. (For purposes of comparison, the power curve for a test based upon a sample of eight cases, previously presented in Figure 7-5, is reproduced in Figure 7-7.) The results obtained in the examples worked above may be read from this figure by noting the height of the two curves

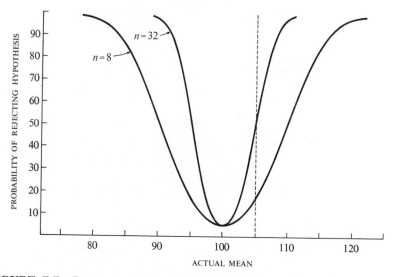

FIGURE 7-7 *Power curves for two sample sizes, $n = 8$ and $n = 32$. Both curves are based on the values $\sigma^2 = 200$ and $\alpha = .05$; the hypothesis tested is that $\mu = 100$.*

at the dashed line erected at $\mu_A = 105$. In agreement with the results given above, we see that for $n = 8$, power is .17; for $n = 32$, power is .52. More generally, we see that for all values of μ_A power is greater for a test based upon a sample of 32 cases than for a test based upon a sample of eight cases. As the value of μ_A approaches 100 (the value specified by the hypothesis being tested) power approaches .05 (the value of α) for both sample sizes.

FACTORS AFFECTING POWER: LEVEL OF SIGNIFICANCE

To demonstrate the effect on power of changing the level of significance employed, the computations of the original problem concerning power (page 127) will be repeated with α changed from .05 to .01. For a test at the .01 level of significance, the critical values of $\overline{X}$ are $100 - 2.576(5) \approx 87.1$ and $100 + 2.576(5) \approx 112.9$. This result is represented in Figure 7-8, in which critical values for a test at the .01 level of significance are represented by solid lines. For purposes of comparison, critical values for a test at the .05 level of significance are represented in

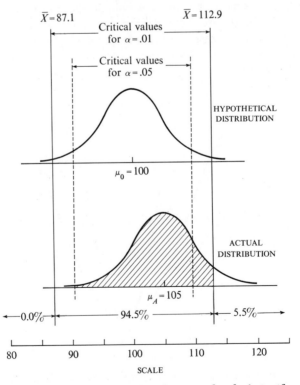

FIGURE 7-8 *The effect on power of a change in level of significance. Based upon the same conditions as Figure 7-3, except that $\alpha = .01$ rather than .05.*

the same figure by dashed lines. It will be noted that the critical values for a test at the .01 level are set further apart than those for the .05 level, thus including a greater proportion of the area of the hypothetical distribution. Just as the wider acceptance region for the .01 level includes more of the area of the hypothetical distribution, it also includes more of the area of the actual distribution. The distances of these critical values from the mean of the actual distribution, in standard-error units, are $z \approx (112.9 - 105)/5 = 1.58$ and $z \approx (87.1 - 105)/5 = -3.58$. Reading Table A-2 to the nearest tabled values of z, the proportions of the area of the actual distribution lying below these values of z are found to be approximately .945 and .000, respectively; the proportion of the area lying between these values is .945—roughly 94 per cent. The power of the test to reject the false hypothesis being tested is $1 - .94 = .06$. This value is seen to be considerably lower than the corresponding value of .17 for the same test at the .05 level of significance.

The above analysis serves to illustrate the point made earlier, that as α is decreased and less risk is taken of a Type I error, there is a corresponding decrease in power and an increased risk of a Type II error. It is this relationship that limits the extent to which we can reduce α. Although we should like to make α very small, it is not practical to reduce this quantity beyond a certain point, for the power of the test eventually becomes so attenuated that the test has little value. The value of α selected for purposes of testing a hypothesis must be chosen so as to strike a reasonable balance between the risks of the two possible types of error.

The effect on the power curve of changing α is shown in Figure 7-9.

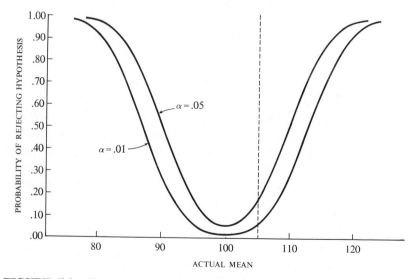

FIGURE 7-9 *Power curves for* $\alpha = .05$ *and* $\alpha = .01$. *Both curves are based on the values* $\sigma^2 = 200$ *and* $n = 8$; *the hypothesis tested is that* $\mu = 100$.

The two power curves shown in this figure—one for a test in which $\alpha = .05$, the other for a test in which $\alpha = .01$—are both based upon a test of the hypothesis that $\mu = 100$ assuming the population variance is known to be 200 and a sample of eight cases is employed.   It will be noted that the power of the test in which $\alpha = .05$ is uniformly higher than that of the test in which $\alpha = .01$.   As the value of the actual mean approaches 100 (the value of μ according to the hypothesis being tested), power approaches the respective value of α—.05 or .01.   The values of power obtained in the examples worked above, in which μ_A was assumed to be 105, may be obtained from the curves shown in Figure 7-9 by determining the heights of the curves at the vertical line erected at $\mu_A = 105$.   In agreement with the values obtained above, power is seen to be .17 for the test in which $\alpha = .05$ and .06 for the test in which $\alpha = .01$.

SIMPLIFYING THE COMPUTATIONS IN TESTING A HYPOTHESIS ABOUT μ

We have seen that in testing a hypothesis at the .05 level of significance, the critical values of $\overline{X}$ are $\overline{X}_{.025}$ and $\overline{X}_{.975}$, the values of $\overline{X}$ below which 2.5 per cent and 97.5 per cent, respectively, of the sampling distribution of $\overline{X}$ are located.   The procedure we followed to compute these critical values was to select appropriate values of z, -1.960 and 1.960, from the table of the normal distribution, substitute in Formula (6-4), and solve the equation for the corresponding values of $\overline{X}$.   The same result may be obtained with less labor simply by substituting the observed value of $\overline{X}$ in Formula (6-4) and computing the corresponding value of z.   For example, applying this procedure to the gunsight problem considered at the beginning of this chapter, we would compute $z = (\overline{X} - \mu_0)/\sigma_{\overline{X}} = (.2 - 0)/.7 = .29$.   If the observed value of $\overline{X}$ is less than $\overline{X}_{.025}$, the computed value of z will be less than -1.960; similarly, if the observed value of $\overline{X}$ is greater than $\overline{X}_{.975}$, the computed value of z will be greater than 1.960.   In other words, whenever the observed value of $\overline{X}$ is located in the acceptance region, the computed value of z is between -1.960 and 1.960; whenever the observed value of $\overline{X}$ is in the rejection region, the computed value of z is either less than -1.960 or greater than 1.960. The computed value of z for the gunsight problem, $z = .29$, indicates that the observed value of $\overline{X}$ is located in the acceptance region, this conclusion being in agreement with that reached earlier.

Being based upon observations in a sample, a value of z computed in the above manner is a statistic and, like other statistics, is subject to sampling fluctuations.   Just as we may conceptualize a sampling distribution of $\overline{X}$, we may imagine a sampling distribution of z.   When the population sampled is normal and the hypothesis being tested is true, the sampling distribution of z is the so-called *unit normal distribution*, i.e., a normal distribution having a mean of zero and a standard deviation of unity. The percentiles of this distribution may be read directly from tables of the normal distribution such as Tables A-2 and A-3; thus $z_{.025}$ and $z_{.975}$, the critical values of z for a test at the .05 level of significance, are -1.960 and 1.960, respectively (Table A-3); similarly, $z_{.005}$ and $z_{.995}$, the critical values of z for a test at the .01 level of significance, are -2.576 and 2.576.

PROBLEMS IN WHICH σ^2 IS UNKNOWN

In most problems encountered in practice the variance of the population from which a sample is drawn is not known and it is therefore not possible to compute $\sigma_{\overline{X}}^2$, the variance of the sampling distribution of $\overline{X}$. However, taking s^2 as an estimate of σ^2, we may compute $s_{\overline{X}}^2$, an estimate of $\sigma_{\overline{X}}^2$, as follows:

$$s_{\overline{X}}^2 = \frac{s^2}{n} \tag{7-1}$$

The formula for $s_{\overline{X}}^2$ is seen to be the same as Formula (6-2) for $\sigma_{\overline{X}}^2$, except that s^2 is substituted for σ^2. The statistic corresponding to z—upon which is based the decision to accept or reject the hypothesis being tested—is t, defined as follows:

$$t = \frac{(\overline{X} - \mu_0)}{s_{\overline{X}}} \tag{7-2}$$

The formula for t is seen to be completely analogous to the formula for z, the only difference being that $s_{\overline{X}}$, the square root of $s_{\overline{X}}^2$, is substituted for $\sigma_{\overline{X}}$ in the denominator.

It is apparent from Formula (7-2) that when the value of $\overline{X}$ observed in a sample is close to the value of μ_0, the value of t will be close to zero. On the other hand, if the sample mean deviates widely from μ_0, then the value of t will be either a large positive number or a large negative number, depending upon whether $\overline{X}$ is above or below μ_0. Thus, a value of t differing widely from zero is taken to indicate that the hypothesis being tested should be rejected.

In order to limit the probability of a Type I error to an acceptable level, say $\alpha = .05$, it is necessary to determine critical values of t above and below which the required proportions of the area of the sampling distribution of t are located—a problem requiring for its solution detailed knowledge concerning the areas of the sampling distribution of t. This important problem was solved by W. S. Gosset, who published his findings under the pseudonym "Student" (1908). (In honor of this discovery the statistic t is often referred to as *"Student's"* t.) In contrast to the sampling distribution of z, which does not vary with sample size, the sampling distribution of t depends upon the size of the sample used in computing s^2.   In other words, there is a different sampling distribution of t for every sample size.   For this reason it is not practical to present as extensive tables of the t distribution as of the normal distribution. Instead, values of t are usually presented only for percentage points of special interest.   Because the t distribution is used primarily for tests of significance and related procedures, tables of t are usually organized in terms of critical values for various levels of significance.   Table A-4 of Appendix A is an example of such a table.   Each row of this table represents a different distribution of t, identified by number of *degrees of freedom,* equal to $n - 1$, one less than the number of cases used in computing s^2.   (The significance of the concept of degrees of freedom to the mathematician need not concern us here; for present purposes we may regard degrees of freedom simply as a means of identifying the appropriate t distribution in a given problem.)   Each critical value presented in Table A-4 should be interpreted as representing two numerically equivalent values of opposite sign, the two values constituting the upper and lower limits of an acceptance region.   Making a test based upon five degrees of freedom at the .05 level of significance, for example, the tabled value of t is 2.571.   This entry is interpreted to mean that the critical values of t are -2.571 and 2.571, with any value of t between these two values leading to acceptance of the hypothesis being tested and any value outside this range leading to rejection.

As might be expected on the basis of the similarity of the formulae for t and z, the shape of the sampling distribution of t is very similar in its general features to the (normal) distribution of z.   For purposes of comparison, schematic representations of the t distribution for four degrees of freedom and of the normal distribution are superimposed in Figure 7-10.

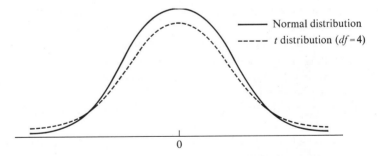

FIGURE 7-10 *Comparison of normal distribution with t distribution for four degrees of freedom.*

Both distributions are symmetrically located about a mean of zero.   The chief difference is that a relatively greater proportion of the t distribution is located in the tails of the distribution.   Consequently, the critical values of t for a given level of significance, i.e., the values setting off the extreme 5 per cent or 1 per cent of the distribution, are numerically larger than the corresponding critical values of z.   For example, with four degrees of freedom the critical values of t for a test at the .05 level of significance are ± 2.776, compared to ± 1.960, the critical values of z for the same level of significance.   As the number of degrees of freedom increases, the t distribution approximates the normal distribution more and more closely until, in the limiting case with infinite degrees of freedom, the two distributions are identical.   (The identity of the two distributions in this special case becomes apparent when the critical values of t for infinite degrees of freedom are compared with the critical values of z.   For a test at the .05 level of significance, for example, the critical values of both statistics are ± 1.960.)   The difference between the t distribution and the normal distribution is also apparent from their respective cumulative distribution curves, presented in Figure 7-11.

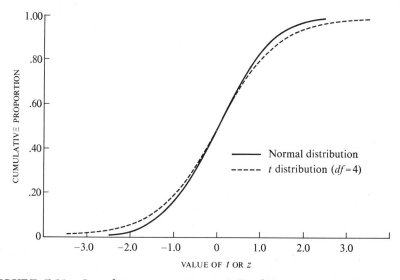

FIGURE 7-11   *Cumulative curves of normal distribution and t distribution for four degrees of freedom.*

These curves are like cumulative polygons, discussed in Chapter 2, the only difference being that the cumulative distributions presented in Figure 7-11 are represented by smooth curves rather than a series of straight line segments.   The greater dispersion of the t distribution is indicated by the somewhat more gradual slope of the cumulative curve for this distribution.

The use of the t statistic to test a hypothesis concerning the mean of a population may be illustrated by an experiment designed to determine whether an illusion occurs in comparing the lengths of a vertical and horizontal line.

> If a vertical line and a horizontal line of equal length are arranged in the form of an inverted T, the vertical line appears to be considerably longer than the horizontal line, a phenomenon commonly known as the *vertical-horizontal illusion*. This name suggests that the illusion is a consequence of the orientation—vertical or horizontal—of the two lines. It is possible, however, that the horizontal line looks relatively shorter, not because of its position, but because it is bisected by the vertical line. It is of interest, therefore, to determine whether a similar illusion occurs when the two lines are arranged in the form of the letter L, an arrangement in which neither line bisects the other. One way of investigating this problem is to construct an apparatus in which the length of the horizontal line is fixed and the length of the vertical line is adjustable. We can then ask a subject to adjust the vertical line so that it appears equal to the horizontal line. Using a horizontal line 100 mm. in length, the lengths of ten settings of the vertical line by one subject were 96, 101, 97, 96, 100, 94, 103, 100, 100, and 101 mm. These ten settings may be regarded as a sample of all possible settings by this particular subject. The question we seek to answer is whether the mean of this population is equal to 100 mm., the length of the fixed horizontal line. One way of answering this question is to test the hypothesis that $\mu = 100$ mm. If the mean of our sample is sufficiently close to this value, we will accept the hypothesis and conclude that no illusion occurs with this arrangement of lines; otherwise, we will reject the hypothesis and conclude that an illusion does occur.

The mean of the sample described above is 98.8 mm., somewhat less than the hypothetical value of μ. To evaluate the discrepancy of $\overline{X}$ from the hypothetical value of 100 mm. we compute t. As a first step in determining $s_{\overline{X}}$, the denominator of the formula for t, we compute s^2, the sample variance. Using Formula (3-7), the value of s^2 is found to be 8.178. Substituting in Formula (7-1), we compute the estimated variance of the mean as follows: $s_{\overline{X}}^2 = s^2/n = 8.178/10 = .8178$; taking the square root of .8178, we obtain $s_{\overline{X}} \approx .904$. Substituting in Formula (7-2), we obtain $t \approx (98.8 - 100)/.904 = -1.2/.904 \approx -1.33$. The number of degrees of freedom for evaluating this value of t is $10 - 1 = 9$. Entering Table A-4 with nine degrees of freedom, we find that the critical values of t for the .05 level of significance are -2.262 and 2.262. We note that the obtained value of t, -1.33, lies between these two critical values, so we accept the hypothesis that $\mu = 100$ mm. So far as the present data are concerned, we have no basis for concluding that an illusion occurs for this subject under the conditions described.[2]

It should be noted that the statistical hypothesis tested by an investigator is not necessarily one which the investigator believes to be true; more typically, the hypothetical value of μ selected for purposes of a test is a specific value whose rejection would be of interest. For example, certain

---

[2] A fuller and more systematic investigation of the vertical-horizontal illusion has been reported by Finger and Spelt (1947).

theoretical considerations might lead one investigator to expect that in the experimental situation described in the preceding example μ is greater than 100 mm., other theoretical considerations might lead a second investigator to expect that μ is equal to 100 mm., and still others might lead a third investigator to expect that μ is less than 100 mm. Regardless of his expectations based on theory, each of these investigators might test the hypothesis $\mu = 100$ mm. because this hypothesis specifies a particular value of μ whose rejection would be of special interest. Accordingly, it is useful to distinguish between an investigator's *research hypothesis* (his expectations concerning the outcome of an experiment) and the *statistical hypothesis* that he tests. Although the statistical hypothesis tested is formulated so that its acceptance or rejection is relevant to an investigator's research hypothesis, the one is not necessarily identical to the other.

Strictly speaking, the use of the t distribution to test a hypothesis concerning μ is appropriate only when the population sampled is normal, for it is under this condition that the sampling distribution of the t statistic coincides with the theoretical distribution upon which critical values of t are based. When the population is not normal, the exact sampling distribution of t is not known; consequently, the use of t in testing a hypothesis under these circumstances may involve a higher probability of a Type I error than intended. The extent of the discrepancy between the actual probability of a Type I error and the nominal value of α (i.e., the probability of a Type I error according to the theoretical distribution of t) depends upon the size of the sample and the degree to which the population departs from a normal distribution. For a given size sample, the greater the departure of the population in question from a normal distribution, the greater the error is likely to be; on the other hand, for a given population, the greater the sample size, the smaller is the error. Because the error involved depends upon the shape of the population, it is not possible to lay down a general rule concerning the sample size needed in order to obtain a satisfactory approximation of the intended value of α. However, as a rule of thumb it may be assumed that with most populations encountered in actual research the error involved will be negligible if a sample of 30 cases or more is employed. Of course, if the departure from normality is only slight, the theoretical t distribution provides a very good approximation with even smaller samples.

ONE-SIDED TESTS

Using the test procedures described above, a test has the same power when the value of μ_A is above μ_0 as when the value of μ_A is a corresponding distance below μ_0. For example, a value of μ_A, say, 20 units above μ_0 results in the same probability of rejection of the hypothesis being tested as does a value of μ_A 20 units below μ_0. Because of this characteristic (equal power against values of μ_A above and below μ_0), the procedures considered thus far are referred to as *two-sided tests*.

In contrast to the situations considered thus far, there are problems in which the investigator wishes to reject the hypothesis being tested only if the actual mean differs from the hypothetical one in a certain direction. A test of this sort is appropriate when the investigator wishes to determine whether the mean of a population (1) falls short of certain minimum standards or (2) exceeds a maximum permissible value.   To illustrate the former situation let us imagine a hypothetical manufacturer of light bulbs who, for purposes of quality control, specifies that the light bulbs produced by his factory must have an average life of at least 2,000 hours in use. We will suppose that periodically the manufacturer draws a sample of light bulbs from his production line and tests them to determine how long they can be used before burning out.   If the population average is equal to or better than the 2,000-hour specification, no corrective action is required; on the other hand, if the population average is below the minimum specification, then steps must be taken to find and correct the cause of the deficiency.   In other words, the manufacturer will reject the hypothesis that the mean life of the population of light bulbs is up to specifications only if the mean life of the bulbs in the sample is too low.   The second type of problem—whether μ exceeds a maximum permissible value—may be illustrated with reference to the job of a city health inspector concerned with the bacteria count of dishes in public restaurants.   Such an investigator would be primarily interested in determining whether the average bacteria count of the dishes in a given restaurant exceeds the maximum permissible value; it is of little concern to him if the average falls below the maximum allowed.   The procedures to be described in this subsection—so-called *one-sided tests*—are appropriate in situations of the kinds illustrated above.   These tests are designed to reject the hypothesis being tested when the actual mean differs from the hypothetical mean in a particular direction, either above or below it, as the situation requires.

In the case of two-sided tests the hypothesis tested is of the general form $\mu = a$, in which a is some constant; the alternative to this type of hypothesis has the general form $\mu \neq a$.   In the case of one-sided tests, on the other hand, the hypothesis and its alternative are somewhat modified. For example, the manufacturer of light bulbs described above wishes to test the hypothesis that the average life of all bulbs is *equal to or greater than* 2,000 hours.   Written symbolically, this hypothesis may be stated as follows: $\mu \geq 2,000$.   The alternative to this hypothesis—the conclusion drawn if the hypothesis is rejected—is that the mean life is less than 2,000 hours, written symbolically $\mu < 2,000$.   It will be noted that no attempt is made to distinguish whether $\mu = 2,000$ or $\mu > 2,000$; the distinction is unimportant in terms of the decision to be made, and these two states of affairs are coalesced into a single hypothesis to be distinguished jointly from the alternative $\mu < 2,000$.

To illustrate the procedure followed in making a one-sided test let us suppose that the light-bulb manufacturer in the above example based his test for a given day upon a sample of 20 bulbs.   We have already noted that he will reject the hypothesis that $\mu \geq 2{,}000$ only if the observed value of $\overline{X}$ is below 2,000 hours, i.e., if a sufficiently large negative value of t is obtained.   Assuming the manufacturer wishes to set α equal to .05, the critical value of t for his test will be the value below which 5 per cent of the area of the sampling distribution of t is located.   This value of t may be obtained by reading the value of t for a two-sided test with $\alpha = .10$. To illustrate, Table A-4 indicates that with 19 degrees of freedom 5 per cent of the area of the sampling distribution of t is below $t = -1.729$ and 5 per cent of the distribution is above $t = 1.729$, these values of t being the critical values for a two-sided test with $\alpha = .10$.   Thus, if the manufacturer takes as his rejection region all values of t less than -1.729, the probability of a Type I error (rejecting the hypothesis that $\mu \geq 2{,}000$) will be .05 when μ is, in fact, equal to 2,000 hours.   The critical value of t and the acceptance and rejection regions for this test are represented graphically in Figure 7-12.

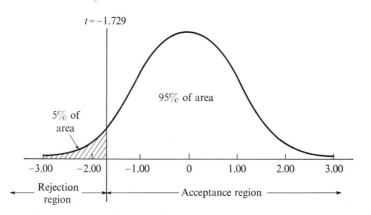

FIGURE 7-12   *Acceptance and rejection regions for a one-sided test.   The hypothesis tested is that $\mu \geq 2{,}000$ hours.*

The determination of critical values for a one-sided test may be described in general terms as follows: Using a table such as Table A-4, in which values of α are specified in terms of a two-sided test, obtain values of α for a one-sided test by halving the values of α (not the values of t) indicated in the table.   For example, for a one-sided test with $\alpha = .05$, enter the column headed $\alpha = .10$; for a one-sided test with $\alpha = .01$, enter the column headed $\alpha = .02$; and so on.

While the decision to employ a one-sided test is usually clear-cut in applied problems of the kinds illustrated above, there has been some controversy concerning the conditions under which a one-sided test is appropriate in scientific investigations. The practice followed by some investigators of using a one-sided test when a certain outcome is predicted on theoretical grounds has been criticized by some writers. To illustrate the procedure in question, if an investigator had theoretical grounds for expecting that in the illusion experiment described earlier the mean setting of the subject would be less than 100 mm., he might perform a one-sided test. Whereas in making a two-sided test the hypothesis tested was $\mu = 100$ mm., in making a one-sided test the hypothesis tested would be $\mu \geq 100$ mm., the alternative—that presumed in our illustration to be predicted by theory—being $\mu < 100$ mm. (It will be noted that the statistical hypothesis adopted by the experimenter is not that $\mu \leq 100$ mm. Assuming the investigator tested this hypothesis and accepted it, his conclusion would be that μ is either equal to 100 mm. or less than 100 mm. By testing the hypothesis that $\mu \geq 100$ mm., the investigator can, if this hypothesis is rejected, make the more definite assertion that μ is less than 100 mm.—a statement that unambiguously supports his theoretical expectations.)

The advantage of using a one-sided test is that it affords a higher probability than a two-sided test of rejecting a false hypothesis concerning μ when the actual mean differs in the predicted direction from the value of μ specified by the hypothesis. For example, if μ is actually less than 100 mm., then the one-sided test described above has a greater probability of rejecting the hypothesis that $\mu \geq 100$ mm. than a two-sided test has of rejecting the hypothesis that $\mu = 100$ mm. The disadvantage of the one-sided test is that if a large positive value of t were observed, it would not be possible to concluded that $\mu > 100$; in such an event, the investigator could only accept the hypothesis that $\mu \geq 100$.

The question of whether it is appropriate or desirable to use one-sided tests in scientific investigations is not a statistical question, but a question of scientific strategy. Statistical theory merely tells us that if an investigator wishes to reject a hypothesis regardless of the direction of the outcome, a two-sided test should be employed; that, on the other hand, if he wishes to distinguish, say, $\mu < a$ from $\mu \geq a$, but does not wish to distinguish $\mu = a$ from $\mu > a$, then a one-sided test is best suited to his needs. However, statistical theory does not tell us which approach is better scientific strategy in a given situation, i.e., whether it is wise to use a test that leads us to ignore results not in accord with our expectations. Indeed, there is no well-formulated theory or generally agreed upon set of principles to guide such decisions, and it seems questionable whether the issue of one-sided tests versus two-sided tests in science will ever be settled in a definitive manner. Without going into the details of this complex issue, it will merely be suggested that when there is any doubt, the use of a two-sided test would seem to be the more conservative procedure.

CONFIDENCE LIMITS FOR μ

In some problems it is of interest to specify two numerical values between which μ may, with a known degree of confidence, be asserted to lie. Such values are called *confidence limits* and the interval between them is known as a *confidence interval*. The procedure for computing confidence limits and the manner in which these limits may be interpreted will first be described without proof. Following this introduction, the theory underlying the method will be explained.[3]

The computation of confidence limits may be illustrated with reference to the problem discussed earlier in which a vertical line was adjusted to apparent equality with a horizontal line. The values needed for present purposes, taken from our earlier discussion of this problem, are $n = 10$, $\overline{X} = 98.8$ mm., and $s_{\overline{X}} = .904$ mm. Before computing confidence limits for μ, we must decide upon the value of α, the probability we are willing to risk that our confidence limits will fail to bracket μ. (For illustrative purposes we will take $\alpha = .05$.) Then we determine the values of t corre-Next, each of these values of t is multiplied by $s_{\overline{X}}$. In our illustrative problem there are nine degrees of freedom for estimating s^2, so the values of t corresponding to $\alpha = .05$, i.e., the values of t between which 95 per cent of the area of the t distribution is located, are -2.262 and 2.262. Next, each of these values of t is multiplied by $s_{\overline{X}}$. In our illustrative problem these products are $-2.262(.904) \approx -2.04$ mm. and $2.262(.904)$ ≈ 2.04 mm. Finally, confidence limits for μ are obtained by adding each of these products to $\overline{X}$. In the problem at hand, we obtain $98.8 - 2.04$ $= 96.76$ mm. as the lower limit of the confidence interval and $98.8 + 2.04$ $= 100.84$ mm. as the upper limit. Thus, μ, the mean of the population of all possible settings by the subject tested, is estimated to lie between 96.76 and 100.84 mm.

The proportion of the t distribution lying below $t = -2.262$ is .025; that below $t = 2.262$ is .975. Accordingly, these values of t may be designated as $t_{.025}$ and $t_{.975}$, respectively. Using this notation, the lower and upper confidence limits for μ may be described in general terms as $\overline{X} + t_{.025}s_{\overline{X}}$ and $\overline{X} + t_{.975}s_{\overline{X}}$, respectively, when $\alpha = .05$. Since $t_{.025}$ is always a negative number and $t_{.975}$ is always a positive number, the first of the above quantities is always below $\overline{X}$; the latter, always above.

In the procedure followed above, the probability of error (i.e., of

---

[3] The procedure described for computing confidence limits and the theory upon which that procedure is based follow from a general theory of statistical estimation developed by Neyman (1937). A more recent discussion of this theory and a comparison of it with an alternative theory of estimation (the so-called *fiducial* theory of estimation) appears in Neyman (1952).

obtaining an interval that does not contain μ) is .05 and the probability of being correct is .95; accordingly, the limits computed are called *95 per cent confidence limits*. When $\alpha = .01$, the limits computed are called *99 per cent confidence limits*. The price paid for the greater confidence afforded by taking $\alpha = .01$ is a wider interval. For example, had we computed 99 per cent confidence limits in the above problem, the values of t employed would have been -3.250 and 3.250, and the resulting confidence limits would have been 95.86 and 101.74 mm.—a somewhat broader interval than that delimited by 95 per cent limits. In general, the smaller the value of α, the broader will be the interval within which μ is estimated to lie.

The width of a confidence interval for μ also depends upon the precision of $\overline{X}$. It is apparent from the manner in which confidence limits are computed that the width of a confidence interval is twice the product $t_{.975}s_{\overline{X}}$. Inasmuch as $s_{\overline{X}}^2 = s^2/n$, it follows that the width of a confidence interval may be decreased either by reducing σ^2 (the expected value of s^2) or by increasing n. These two methods of increasing the precision of $\overline{X}$ have been discussed in some detail in Chapter 6 and therefore will not be considered in detail here.

It was stated above that in computing 95 per cent confidence limits the risk of error is .05. The meaning of this statement may be clarified by considering confidence limits computed for a series of samples all drawn from the same population. For illustrative purposes six samples of five cases each were randomly selected from the model population described in Table 7-2. The values in this population are distributed with $\mu = 10$ and

TABLE 7-2 *Model population approximating a normal distribution with $\mu = 10$ and $\sigma^2 = 5$*

X	Probability
17	.01
16	.00
15	.01
14	.03
13	.07
12	.12
11	.17
10	.18
9	.17
8	.12
7	.07
6	.03
5	.01
4	.00
3	.01

TABLE 7-3 *Ninety-five per cent confidence limits based upon six samples from the same population*

			Sample Number			
	1	*2*	*3*	*4*	*5*	*6*
			Values of X			
	9	10	9	10	9	8
	14	10	3	7	12	8
	9	3	13	14	10	12
	8	8	11	11	14	11
	9	10	10	7	12	11
$\overline{X}$	9.8	8.2	9.2	9.8	11.4	10.0
$s_{\overline{X}}$	1.068	1.356	1.685	1.319	.872	.837
Upper Limit	12.76	11.96	13.88	13.46	13.82	12.32
Lower Limit	6.84	4.44	4.52	6.14	8.98	7.68

$\sigma^2 = 5$, and the shape of the distribution is approximately normal. The six samples drawn from this population are described in Table 7-3. The values of $\overline{X}$ and $s_{\overline{X}}$ for each sample and the confidence limits based upon these

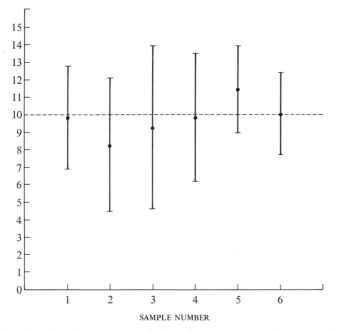

FIGURE 7-13 *Confidence intervals based upon six samples drawn from the same population. The dashed line represents the value of μ.*

values are listed at the bottom of the table.   The confidence intervals based upon the six samples are represented graphically in Figure 7-13.

It is apparent that the centers of the intervals vary depending upon the value of $\overline{X}$ for the sample in question and that the intervals vary in width depending upon the value of $s_{\overline{X}}$ (which in turn depends upon s^2, the variance of the corresponding sample).   The value of the population mean, $\mu = 10$, is represented in Figure 7-13 by a dashed horizontal line. It will be noted that the confidence interval obtained in each of the six samples includes μ.   However, if sampling were continued, confidence intervals would occasionally be obtained that did not include μ, either because of an extreme value of $\overline{X}$, a small value of $s_{\overline{X}}$, or both.   If, as in Table 7-3 and Figure 7-13, the limits computed are 95 per cent confidence limits, an interval not including μ will be obtained in about 5 per cent of the samples; if 99 per cent confidence limits are computed, intervals not including μ will be obtained in about 1 per cent of the samples.   In actual practice, a single sample is drawn from a population and the limits obtained either include μ or they do not.   We do not know whether the limits computed in a given sample actually include μ, but we know we have employed a procedure that will lead to correct results a specified proportion of the time.

THEORY UNDERLYING CONFIDENCE LIMITS

In this subsection a proof will be given that, when 95 per cent confidence limits are computed in the manner described above, the probability is .95 that the limits will include μ.   To lay the groundwork for the proof that follows, three rules from the algebra of inequalities will be briefly reviewed.

RULE 1.   *If a constant is added to each of a series of unequal quantities, the results are unequal in the same direction.*   To illustrate this rule we start with the following double inequality: $-6 < 3 < 4$.   If some constant, say 5, is added to each of these quantities, we obtain $-1 < 8 < 9$.   We note that the order of magnitude of the new quantities is the same as that of the original ones, i.e., the first number is less than either of the others and the last number is greatest.

RULE 2.   *If each of a series of unequal quantities is multiplied by a constant of positive sign, the results are unequal in the same direction.* Starting with the double inequality $-6 < 3 < 4$ and multiplying each value by the constant 2, we obtain $-12 < 6 < 8$.   Again, the ordering of the new values is the same as that of the original ones.

RULE 3.   *If each of a series of unequal quantities is multiplied by a constant of negative sign, the results are unequal in the opposite direction.* Starting with the double inequality $-6 < 3 < 4$ and multiplying each value by the constant -2, we obtain $12 > -6 > -8$.   Here, the ordering of the new series is reversed from that of the original, -8 being the least, and 12 the greatest, of the new quantities.

Our point of departure in deriving the procedure described in the preceding section for computing confidence limits is the following assertion: *For samples drawn at random from a normal population the quantity* $(\overline{X} - \mu)/s_{\overline{X}}$ *is distributed as "Student's" t.* In other words, percentiles of the sampling distribution of $(\overline{X} - \mu)/s_{\overline{X}}$ are given by tables describing the theoretical distribution of t. This statement is a theorem from mathematical statistics and will here be taken without proof. (Although not previously stated in precisely this form, this theorem was the basis of the procedures described earlier for testing hypotheses concerning μ.) A corollary of the above theorem is the following: *The probability is .95 that the quantity* $(\overline{X} - \mu)/s_{\overline{X}}$ *based upon a random sample from a normal population will lie between* $t_{.025}$ *and* $t_{.975}$. Making use of the symbols for writing inequalities, this corollary may be written as follows:

$$\text{The probability is .95 that } \left(t_{.025} < \frac{\overline{X} - \mu}{s_{\overline{X}}} < t_{.975} \right)$$

We next perform a series of algebraic operations—multiplication and addition using constants—on the double inequality in parentheses. First, we multiply each of the three parts of the inequality by $s_{\overline{X}}$. Applying our second rule for inequalities, we obtain:

$$\text{The probability is .95 that } (t_{.025}s_{\overline{X}} < \overline{X} - \mu < t_{.975}s_{\overline{X}})$$

To change the sign of μ from *minus* to *plus* we multiply each term by -1. This operation has the effect of changing the sign of every term in the inequality and, according to our third rule of inequalities, of reversing the direction of the inequality as follows:

$$\text{The probability is .95 that } (-t_{.025}s_{\overline{X}} > -\overline{X} + \mu > -t_{.975}s_{\overline{X}})$$

The term $-\overline{X}$ may be removed from the middle part of the inequality by adding $\overline{X}$ to each of the three parts of the inequality. According to our first rule of inequalities, this operation gives us the following statement:

$$\text{The probability is .95 that } (\overline{X} - t_{.025}s_{\overline{X}} > \mu > \overline{X} - t_{.975}s_{\overline{X}})$$

Finally, we seek to change the sign of the two products, $-t_{.025}s_{\overline{X}}$ and $-t_{.975}s_{\overline{X}}$, from *minus* to *plus*. We note that the values of $t_{.025}$ and $t_{.975}$ are the same except for sign, i.e., $t_{.025} = -t_{.975}$, and $t_{.975} = -t_{.025}$. Substituting $t_{.975}$ for $-t_{.025}$, and $t_{.025}$ for $-t_{.975}$, we obtain the following:

$$\text{The probability is .95 that } (\overline{X} + t_{.975}s_{\overline{X}} > \mu > \overline{X} + t_{.025}s_{\overline{X}})$$

According to this last statement, the probability is .95 that the two numbers $(\overline{X} + t_{.975}s_{\overline{X}})$ and $(\overline{X} + t_{.025}s_{\overline{X}})$ computed on the basis of a random sample will bracket μ. It will be noted that these two numbers are 95 per cent confidence limits computed as described in the preceding section. It has thus been shown that a confidence interval computed in this manner has a probability of .95 of including μ. The proof given can be readily extended to confidence limits based upon other values of α.

In concluding this discussion of confidence-interval estimates it is reiterated that the method described, being based upon the t distribution, presupposes that the population from which the sample is drawn is normally distributed. Although moderate departures from normality usually do not result in errors of any consequence, the actual value of α may differ from the value intended by the investigator if the departure from normality is marked, particularly if the sample size is small.

PROBLEMS

1. An experimenter draws a sample of ten cases from a population and wishes to test the hypothesis that $\mu = 80$. (*a*) Assuming the population variance is known to be 160, what are the critical values of $\overline{X}$ for a test at the .05 level of significance? (*b*) Assuming the value of $\overline{X}$ based upon the sample of ten observations has a value of 71, would the hypothesis that $\mu = 80$ be accepted or rejected?

2. Assume that the variance of a normally distributed population is known to be 72, but that the value of μ is uncertain. An investigator plans to draw a random sample of eight cases and test, at the .05 level of significance, the hypothesis that $\mu = 200$. Unknown to the investigator, the value of μ is actually 202. (*a*) What are the critical values of $\overline{X}$ for the test described above? (*b*) What is the probability that the investigator will make a Type II error? (*c*) What is the power of his test to reject the false hypothesis that $\mu = 200$?

3. Assume all the circumstances are as described in Problem 2, except that the .01 level of significance is adopted. (*a*) What are the critical values of $\overline{X}$ for a test at the .01 level? (*b*) What is the power of the test to reject the false hypothesis that $\mu = 200$? (*c*) State the general rule relating changes in power to changes in α.

4. Assume all the circumstances are as described in Problem 2, except that $\overline{X}$ is based upon a sample of 18 cases (rather than eight). (*a*) What are the critical values of $\overline{X}$ for a test at the .05 level of significance? (*b*) What is the power of the test to reject (at the .05 level) the false hypothesis that $\mu = 200$? (*c*) State the general rule relating power to sample size.

5. Assume all the circumstances are as described in Problem 2, except that the actual mean is 205 (rather than 202). (*a*) What are the critical values for a test, at the .05 level of significance, of the hypothesis that $\mu = 200$? (*b*) What is the power of the test to reject (at the .05 level) the false hypothesis that $\mu = 200$? (*c*) Formulate a general rule relating power to the discrepancy between the actual value of μ and the value according to the hypothesis being tested. (*d*) What are the limiting values of power (lowest and highest values possible) as the actual state of affairs varies?

6. Test the hypothesis stated in Problem 1 by computing z based upon the observed value of $\overline{X}$. (*a*) What is the value of z based on the observed

value of $\bar{X}$?   (*b*) What are the critical values of z for a test at the .05 level of significance?   Adopting the .05 level of significance, would the hypothesis be accepted or rejected?   (*c*) What are the critical values of z for a test at the .01 level of significance?   Adopting the .01 level of significance, would the hypothesis be accepted or rejected?

7. Tom took five different forms (repeated measures) of an intelligence test, obtaining the following scores: 95, 101, 93, 97, 99.   Adopting the .05 level of significance, would you accept or reject the hypothesis that Tom's "true" score (i.e., the mean of the hypothetical population of all possible repeated measures) is 100?

8. In a random sample of four observations the values of X were as follows: 9, 10, 7, 6.   Test, at the .05 level of significance, the hypothesis that the mean of the population from which these observations were drawn is 12.

9. (*a*) Assume that in Problem 7 it is desired to make a one-sided test, at the .05 level of significance, of the hypothesis $\mu \geq 100$.   What is the critical value of t for such a test?   (*b*) Assume that in Problem 8 it is desired to make a one-sided test, at the .01 level of significance, of the hypothesis $\mu \leq 12$. What is the critical value of t for such a test?

10. (*a*) Using the data presented in Problem 7, determine 95 per cent confidence limits for μ.   (*b*) Using the same data, determine 99 per cent confidence limits for μ.

11. (*a*) Using the data presented in Problem 8, determine 95 per cent confidence limits for μ.   (*b*) Using the same data, determine 99 per cent confidence limits for μ.

REFERENCES

FINGER, F. and D. F. SPELT.   The illustration of the horizontal-vertical illusion. *J. exp. Psychol.,* 1947, **37**, 243–250.

NEYMAN, J.   Outline of a theory of statistical estimation based on the classical theory of probability.   *Philos. Trans. Royal Soc.,* Series A, 1937, **236,** 333–380.

————.   *First course in probability and statistics.*   New York: Holt, 1950.

————.   *Lectures and conferences on mathematical statistics and probability* (2d ed.).   Washington: Graduate School, U.S. Department of Agriculture, 1952.

NEYMAN, J. and E. S. PEARSON.   On the problem of the most efficient tests of statistical hypotheses.   *Philos. Trans. Royal Soc.,* Series A, 1933, **231,** 289–337.

"Student" (W. S. GOSSET).   On the probable error of the mean.   *Biometrika,* 1908, **6,** 1–25.

ADDITIONAL READINGS

COHEN, J.   The statistical power of abnormal-social psychological research: a review.   *J. abn. soc. Psychol.,* 1962, **65,** 145–153.   A survey of research published in the *Journal of Abnormal and Social Psychology* during a one-year period, with the conclusion that the probability of rejecting a false hypothesis was in most cases disconcertingly low.

DIXON, W. J. and F. J. MASSEY, JR.   *Introduction to statistical analysis* (2d ed). New York: McGraw-Hill, 1957.   Chaps. 7 and 14.   An elementary discussion of the theory of hypothesis testing with attention to the probability of accepting a false hypothesis.

GOLDFRIED, M. R.   Theoretical note: one-tailed tests and "unexpected" results. *Psychol. Rev.,* 1959, **66,** 79–80.   Discusses the use of one-sided tests in science and critically examines the practice, followed by some investigators, of using either a one-sided test or a two-sided test, depending upon the outcome of an experiment.

WALKER, HELEN M. and J. LEV.   *Statistical inference.*   New York: Holt, 1953. Chaps. 2 and 7.   An elementary discussion of hypothesis testing and confidence-interval estimation.

CHAPTER 8

statistical inference (2):

the comparison of two populations

MANY PSYCHOLOGICAL INVESTIGATIONS SEEK TO DETERMINE WHETHER the distribution of values in one population differs from the distribution in another. For example, an investigator might wish to find out whether performance of the hypothetical population of individuals tested under one experimental treatment differs from that of the population tested under another treatment. Alternatively, it might be desired to compare two naturally occurring populations—for example, men and women. It is possible to test very general hypotheses (e.g., that a given measure is distributed identically in two populations) or more specific ones (e.g., that two populations have identical means or identical variances). In this chapter we shall examine what are probably the most widely used of all statistical tests, those designed for determining whether two populations differ in central tendency.

THE DISTRIBUTION OF A DIFFERENCE

As theoretical background for the procedures to be considered in this chapter, we will examine two theorems from the theory of probability concerning the distribution of a difference between two independent random variables. In this discussion values of one random variable will be represented by the letter X, values of the second random variable by the letter Y, and the difference between them by the expression $X - Y$. For purposes of illustration, let us imagine two ordinary dice, one white and the other red. We will define the random variable X as the outcome of a throw of the white die and the random variable Y as the outcome of a throw of the red one. Let us suppose that each of the dice is thrown once and the difference $X - Y$ is computed. The possible outcomes of such a procedure are listed in Table 8-1.

TABLE 8-1 *Possible values of* $X - Y$ *for throws of two dice*

VALUE OBTAINED ON WHITE DIE X	VALUE OBTAINED ON RED DIE Y					
	1	2	3	4	5	6
1	0	−1	−2	−3	−4	−5
2	1	0	−1	−2	−3	−4
3	2	1	0	−1	−2	−3
4	3	2	1	0	−1	−2
5	4	3	2	1	0	−1
6	5	4	3	2	1	0

There are 36 possible outcomes; since these are all equally likely, the probability of each outcome is 1/36. It will be noted that certain values of $X - Y$ occur in only one outcome, while others occur in several. For example, the value $X - Y = 5$ occurs in only one of the possible outcomes; the probability of this value is therefore 1/36. On the other hand, the value $X - Y = 4$ occurs in two of the possible outcomes; hence, the probability of this value is 2/36. The probabilities of the remaining values of $X - Y$ may be determined in a similar manner. A listing of all possible values of $X - Y$ and the probability of each, i.e., a description of the probability distribution of $X - Y$, is given in Table 8-2.

TABLE 8-2 *Probability distribution of* $X - Y$

$X - Y$	−5	−4	−3	−2	−1	0	1	2	3	4	5
PROBABILITY	$\frac{1}{36}$	$\frac{2}{36}$	$\frac{3}{36}$	$\frac{4}{36}$	$\frac{5}{36}$	$\frac{6}{36}$	$\frac{5}{36}$	$\frac{4}{36}$	$\frac{3}{36}$	$\frac{2}{36}$	$\frac{1}{36}$

In the discussion that follows it will be necessary to distinguish the parameters of three different theoretical distributions—the probability distribution of X, the probability distribution of Y, and the probability distribution of $X - Y$. Accordingly, the parameters of these distributions will be distinguished by subscripts as follows: the mean and variance of the distribution of X will be represented by μ_X and σ_X^2, respectively; those of the distribution of Y, by μ_Y and σ_Y^2; and those of the distribution of $X - Y$, by μ_{X-Y} and σ_{X-Y}^2. Inasmuch as the distributions of X and Y are identical to distributions considered in Chapter 4, we know from our previous calculations that $\mu_X = \mu_Y = 3.5$ and $\sigma_X^2 = \sigma_Y^2 = 2\frac{11}{12}$.

The theorems in which we are interested concern the relationship between the mean and variance of the probability distribution of $X - Y$ and the corresponding parameters of the probability distributions of X and Y. These theorems will be presented without proof; the interested reader will find a proof in most elementary texts on probability theory.

The first theorem is the following: *The mean of the probability distribution of a difference between two independent random variables is equal to the difference between the means of the probability distributions of the two separate variables, i.e.,*

$$\mu_{X-Y} = \mu_X - \mu_Y \tag{8-1}$$

Substituting the values of μ_X and μ_Y for our illustrative problem, we obtain $\mu_{X-Y} = 3.5 - 3.5 = 0$. This value may be verified by direct calculation of μ_{X-Y} by substitution in Formula (4-6) of the values given in Table 8-2.

The second theorem is the following: *The variance of the probability distribution of a difference between two independent random variables is equal to the sum of the variances of the two separate variables, i.e.,*

$$\sigma_{X-Y}^2 = \sigma_X^2 + \sigma_Y^2 \tag{8-2}$$

Substituting the values of σ_X^2 and σ_Y^2 for our illustrative problem, we obtain $\sigma_{X-Y}^2 = 2\frac{11}{12} + 2\frac{11}{12} = 5\frac{5}{6}$. This value may be verified by direct calculation of σ_{X-Y}^2 using Formula (4-7).

At first glance it may seem strange that the variance of a difference should be greater than the variance of the components upon which it is based. However, this impression is dispelled by an examination of the ranges of the quantities involved. It will be noted that the lowest possible value of X is 1 and the highest possible value is 6—a range of 5. The range of possible values of Y is the same. On the other hand, the lowest possible value of $X - Y$ is -5 and the highest possible value is 5—a range of 10. The range of possible values of the difference is thus seen to be equal to the sum of the ranges of the two component variables, a relationship that holds generally and parallels the relationship between the corresponding variances.

The statistical procedures to which we now turn may be divided into two broad classes: (1) those that are applicable when the populations in question, or certain derivative distributions, are normally distributed and (2) those that are applicable under more general conditions—so-called *nonparametric* methods. We shall consider these two major categories separately, beginning with the former.

PROCEDURES APPLICABLE TO NORMAL DISTRIBUTIONS

INDEPENDENT SAMPLES: THE SAMPLING DISTRIBUTION OF $\overline{X}_1 - \overline{X}_2$

Let us begin by considering the following illustrative problem: An investigator wishes to determine whether performance under one set of conditions (Treatment *1*) differs from performance under another set of conditions (Treatment *2*). More specifically, he wishes to determine whether μ_1, the mean of a hypothetical population of individuals tested under Treatment *1*, differs from μ_2, the mean of a population of individuals tested under Treatment *2*. In a problem of this type the investigator may have theoretical or other grounds for believing that μ_1 and μ_2 differ, but he may not know the extent of the difference, if any. Because the hypothesis that $\mu_1 \neq \mu_2$ is not specific enough for purposes of performing a statistical test, the procedure followed under such circumstances is to test the opposite and more specific hypothesis that $\mu_1 = \mu_2$. This hypothesis is called the *null hypothesis* because it involves the assumption that there is no difference between μ_1 and μ_2.[1]

We will assume that to test the hypothesis that $\mu_1 = \mu_2$ an experiment is performed using ten subjects. By means of a table of random numbers five of the ten subjects are selected for testing under Treatment *1*, and the rest are tested under Treatment *2*. The means of these two samples of subjects will be represented by $\overline{X}_1$ and $\overline{X}_2$, respectively. The statistic of interest is the difference between these two means, $\overline{X}_1 - \overline{X}_2$. Although represented by a complex expression, the difference $\overline{X}_1 - \overline{X}_2$ should be regarded as a unitary quantity—a single statistic based upon the outcome of one experiment.

> To illustrate the formal characteristics of such an experiment and the manner in which the data are analyzed, two model populations were constructed—one representing subjects tested under Treatment *1*, the other representing subjects tested under Treatment *2*—and a sample of five cases drawn from each. The two populations were identical: each consisted of 20 dice (representing individual subjects) having the values of X indicated in Table 4-4. A sample of five observations representing

---

[1] It should be added that the designation *null hypothesis* is commonly used to refer not only to a hypothesis of the form $\mu_1 = \mu_2$ but to any hypothesis subjected to a statistical test. Thus, in testing a hypothesis concerning the mean of a single population (i.e., a hypothesis of the form $\mu = a$), the hypothesis tested may be referred to as the *null hypothesis*, although in such cases the import of the modifier *null* is not always clear.

the scores of five subjects tested under Treatment *1* was obtained by a procedure equivalent to drawing dice one at a time from Population *1*, rolling each die once, and recording the value of X obtained; a sample of five observations representing the scores of five subjects tested under Treatment *2* was obtained by sampling Population *2* in a similar manner. The results are presented in Table 8-3, where the difference between the two sample means, $\overline{X}_1 - \overline{X}_2$, is shown to be 8.6.

TABLE 8-3　*Simulated experiment: random samples from two identical populations*

SCORES OF SUBJECTS TESTED UNDER TREATMENT *1*	SCORES OF SUBJECTS TESTED UNDER TREATMENT *2*
111	106
28	97
102	59
89	6
46	65
$\overline{X}_1 = \dfrac{376}{5} = 75.2$	$\overline{X}_2 = \dfrac{333}{5} = 66.6$

$$\overline{X}_1 - \overline{X}_2 = 75.2 - 66.6$$
$$= 8.6$$

(Since the populations from which these samples were drawn had identical distributions of X, these populations represent a situation in which the null hypothesis is true, i.e., in which there is no difference on the average between the two treatments being compared. To represent a situation in which performance differs under the two treatments of interest—and, hence, in which the null hypothesis is false—we would construct two populations having different means. For example, we might construct the second population so that each value of X was 5 units higher than the corresponding value of X in the first population.)

Just as the two sample means, $\overline{X}_1$ and $\overline{X}_2$, are subject to sampling errors depending upon the particular individuals included in the samples, so is the difference $\overline{X}_1 - \overline{X}_2$. Extending the concepts developed in Chapter 6, we may conceptualize a sampling distribution of $\overline{X}_1 - \overline{X}_2$, i.e., a distribution that may be described by specifying all possible values of $\overline{X}_1 - \overline{X}_2$ and the probability of each. Indeed, in order to develop a procedure for testing the hypothesis that $\mu_1 = \mu_2$, we must have detailed knowledge concerning this important theoretical distribution.

In considering the sampling distribution of $\overline{X}_1 - \overline{X}_2$, it is helpful to distinguish the five theoretical distributions represented schematically in

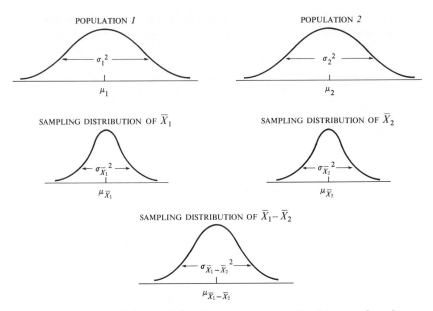

FIGURE 8-1   *Five theoretical distributions conceptualized in tests based upon the means of independent samples.*

Figure 8-1.   The "parent" populations, the properties of which determine the properties of the derivative distributions, are represented at the top of the figure.   In terms of the example given above, Population *1* consists of all subjects of a given kind that could be tested under Treatment *1;* Population *2*, of all subjects of a given kind that could be tested under Treatment *2*.   Immediately below the parent populations are represented two sampling distributions—one the sampling distribution of $\overline{X}$ for samples drawn from Population *1,* the other the sampling distribution of $\overline{X}$ for samples drawn from Population *2*.   These two sampling distributions will be designated the *sampling distribution of $\overline{X}_1$* and the *sampling distribution of $\overline{X}_2$*, respectively.   Finally, at the bottom of the figure is represented the sampling distribution of the difference $\overline{X}_1 - \overline{X}_2$.   (The reader should note the subscripts used to identify the means and variances of the five distributions.)

The properties of the sampling distribution of $\overline{X}_1 - \overline{X}_2$ are dependent upon the properties of the sampling distributions of $\overline{X}_1$ and $\overline{X}_2$.   Applying Formula (8-1) to the present problem, noting that here we are dealing with a difference between means rather than between individual observations, we obtain the following general result: $\mu_{\overline{X}_1-\overline{X}_2} = \mu_{\overline{X}_1} - \mu_{\overline{X}_2}$.   Inasmuch as $\mu_{\overline{X}_1}$ and $\mu_{\overline{X}_2}$ are equal to μ_1 and μ_2, respectively, the above relationship may be written in terms of the parameters of the parent populations as follows:

$$\mu_{\bar{X}_1-\bar{X}_2} = \mu_1 - \mu_2 \qquad (8\text{-}3)$$

Intuitively, this result seems reasonable. If the two populations in question have equal means, i.e., if $\mu_1 = \mu_2$, then $\bar{X}_1 - \bar{X}_2$ is distributed with a mean of zero. On the other hand, if $\mu_1 \neq \mu_2$, then $\bar{X}_1 - \bar{X}_2$ is distributed with a mean other than zero—for example, if $\mu_1 = 10$ and $\mu_2 = 8$, then $\bar{X}_1 - \bar{X}_2$ is distributed with a mean of 2.

Applying Formula (8-2) to the present problem, it is seen that the variance of the sampling distribution of $\bar{X}_1 - \bar{X}_2$ is equal to the sum of the variances of $\bar{X}_1$ and $\bar{X}_2$, i.e.,

$$\sigma_{\bar{X}_1-\bar{X}_2}^2 = \sigma_{\bar{X}_1}^2 + \sigma_{\bar{X}_2}^2 \qquad (8\text{-}4)$$

Letting n_1 represent the number of observations in the sample from Population *1*, n_2 the number in the sample from Population *2*, the values of $\sigma_{\bar{X}_1}^2$ and $\sigma_{\bar{X}_2}^2$ are given by the following equalities: $\sigma_{\bar{X}_1}^2 = \sigma_1^2/n_1$ and $\sigma_{\bar{X}_2}^2 = \sigma_2^2/n_2$. Substituting in Formula (8-4), we obtain the following equation relating the variance of $\bar{X}_1 - \bar{X}_2$ to the variances of Populations *1* and *2:*

$$\sigma_{\bar{X}_1-\bar{X}_2}^2 = \frac{\sigma_1^2}{n_1} + \frac{\sigma_2^2}{n_2} \qquad (8\text{-}5)$$

In preparing the way for further developments, it will be useful to derive a formula for the special case in which the two parent populations have equal variances, i.e., in which $\sigma_1^2 = \sigma_2^2 = \sigma^2$. Under this condition Formula (8-5) is modified as follows: $\sigma_{\bar{X}_1-\bar{X}_2}^2 = (\sigma^2/n_1) + (\sigma^2/n_2)$. Factoring the common term σ^2, we obtain the following: $\sigma_{\bar{X}_1-\bar{X}_2}^2 = \sigma^2[(1/n_1) + (1/n_2)]$. Finally, taking the square root of both sides of this last equation, we obtain the following formula for the standard error of $\bar{X}_1 - \bar{X}_2$ for the special case in which $\sigma_1^2 = \sigma_2^2 = \sigma^2$:

$$\sigma_{\bar{X}_1-\bar{X}_2} = \sqrt{\sigma^2\left(\frac{1}{n_1} + \frac{1}{n_2}\right)} \qquad (8\text{-}6)$$

Lastly, we consider the shape of the sampling distribution of $\bar{X}_1 - \bar{X}_2$. This statistic is distributed normally if the two components upon which it is based, $\bar{X}_1$ and $\bar{X}_2$, are both normally distributed. In turn, $\bar{X}_1$ and $\bar{X}_2$ are normally distributed if the respective parent populations are both normal. It follows that the sampling distribution of $\bar{X}_1 - \bar{X}_2$ is normal if the two parent populations are both normal; otherwise, the sampling distribution of $\bar{X}_1 - \bar{X}_2$ is not normal. However, even when the parent populations are not normal, the distribution of $\bar{X}_1 - \bar{X}_2$ is approximately normal when both samples are sufficiently large. For populations encountered in actual research, the approximation is usually very good when both samples include 30 or more observations.

INDEPENDENT SAMPLES: TESTING THE NULL HYPOTHESIS

When the values of σ_1^2 and σ_2^2 are unknown—which is almost always the case in actual practice—the hypothesis that $\mu_1 = \mu_2$ is tested by computing t as follows:

$$t = \frac{(\overline{X}_1 - \overline{X}_2) - \mu_{\overline{X}_1 - \overline{X}_2}}{s_{\overline{X}_1 - \overline{X}_2}} \tag{8-7}$$

This formula is seen to be analogous to Formula (7-2) for testing a hypothesis concerning the mean of a single population: the numerator is the discrepancy between (*a*) the observed value of $\overline{X}_1 - \overline{X}_2$ and (*b*) the mean of the sampling distribution of $\overline{X}_1 - \overline{X}_2$ according to the hypothesis being tested; the denominator is an estimate of the standard error of $\overline{X}_1 - \overline{X}_2$, the computation of which will be described below. It is apparent that, if the observed value of $\overline{X}_1 - \overline{X}_2$ is close to the value of $\mu_{\overline{X}_1 - \overline{X}_2}$ implied by the hypothesis being tested, then the computed value of t will be close to zero; on the other hand, if the observed value of $\overline{X}_1 - \overline{X}_2$ departs widely from the hypothetical value of $\mu_{\overline{X}_1 - \overline{X}_2}$, the computed value of t will not be close to zero, leading to rejection of the hypothesis being tested.

Strictly speaking, the use of Formula (8-7) is based upon two assumptions: (1) that both parent populations are normal and (2) that both populations have the same variance, i.e., that $\sigma_1^2 = \sigma_2^2 = \sigma^2$. Putting the matter somewhat differently, when the above assumptions are satisfied, the sampling distribution of t computed using Formula (8-7) will coincide with "Student's" t distribution, the theoretical distribution upon which the critical values of t presented in Table A-4 are based. When the above assumptions are not satisfied, the exact sampling distribution of t is not known and exact critical values for a given value of α cannot be specified.

Because both populations are assumed to have the same variance, the data of both samples are used to estimate σ^2, the common variance. Called the *pooled estimate of variance,* the statistic estimating σ^2 is designated s_p^2 and is computed as follows:

$$s_p^2 = \frac{\Sigma x_1^2 + \Sigma x_2^2}{(n_1 - 1) + (n_2 - 1)} \tag{8-8}$$

Formula (8-8) may be viewed as an elaboration of Formula (3-5) for s^2. The quantity Σx_1^2 in the numerator of Formula (8-8) is the sum of squares of deviations of the observations in Sample *1* around $\overline{X}_1$; Σx_2^2 is the sum of squares of deviations of the observations in Sample *2* around

$\overline{X}_2$. These quantities may be computed using Formula (3-9) as follows:

$$\Sigma x_1^2 = \frac{n_1 \Sigma X_1^2 - (\Sigma X_1)^2}{n_1} \quad \text{and} \quad \Sigma x_2^2 = \frac{n_2 \Sigma X_2^2 - (\Sigma X_2)^2}{n_2}$$

The denominator of Formula (8-8) is the sum of the degrees of freedom for the separate samples.[2]

The statistic $s_{\overline{X}_1 - \overline{X}_2}$, an estimate of the standard error of $\overline{X}_1 - \overline{X}_2$, is obtained by substituting s_p^2 in place of σ^2 in the right-hand side of Formula (8-6) as follows:

$$s_{\overline{X}_1 - \overline{X}_2} = \sqrt{s_p^2 \left(\frac{1}{n_1} + \frac{1}{n_2} \right)} \tag{8-9}$$

Substituting for $s_{\overline{X}_1 - \overline{X}_2}$ in Formula (8-7), and simplifying the numerator by omitting $\mu_{\overline{X}_1 - \overline{X}_2}$ (which according to the null hypothesis is zero), we obtain the following formula for t for testing the hypothesis that $\mu_1 = \mu_2$:

$$t = \frac{\overline{X}_1 - \overline{X}_2}{\sqrt{s_p^2 \left(\frac{1}{n_1} + \frac{1}{n_2} \right)}} \tag{8-10}$$

The number of degrees of freedom associated with this value of t is $(n_1 - 1) + (n_2 - 1)$, the number of degrees of freedom available for computing s_p^2.

The use of Formula (8-10) will be illustrated by calculating t for the data presented in Table 8-3. The calculation of $\overline{X}_1 - \overline{X}_2$ is shown in Table 8-3; the calculation of the sums of squares of deviations, Σx_1^2 and Σx_2^2, is shown in Table 8-4. Substituting the latter quantities in Formula (8-8), the pooled estimate of σ^2 is computed as follows:

$$s_p^2 = \frac{5{,}270.8 + 6{,}209.2}{4 + 4} = \frac{11{,}480}{8} = 1{,}435$$

(The value of s_p^2 is seen to be a fair approximation of $\sigma^2 = 1{,}199^{11}\!/_{12}$.) Finally, substituting the above results in Formula (8-10), t is computed as follows:

$$t = \frac{75.2 - 66.6}{\sqrt{1{,}435 \left(\frac{1}{5} + \frac{1}{5} \right)}} = \frac{8.6}{\sqrt{1{,}435 \left(\frac{2}{5} \right)}} \approx \frac{8.6}{23.96} \approx 0.36$$

[2] Alternatively, s_p^2 may be viewed as a weighted average of s_1^2 and s_2^2, the variances of Samples *1* and *2*, respectively. Solving the equation $s_1^2 = \Sigma x_1^2/(n_1 - 1)$ for Σx_1^2, we obtain $\Sigma x_1^2 = (n_1 - 1)s_1^2$; similarly, $\Sigma x_2^2 = (n_2 - 1)s_2^2$. Substituting for Σx_1^2 and Σx_2^2 in Formula (8-8), we obtain $s_p^2 = \dfrac{(n_1 - 1)s_1^2 + (n_2 - 1)s_2^2}{(n_1 - 1) + (n_2 - 1)}$. It is evident from the latter formula, which is algebraically equivalent to Formula (8-8), that s_p^2 is a weighted average of s_1^2 and s_2^2, each of the sample variances being weighted by the number of degrees of freedom on which it is based.

TABLE 8-4   *Computation of Σx_1^2 and Σx_2^2*

SUBJECTS TESTED UNDER TREATMENT *1*		SUBJECTS TESTED UNDER TREATMENT *2*	
X	X^2	X	X^2
111	12,321	106	11,236
28	784	97	9,409
102	10,404	59	3,481
89	7,921	6	36
46	2,116	65	4,225
376	33,546	333	28,387

$$\Sigma x_1^2 = \frac{5(33,546) - (376)^2}{5}$$
$$= 5,270.8$$

$$\Sigma x_2^2 = \frac{5(28,387) - (333)^2}{5}$$
$$= 6,209.2$$

The number of degrees of freedom is eight—four from one sample and four from the other. With eight degrees of freedom the critical values of t for a test at the .05 level of significance are -2.306 and 2.306. Since the computed value of t lies between these critical values, the hypothesis that $\mu_1 = \mu_2$ is accepted. In other words, it is concluded that performance does not differ under the two treatments compared. (We happen to know in the present case, as we usually do not know in practice, that the null hypothesis is true. Thus, the value of t obtained in our illustrative problem has led to a correct conclusion—acceptance of a true hypothesis.)

INDEPENDENT SAMPLES: VIOLATIONS
OF THE ASSUMPTIONS UNDERLYING THE t TEST

We have noted that the t test for comparing the means of independent samples is based upon two assumptions—that the populations sampled have equal variances, and that both populations are normally distributed. An empirical study of the effects upon the probability of a Type I error of violations of these assumptions has been reported by Boneau (1960). The general procedure used by Boneau was as follows: First, two populations having known characteristics were constructed. Then a large number of "experiments" were performed, in each of which two samples were selected randomly, one from each population, and the value of t computed using Formula (8-10). This procedure was repeated with a variety of different populations. In every case the means of the two populations were identical, but the assumptions underlying the t test were violated in some fashion. In some instances both populations were normal but had unequal variances; in others, the populations had equal variances but were not normal; in still others, the populations were not normal and the variances were unequal. The purpose of the study was to determine the extent to which violations of the assumptions underlying the t test cause the relative frequency of Type I errors to depart from the nominal value of α, i.e., the theoretical value of α for the critical values employed. If the findings of such a study should indicate that, using critical values for, say, $\alpha = .05$, a true null hypothesis is rejected approximately 5 per cent of the time despite the fact that a given assumption is violated, then fulfillment of that assumption would be regarded as relatively unimportant in practice. On the other hand, if it should be found that violations of a given assumption result in rejection of the null hypothesis considerably more often than 5 per cent of the time, then fulfillment of that assumption would be regarded as important, and it would seem inadvisable to employ the t test under circumstances in which that assumption is not met.

Boneau found that when both populations were normal but had unequal variances ($\sigma_1^2 = 4$, $\sigma_2^2 = 1$) the t test was seriously in error if the samples were unequal in size. For example, with $n_1 = 5$ and $n_2 = 15$, 16 per cent of the observed values of t exceeded the critical values of t for $\alpha = .05$, and 6 per cent exceeded the critical values for $\alpha = .01$. However, with samples of equal size the relative frequency of rejection conformed much more closely to the nominal value of α. With small samples ($n_1 = n_2 = 5$) the agreement was fair: using critical values for $\alpha = .05$, 6.4 per cent of the obtained values of t led to rejection of a true null hypothesis; using critical values for $\alpha = .01$, 1.8 per cent of the obtained values led to rejection. With samples of moderate size ($n_1 = n_2 = 15$) the agreement was still better, 4.9 per cent and 1.1 per cent of the obtained values of t leading to rejection using critical values for $\alpha = .05$ and $\alpha = .01$, respectively. These findings indicate that, for experiments employing moderately large samples of equal size, a violation of the assumption that the population variances be equal is relatively unimportant, for the risk of a Type I error conforms closely to the nominal value of α even when this assumption is violated.

In the remaining situations studied by Boneau one or both of the populations differed radically in shape from the normal distribution. (In these situations the distribution of t was investigated only for experiments employing samples of equal size.) With small samples ($n_1 = n_2 = 5$) the correspondence between the relative frequency of rejection of the null hypothesis and the nominal value of α was fair: using critical values for $\alpha = .05$, the rejection rate varied between 3.1 per cent and 8.3 per cent depending on the populations involved; using critical values for $\alpha = .01$, the rejection rate varied between 0.3 per cent and 3.3 per cent. With samples of moderate size ($n_1 = n_2 = 15$) the agreement was quite good: the rejection rate varied between 4.0 per cent and 5.6 per cent for tests based upon critical values for $\alpha = .05$, and between 0.4 per cent and 1.6 per cent for tests based upon critical values for $\alpha = .01$. Since the populations studied by Boneau violated the assumptions of the t test for independent samples to as great an extent as is likely to occur in practice, it appears that for almost any population encountered in psychological research the frequency of rejection of the null hypothesis may be expected to conform closely to the nominal value of α if the t test is based upon samples of moderate (and equal) size, and that even with small samples the errors resulting from violations of the assumption of normality are not extreme.

One qualification concerning the above conclusion should be noted. When one of the populations sampled was symmetrical and the other skewed, the distribution of t also tended to be skewed so that the total number of values of t lying in the rejection region was not divided equally between the two parts of the rejection region, i.e., below $t_{.025}$ and above $t_{.975}$. Thus, while the total number of rejections of the null hypothesis approximated α in such cases, the preponderance of the observed values of t leading to rejection was located in one tail of the empirical distribution. In such cases a one-sided test would be seriously in error, i.e., would lead either to too many or too few rejections of the null hypothesis, depending upon the hypothesis tested. However, with sufficiently large samples ($n_1 = n_2 = 25$), the distribution of observed values of t was found to be very nearly symmetrical, with the result that this difficulty disappeared.

Finally, although increasing sample size reduces the extent to which the t test is disturbed by violations of the assumptions concerning the shape and variance of the populations sampled, it is emphasized that the use of large samples in no way compensates for faults of experimental design leading to systematic errors. For example, if subjects are not assigned to experimental treatments in a random fashion, with the result that one or more extraneous variables are confounded with the independent variable, this condition is in no way corrected by employing large samples.

PAIRED OBSERVATIONS: THE SAMPLING DISTRIBUTION OF $\overline{D}$

Thus far we have considered experiments in which the two samples observed are drawn from their respective populations independently. That is to say, both samples are selected randomly, and in drawing one sample, no account is taken of the characteristics of the individuals in the other sample. Consequently, even when μ_1 is equal to μ_2, a difference may arise between $\overline{X}_1$ and $\overline{X}_2$ because more high-scoring individuals happen to be chosen in one sample than in the other. In contrast to experiments employing independent samples, it is possible in some experimental situations to restrict the extent to which individuals in the two samples differ—aside from the difference deliberately introduced by the investigator—by pairing, or matching, the individuals in the two samples in some manner. Four methods by which the subjects receiving one experimental treatment may be matched with those receiving the other treatment are the following:

1. In some investigations an effective form of matching is to measure each individual twice, once under one experimental treatment and once under the other. When the two tests are administered successively, the effects of such factors as practice and fatigue may be prevented from systematically favoring or impairing performance under either of the two treatments by randomly varying the sequence of the two treatments among subjects, some of the subjects being tested under one treatment first and others being tested under the other treatment first. A limitation of this method of matching is that it cannot be employed with observations of a kind in which measuring a subject once renders him unsuited for further measures of the same type. For example, if the measure employed is the time required to complete a problem requiring insight for its solution, a subject who had once solved the problem would not be suitable for further testing on the same problem under another experimental treatment.

2. It is sometimes possible to take advantage of natural pairing of subjects in assigning individuals to experimental treatments. For example, if ten pairs of twins are available for a study, the two samples could be matched by splitting each pair of twins and randomly assigning one member of each pair to one treatment and one to the other. Following this procedure, each individual in one sample would be matched by his twin in the other. For this type of matching to be effective, the two members within each pair must resemble one another with respect to the dependent variable being measured. For example, if the dependent variable being recorded is number of trials required to learn a standard task, matching in the manner described here would be effective only if the two individuals within a given pair are alike with respect to learning ability; otherwise, nothing is accomplished by matching.

3. When twins or other such natural pairs are not available, pairing may be based upon preliminary measurements of the subjects. For example, in studying the effects of two diets on weight, subjects might be paired on the basis of preliminary measurements of weight obtained before starting the diet. If for some reason it were not possible to obtain preliminary weight measures, measurements of a related variable (e.g., height) could be used as a basis for pairing.

4. Pairing may also be based upon certain conditions that vary over the course of an experiment but that can be held constant for pairs of subjects. Pairing on a basis of this sort may be illustrated by a hypothetical animal study designed to compare learning performance under two conditions of motivation—for example, food deprivation versus water depriva-

tion.   If the investigator's schedule permits him to run only two subjects at a time, and subjects are spaced so that two are run, say, in the fall, two in the winter, and so on, the investigator could elect to pair observations by splitting each (seasonal) pair of subjects, assigning one member of each pair to one experimental treatment and one member to the other. (The alternative method, requiring analysis by the procedures described above for independent samples, would be to disregard the seasonal pairing of subjects and simply assign half of the total number of subjects to one experimental treatment at random.   Unlike the procedure followed in pairing observations, the alternative procedure permits two subjects tested during the same season to be assigned to the same experimental treatment.)

To illustrate the theoretical considerations involved in dealing with paired observations let us imagine a hypothetical investigation in which each subject is tested twice on a standard task, once with a distracting noise present (Treatment *1*) and once without the noise (Treatment *2*).

The results of such an experiment may be simulated by sampling the two model populations described earlier in the chapter, i.e., two identical populations each consisting of 20 dice having the values indicated in Table 4-4.   (Here, as before, the use of two identical populations represents a situation in which performance is the same under the two treatments compared, i.e., in which the null hypothesis is true.   A situation in which performance differs under the two treatments would be represented by a model in which the distribution of X differs in the two populations, with the result that μ_1 and μ_2 differ in value.)   In this analogy the 20 dice in Population *1* represent a population of individuals tested under Treatment *1*; the dice in Population *2* represent the same 20 individuals tested under Treatment *2*.   That is to say, the probability distribution of X for a given die in Population *1* represents the potential performance of a specific individual tested under Treatment *1*; the (identical) probability distribution of X for the corresponding die in Population *2* represents the potential performance of the same individual tested under Treatment *2*.

Using this model, the results of an experiment in which several individuals are each measured twice, once under Treatment *1* and once under Treatment *2*, may be simulated as follows: The individuals to be included in the sample are first determined randomly—for example, by using a table of random numbers.   The value of X for a given individual under Treatment *1* is determined by selecting the appropriate die from Population *1* and rolling it once; the value of X for the same individual under Treatment *2* is obtained by selecting the corresponding die from Population *2* and rolling it once.   This procedure is repeated for each individual in the sample.   (It will be noted that this procedure differs from that used in simulating the results of an experiment employing independent samples: in the latter procedure the samples from the two populations were drawn independently so there was no correspondence between the observations in one sample and those in the other.)

The results of an experiment such as described above are shown in Table 8-5.   The first column identifies the five individuals included in the

TABLE 8-5 *Simulated experiment: five individuals tested under two different treatments*

INDIVIDUAL	SCORE UNDER TREATMENT 1 X_1	SCORE UNDER TREATMENT 2 X_2	DIFFERENCE D	D^2
1	5	4	1	1
4	23	20	3	9
11	63	65	−2	4
13	78	78	0	0
16	92	96	−4	16
	261	263	−2	30

$$\overline{X}_1 = \frac{261}{5} = 52.2$$

$$\overline{X}_2 = \frac{263}{5} = 52.6 \qquad\qquad \overline{D} = \frac{-2}{5} = -.4$$

$$\overline{X}_1 - \overline{X}_2 = -.4$$

sample; the second column lists the values of X_1, the performance measures of the five subjects under Treatment *1*; and the third column lists the values of X_2, the performance measures of the same subjects under Treatment *2*. (The remaining two columns will be explained below.)

Inspection of Table 8-5 indicates that there is close agreement between the two scores for any given individual: the individual having the lowest score under Treatment *1* also has the lowest score under Treatment *2*; the individual having the next-to-lowest score under Treatment *1* also has the next-to-lowest score under Treatment *2*; and so on. This consistency in the relative standing under the two treatments of the two observations of a given pair is the aim of pairing. When such consistency is achieved, a low score under one treatment is matched by a corresponding low score under the other treatment; an intermediate score, by an intermediate score; and so on. As a consequence of the close matching of the two scores of each pair, the difference $\overline{X}_1 - \overline{X}_2 = -.4$ in the present experiment gives a closer approximation of $\mu_1 - \mu_2 = 0$, the difference between the population means, than did the corresponding difference $\overline{X}_1 - \overline{X}_2 = 8.6$ based upon independent samples (Table 8-3).

Speaking in more general terms, the effect of pairing is to reduce the variance of the sampling distribution of the difference $\overline{X}_1 - \overline{X}_2$. It is not surprising, therefore, that the method of estimating the variance of the difference between means (and, hence, of evaluating the significance of an observed difference) is not the same in an experiment employing paired observations as in an experiment employing independent samples. Although the reasons are not at first obvious, in an experiment employing paired observations information concerning the sampling distribution of $\overline{X}_1 - \overline{X}_2$ may be derived by considering the differences computed pair by pair. The differences for the data presented in Table 8-5 are listed in the column headed D. (Note that the direction of each difference is indicated by its sign: if X_1 is greater than X_2, the difference is positive; if X_2 is greater than X_1, the difference is negative.) In the bottom portion of the table it is shown that the mean difference, $\overline{D}$, is equal to $-.4$. It will be noted that the value of $\overline{D}$ is the same as the value of $\overline{X}_1 - \overline{X}_2$. This important relationship will always obtain: in an experiment involving paired observations, the difference between the treatment means, $\overline{X}_1 - \overline{X}_2$, is always equal to $\overline{D}$, the mean of the differences computed separately for each pair. Accordingly, *for experiments employing paired observations the sampling distribution of $\overline{X}_1 - \overline{X}_2$ is the same as the sampling distribution of $\overline{D}$.*

The various theoretical distributions that must be conceptualized in using paired observations to test the hypothesis that $\mu_1 = \mu_2$ are represented schematically in Figure 8-2. The two distributions pictured at the top of this figure represent the distribution of X *for all possible*

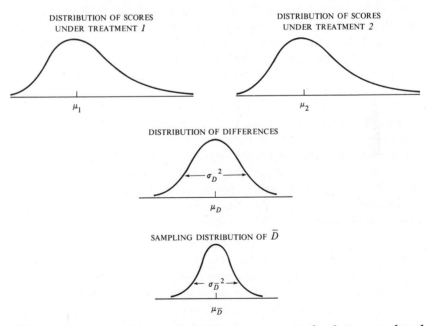

FIGURE 8-2 *Four theoretical distributions conceptualized in tests based upon paired observations.*

individuals tested under Treatment *1* and the distribution for all possible individuals tested under Treatment 2. Both of these distributions have been pictured as asymmetrical to emphasize the fact that these distributions need not be normally distributed. Below these distributions is pictured the theoretical distribution of differences, i.e., a distribution describing the probabilities of the various possible values of *D*. This distribution of differences is analogous to the population from which a single sample is drawn using the methods of Chapter 7; it is the distribution from which a sample of differences is drawn, and is assumed to be normally distributed. (It will be noted that our model based upon Table 4-4 does not actually meet the requirement that the differences be normally distributed; this characteristic was sacrificed in the model for purposes of simplicity.) The distribution pictured at the bottom of Figure 8-2 is the sampling distribution of $\overline{D}$. This distribution is analogous to the sampling distribution of $\overline{X}$ in the single-sample problems discussed in Chapter 7; it is a theoretical distribution describing the probabilities of the various possible values of $\overline{D}$. The observed value of $\overline{D}$ may be construed as a value selected at random from this distribution, and the properties of this distribution must be taken into account in evaluating whether the observed value of $\overline{D}$ warrants rejection of the null hypothesis.

The parameters of the sampling distribution of $\overline{D}$ may be derived by the same theoretical considerations that apply to the sampling distribution of $\overline{X}$ for samples drawn from a single population. As noted above, the *n* differences upon which the value of $\overline{D}$ is based (e.g., the five differences in Table 8-5) may be regarded as a sample from a theoretical distribution of differences, the mean and variance of which may be designated μ_D and $\sigma_D{}^2$, respectively. The mean and variance of the sampling distribution of $\overline{D}$ are given by equations analogous to Formulae (6-1) and (6-2) for the parameters of the sampling distribution of $\overline{X}$, i.e., $\mu_{\overline{D}} = \mu_D$ and

$$\sigma_{\overline{D}}{}^2 = \frac{\sigma_D{}^2}{n} \tag{8-11}$$

It can be shown that μ_D is equal to the difference between μ_1 (the mean of the hypothetical population of subjects tested under Treatment *1*) and μ_2 (the corresponding mean for Treatment *2*), i.e.,

$$\mu_D = \mu_1 - \mu_2 \tag{8-12}$$

(This relationship is seen to be analogous to that between $\overline{D}$ and $\overline{X}_1 - \overline{X}_2$, shown in Table 8-5.) It follows that, if $\mu_1 = \mu_2$, then $\mu_D = 0$. In other words, if the null hypothesis is true, then the distribution of differences has a mean of zero.

The manner in which experimental data based upon paired observations are used to test the hypothesis that $\mu_1 = \mu_2$ will be demonstrated using the data presented in Table 8-5.   These data, it will be recalled, are the hypothetical scores of five subjects each tested once under Treatment *1* and once under Treatment *2*.

We have seen that if the null hypothesis is true, $\mu_D = 0$.   Accordingly, a test of the null hypothesis is provided by testing the derivative hypothesis that the five differences shown in the fourth column of Table 8-5 are a random sample from a population of differences in which $\mu_D = 0$. This hypothesis may be tested using the procedures described in Chapter 7 for testing a hypothesis when the population variance is unknown.   The test is made using Formula (7-2) with $\overline{D}$ substituted for $\overline{X}$ and $s_{\overline{D}}$ substituted for $s_{\overline{X}}$ as follows: $t = (\overline{D} - \mu_0)/s_{\overline{D}}$.   Inasmuch as μ_0 (the value of μ_D according to the hypothesis being tested) is zero, this equation may be simplified by omitting μ_0 as follows:

$$t = \frac{\overline{D}}{s_{\overline{D}}} \qquad (8\text{-}13)$$

The number of degrees of freedom associated with this value of t is $n - 1$, in which n represents the number of differences.

The denominator of Formula (8-13), the estimated standard error of $\overline{D}$, is computed in two steps.   First, s_D^2, the estimated variance of the distribution of differences, is computed as follows:

$$s_D^2 = \frac{n\Sigma D^2 - (\Sigma D)^2}{n(n-1)} = \frac{5(30) - (-2)^2}{5(4)} = 7.3$$

Next, $s_{\overline{D}}^2$ is computed as follows:

$$s_{\overline{D}}^2 = \frac{s_D^2}{n} = \frac{7.3}{5} = 1.46$$

(The formulae used in computing s_D^2 and $s_{\overline{D}}^2$ are seen to be analogous to Formulae (3-7) and (7-1) for s^2 and $s_{\overline{X}}^2$, respectively.)   Taking the square root of $s_{\overline{D}}^2$, we obtain $s_{\overline{D}} \approx 1.208$.   Substituting in Formula (8-13), we obtain $t \approx -.4/1.208 \approx -.33$.   Inasmuch as our estimate of s_D^2 is based upon five differences, there are four degrees of freedom associated with this value of t.   Accordingly, the critical values for a test at the .05 level of significance are -2.776 and 2.776.   Since the observed value of t $(-.33)$ falls between these critical values, the difference is not statistically significant, i.e., the observed value of $\overline{D}$ does not warrant rejection of the null hypothesis.

Non-normality of the population of differences has the same consequences as non-normality of the population in a single-sample problem of the type considered in Chapter 7, and the remarks made concerning the latter situation apply here. The greater the departure of the distribution of differences from a normal distribution, the greater is the error involved in using the t test likely to be. However, as the number of differences in the sample increases, the extent of the error decreases, and with samples in which n is 30 or more the error resulting from non-normality of the population of differences will in most instances be negligible.

THE POWER OF TESTS BASED UPON
INDEPENDENT SAMPLES AND PAIRED OBSERVATIONS

Using the tests described above—that based upon Formula (8-10) for independent samples and that based upon Formula (8-13) for paired observations—the probability of rejecting the null hypothesis when it is false is determined by the same factors as considered in Chapter 7 in connection with tests concerning the mean of a single population. First, power depends upon the actual difference between μ_1 and μ_2: all other factors being equal, the greater the discrepancy between the hypothetical difference (zero) and the actual difference between μ_1 and μ_2, the greater is the power of the test in question. Second, power depends upon the value of α employed in selecting critical values of t: all other factors being equal, the smaller the value of α, the lower is power. Third, power depends upon the precision of $\overline{X}_1 - \overline{X}_2$ in tests based upon independent samples, and upon the precision of $\overline{D}$ in tests based upon paired observations: all other factors being equal, the smaller the value of $\sigma_{\overline{X}_1 - \overline{X}_2}$ or of $\sigma_{\overline{D}}$, the greater is the power of the test.

In view of its effect upon power, it is of interest to compare the precision of $\overline{X}_1 - \overline{X}_2$ based upon independent samples with that of $\overline{D}$ based upon paired observations. The desired comparison may be made by expressing the values of $\sigma_{\overline{X}_1 - \overline{X}_2}^2$ and $\sigma_{\overline{D}}^2$ in terms of σ_τ^2 (the variation associated with individual differences) and σ_ϵ^2 (the variation of repeated determinations based upon the same individual), which were defined and discussed in detail in Chapter 4.

The comparison will be facilitated if the value of $\sigma_{\overline{X}_1 - \overline{X}_2}^2$ is computed for the special case in which $n_1 = n_2 = n$. Squaring both sides of Formula (8-6), we obtain the following equation for the variance of $\overline{X}_1 - \overline{X}_2$: $\sigma_{\overline{X}_1 - \overline{X}_2}^2 = \sigma^2[(1/n_1) + (1/n_2)]$. In the special case in which $n_1 = n_2 = n$, this relationship simplifies to

$$\sigma_{\overline{X}_1 - \overline{X}_2}^2 = \frac{2\sigma^2}{n} \tag{8-14}$$

We have already noted in Formula (4-8) that $\sigma^2 = \sigma_\tau^2 + \sigma_\epsilon^2$. Substituting in Formula (8-14), we obtain the following equality for the special case in which $n_1 = n_2 = n$: $\sigma_{\overline{X}_1 - \overline{X}_2}^2 = 2(\sigma_\tau^2 + \sigma_\epsilon^2)/n$, which may be written

$$\sigma_{\overline{X}_1 - \overline{X}_2}^2 = \frac{2\sigma_\tau^2}{n} + \frac{2\sigma_\epsilon^2}{n} \tag{8-15}$$

It is thus seen that both individual differences and variation of repeated determinations contribute to the sampling variation of $\overline{X}_1 - \overline{X}_2$ in experiments employing independent samples. In other words, it is to be expected that even when $\mu_1 = \mu_2$ a difference will occur between $\overline{X}_1$ and $\overline{X}_2$ in part as a result of individual inconsistency and in part because more high-scoring individuals happen to be included in one sample than in the other. The joint effect of these two sources of variation is taken into account in the t test described by Formula (8-10); unless the difference between $\overline{X}_1$ and $\overline{X}_2$ is greater than might reasonably be expected on the basis of the estimated value of σ^2, the hypothesis that $\mu_1 = \mu_2$ is judged to be tenable.

Deriving the relationship between $\sigma_{\overline{D}}^2$ and the two components of σ^2 —σ_τ^2 and σ_ϵ^2—is somewhat more complex. As a first step, we consider the probability distribution of D for a single subject. The value of D for a given subject may be written in general terms as follows:

$$D = X_1 - X_2$$

in which X_1 and X_2 represent the observed values of X under Treatments *1* and *2*, respectively, for the subject in question. Since X_1 and X_2 for a given subject are independent random variables, the mean and variance of the probability distribution of D are given by Formulae (8-1) and (8-2), respectively. To illustrate, for Individual *4* the mean of the probability distribution of X_1 is 21.5; assuming the null hypothesis to be true, the mean of the probability distribution of X_2 for this individual is also 21.5. Substituting in Formula (8-1), we may compute μ_D, the mean of the probability distribution of D for Individual *4*, as follows:

$$\mu_D = 21.5 - 21.5 = 0$$

The variance of the probability distribution of X for Individual *4* under Treatment *1*, like that for other subjects, is σ_ϵ^2; the variance under Treatment *2* is the same. Substituting in Formula (8-2), we may express σ_D^2, the variance of the distribution of D for Individual *4*, as follows:

$$\sigma_D^2 = \sigma_\epsilon^2 + \sigma_\epsilon^2 = 2\sigma_\epsilon^2 \tag{8-16}$$

By similar computations it may be shown that, for each of the individuals in our model, D is distributed with $\mu_D = 0$ and $\sigma_D^2 = 2\sigma_\epsilon^2$.

Although in a certain sense we may think of the distribution of D for each individual as being distinct, we have indicated above that all of these distributions are mathematically identical. Thus, the n values of D obtained in an experiment employing paired observations may be treated as if they were a sample from a single population. It follows, as indicated in Formula (8-11), that the variance of the sampling distribution of $\overline{D}$ is equal to $\sigma_D{}^2/n$. Substituting the value of $\sigma_D{}^2$ given in Formula (8-16), we obtain the following formula for the variance of $\overline{D}$:

$$\sigma_{\overline{D}}^2 = \frac{2\sigma_\epsilon{}^2}{n} \qquad (8\text{-}17)$$

A comparison of the variance of $\overline{X}_1 - \overline{X}_2$ for experiments employing independent samples (Formula (8-15)) with that of $\overline{D}$ for experiments employing paired observations (Formula (8-17)) indicates that $\sigma_{\overline{X}_1-\overline{X}_2}^2$ exceeds $\sigma_{\overline{D}}^2$ by an amount equal to $2\sigma_\tau{}^2/n$. In other words, the effect of pairing observations is to eliminate $\sigma_\tau{}^2$, the component of σ^2 due to individual differences, from experimental error. Thus, if $\sigma_\tau{}^2$ constitutes a large portion of σ^2, the use of paired observations will afford a substantial increase in the precision of the experiment, resulting in a greater probability of rejecting the null hypothesis when it is false.

One word of caution is in order concerning the pairing of observations. The increase in power afforded by pairing is to some extent offset by a loss of degrees of freedom. For example, in an experiment employing independent samples in which $n_1 = n_2 = 5$, the number of degrees of freedom for evaluating t is $4 + 4 = 8$; in an experiment employing the same total number of observations but in which the observations are paired, i.e., an experiment employing five pairs, there are only four degrees of freedom. With fewer degrees of freedom the t test based upon paired observations will be less powerful than a test based upon independent samples unless pairing has resulted in a sufficiently large reduction in experimental error. Therefore, pairing is most desirable when $\sigma_\tau{}^2$ constitutes a large portion of σ^2; when $\sigma_\tau{}^2$ constitutes only a small portion of σ^2, a t test based upon independent samples may be more powerful than one based upon paired observations.

A MORE COMPLEX MODEL FOR PAIRED OBSERVATIONS

The model we have employed thus far in discussing paired observations has been made as simple as possible by assuming that the probability distribution of X for a given individual under Treatment *1* is identical to the probability distribution for the same (or corresponding) individual under Treatment *2*. For example, according to Table 4-4 the possible values of X for Individual *1* under Treatment *1* are $1, 2, \cdots, 6$, the probability of occurrence of each value being $1/6$, and we have assumed that the distribution of X for this subject (or the one corresponding to him) under Treatment *2* is exactly the same. In actual practice, however, the situation may not be so simple.   For example, in an experiment in which each subject is tested twice, once under Treatment *1* and once under Treatment *2*, the subject's performance may change as a result of the practice obtained on the first testing.   Such an effect would be represented in the model by a change in the probability distribution of X and hence by a difference between the two treatments in the expected values of X, i.e., in the means of the respective probability distributions for that subject.   (We have already noted that because of this possibility the order in which the two treatments are presented must be determined randomly for each subject, so that one treatment is not systematically favored by practice effects.)   Another complicating factor is that subjects may differ with respect to the treatment under which they perform better: some subjects may find Treatment *1* more favorable, others may find Treatment *2* more favorable.   In other words, it may be that for some subjects the expected value of X is higher under Treatment *1* than under Treatment *2*, whereas for others the reverse is true.   In experiments in which the pairs consist not of the same individual tested under different treatments but of two individuals who have been matched on the basis of some preliminary measure, the two members of any given pair are seldom perfectly matched, i.e., the probability distribution of X for one individual is seldom identical to that of the individual with whom he is matched.   Similarly, the probability distributions of X for two subjects forming a natural pair (e.g., twins), although often similar, are rarely identical.

A model having the characteristics of the more complex situations described above may be constructed by modifying our original model as shown in Table 8-6.

TABLE 8-6   *Modified model for paired observations*

PAIR	TREATMENT *1* Possible Values of X_1						τ_1	TREATMENT *2* Possible Values of X_2						τ_2
1	1	2	3	4	5	6	**3.5**	4	5	6	7	8	9	**6.5**
2	8	9	10	11	12	13	**10.5**	7	8	9	10	11	12	**9.5**
3	12	13	14	15	16	17	**14.5**	14	15	16	17	18	19	**16.5**
.	.	.	.	.	.	.	.	.	.	.	.	.	.	.
.	.	.	.	.	.	.	.	.	.	.	.	.	.	.
.	.	.	.	.	.	.	.	.	.	.	.	.	.	.
20	116	117	118	119	120	121	**118.5**	113	114	115	116	117	118	**115.5**

In contrast to the original model, in which the two probability distributions of X for a given pair were assumed to be the same, in the modified model represented in Table 8-6 the two probability distributions for a given pair —one for Treatment *1*, the other for Treatment *2*—are not identical.

This feature of the model is evident from a comparison of the two values of τ within each pair. It will be noted that for any given pair the value of τ_1 (the mean of the probability distribution for the individual tested under Treatment *1*) is similar in value, but not identical, to the value of τ_2 (the mean of the probability distribution for the individual tested under Treatment *2*). If we examine the difference $\tau_1 - \tau_2$ for each pair, we note that this difference varies in magnitude and direction from pair to pair. For example, for Pairs *1*, *2*, and *3*, the value of this difference is -3, 1, and -2, respectively. When constructed so that the mean value of $\tau_1 - \tau_2$ for all individuals is zero, the model represents a situation in which the null hypothesis is true; otherwise, it represents a situation in which the null hypothesis is false, i.e., one in which the values of X for the two treatments differ on the average.

When the model is modified in the manner described above, differences computed in the manner shown in Table 8-5 vary more from pair to pair than differences based upon the simpler model described originally. In other words, the value of $\sigma_D{}^2$, which is equal to $2\sigma_\epsilon{}^2$ for differences based upon the original model, is greater than $2\sigma_\epsilon{}^2$ for differences based upon the modified model. The increase in the variance of D arises as a consequence of the variation from pair to pair in the modified model of the difference $\tau_1 - \tau_2$, which in the original model was assumed to be constant (zero) for all pairs. In turn, it follows that the value of $\sigma_{\bar{D}}{}^2$ based upon the modified model is greater than indicated in Formula (8-17). However, in all other respects the theory underlying the t test for paired observations is the same as described in connection with the original model. Whether the simple model described originally or the more complex model described in the present subsection applies to a given research situation, the computation of t is the same.

INTERVAL ESTIMATES OF THE DIFFERENCE $\mu_1 - \mu_2$

In most experiments involving the comparison of two experimental treatments the investigator is interested in rejecting the hypothesis that $\mu_1 = \mu_2$, i.e., in demonstrating that performance differs under the two treatments being compared. However, occasionally an investigator is interested in demonstrating that performance under two experimental treatments is the same. (For example, the results of certain learning studies led Bugelski (1962) to hypothesize that, in learning certain types of material by rote, the total time required to attain mastery of the task is the same despite variations among treatments in the rate at which the items to be memorized are presented.) Unfortunately, acceptance of the hypothesis that $\mu_1 = \mu_2$ on the basis of a statistical test is not proof that this hypothesis is true, but merely an indication that it is one of several possible hypotheses that are compatible with the available data. On the other hand, the information afforded by computing confidence limits for the difference between μ_1 and μ_2 is somewhat more specific: the difference may be asserted—with a known risk of error—to lie within a given interval. In some cases the interval may include only values so close to zero that any difference that may exist between μ_1 and μ_2 is judged to be of little practical importance.

The computation of confidence limits for the difference $\mu_1 - \mu_2$ is a simple extension of the method described in Chapter 7 for determining confidence limits for the mean of a single population. In an experiment employing independent samples, the lower and upper 95 per cent confidence limits for the difference $\mu_1 - \mu_2$ are $(\overline{X}_1 - \overline{X}_2) + t_{.025}s_{\overline{X}_1-\overline{X}_2}$ and $(\overline{X}_1 - \overline{X}_2) + t_{.975}s_{\overline{X}_1-\overline{X}_2}$, respectively. The number of degrees of freedom used in entering the t table to determine $t_{.025}$ and $t_{.975}$ is $(n_1 - 1) + (n_2 - 1)$. (A comparison of the above confidence limits with those described in Chapter 7 for the mean of a single population indicates that both sets of limits have the general form $A + t_{.025}s_A$ and $A + t_{.975}s_A$. In problems involving a single sample, A corresponds to $\overline{X}$; in problems involving two independent samples, A corresponds to the difference $\overline{X}_1 - \overline{X}_2$.) The computations involved will be illustrated using the data of Table 8-3. It has already been shown in connection with the t test based upon these data that $\overline{X}_1 - \overline{X}_2 = 8.60$, $s_p^2 = 1,435$, and $s_{\overline{X}_1-\overline{X}_2} = \sqrt{1,435[(1/5) + (1/5)]} \approx 23.96$. Since there are eight degrees of freedom associated with these data, the values of $t_{.025}$ and $t_{.975}$ are -2.306 and 2.306, respectively. Thus, the lower confidence limit for $\mu_1 - \mu_2$ is $8.60 - 2.306(23.96) \approx -46.65$ and the upper confidence limit is $8.60 + 2.306(23.96) \approx 63.85$.

Using paired observations, the lower and upper 95 per cent confidence limits for $\mu_1 - \mu_2$ are $\overline{D} + t_{.025}s_{\overline{D}}$ and $\overline{D} + t_{.975}s_{\overline{D}}$, respectively. In this case the number of degrees of freedom used in entering the t table is $n - 1$, in which n is the number of differences available for computing s_D^2. (Again, the parallel to confidence limits described in Chapter 7 is apparent.) The computation of confidence limits employing paired observations will be illustrated using the data presented in Table 8-5, for which $\overline{D} = -.40$ and $s_{\overline{D}} \approx 1.208$. With four degrees of freedom $t_{.025} = -2.776$ and $t_{.975} = 2.776$. The lower confidence limit for $\mu_1 - \mu_2$ is $-.40 - 2.776(1.208) \approx -3.75$; the upper confidence limit is $-.40 + 2.776(1.208) \approx 2.95$.

A marked contrast will be noted between the width of the confidence interval based upon independent samples (-46.65 to 63.85) and that of the interval based upon paired observations (-3.75 to 2.95). The discrepancy between the widths of the two intervals is a consequence of the difference in precision between $\overline{X}_1 - \overline{X}_2$ based upon independent samples and $\bar{D}$ based upon paired observations for the model upon which the data were based.

NONPARAMETRIC METHODS OF COMPARING TWO POPULATIONS

In some situations an investigator may have reason to doubt that the assumptions underlying the t test are satisfied by the population (or populations) of which his observations are a sample. He may question the validity of the assumptions underlying the t test because the measures with which he is concerned are of a kind known generally not to be normally distributed (e.g., response latencies, trials to a criterion) or because an examination of the distribution of observations in his sample suggests a violation of the assumptions in question. For example, the sample distribution may be highly skewed, suggesting that the population sampled is not normal, or the variances of two samples tested under different experimental treatments may differ markedly, suggesting that the variances of the corresponding populations are not equal. Under such circumstances an investigator may elect to use the t test anyway, regarding the approximation provided by this method as satisfactory. Alternatively, there are available a number of so-called *nonparametric* tests that provide an exact method for testing hypotheses concerning populations that are not normal. In this section two such techniques, both based upon the ranking of observations, will be described. The first technique, the rank-sum test, is for use in studies employing independent samples; the second, the signed-rank test, is for use in studies employing paired observations.

INDEPENDENT SAMPLES: THE RANK-SUM TEST[3]

The use of the rank-sum test will be illustrated using data from an animal study designed to assess the effects of experiences of intense electric shock upon subsequent performance in a novel situation in which shock is encountered anew (Kurtz and Pearl, 1960).

> An experimental group consisting of ten rats received a series of intense electric shocks at approximately one month of age; a control group, also consisting of ten rats, did not receive shock at that time. At approximately two months of age both groups of rats were tested in a novel situation. In this test the animals were trained to jump from a compartment in which they were shocked into an adjoining "safe" compartment, the floor of which was 6 in. above that of the first compartment.

---

[3] The test described in this subsection is an extension by White (1952) of a test described by Wilcoxon (1949). Although the computational procedures are different, this test is mathematically equivalent to the Mann-Whitney U Test (Mann & Whitney, 1947).

The performance measure of interest was the total number of jumps made by the animals after shock in the first compartment was discontinued.

The results are shown in the first and the third columns of Table 8-7.

TABLE 8-7 *Comparison of two treatments using the rank-sum test. Total number of jumps into "safe" compartment*

CONTROL GROUP		EXPERIMENTAL GROUP	
Raw Score	Rank	Raw Score	Rank
0	1	7	5
1	2	48	10.5
2	3	57	12
5	4	61	13
16	6	68	15
20	7	104	16
25	8	122	17
35	9	229	18
48	10.5	318	19
62	14	344	20
	64.5		145.5

NOTE: To illustrate the handling of tied observations, one observation in the control group, actually 47, has been recorded here as 48.

Inspection of these data strongly suggests that the populations in question do not meet the assumptions underlying the t test for independent samples. Both samples, especially that of the experimental group, appear to have come from populations having markedly skewed distributions. Moreover, the variability of observations in the experimental group is substantially greater than in the control group. Accordingly, there is some question whether use of the t test for independent samples would be well-advised with these data.

To test the significance of the difference between these two distributions using the rank-sum test we first rank the complete set of 20 observations without regard to the group to which they belong, as shown in the second and fourth columns of Table 8-7. The ranking of the nine lowest observations is straightforward, but a complication is encountered with the value 48, which occurs twice—once in the experimental group and once in the control group. Had these scores not been tied, they would have received ranks 10 and 11. The difficulty is resolved by assigning to each of these scores the average of the ranks for which they are tied, $(10 + 11)/2 = 10.5$. The next highest score, 57, receives a rank of 12; thereafter ranking is again straightforward. Next, we obtain the sum of ranks for each of the groups. (In general, when the two groups are of unequal size we shall designate the sum of ranks for the smaller group as R_1, that for the larger group as R_2.   When the groups are of equal size, as in our illustrative problem, either total may be arbitrarily designated R_1.) For the data in Table 8-7, $R_1 = 64.5$ and $R_2 = 145.5$.   If the populations represented by these two samples had identical distributions, we would expect the sums of ranks for the two samples to be approximately equal, since the samples are of the same size.   In other words, since the grand total of the ranks from 1 to 20 is 210, we would expect R_1 to be approximately 105, half the grand total.   To evaluate whether the departure of R_1 from the expected value of 105 is statistically significant, we consult Table A-5 of Appendix A, which gives critical values of R_1 for various combinations of sample size.   (The first part of Table A-5 gives critical values of R_1 for $\alpha = .05$; the second part gives critical values for $\alpha = .01$.)   Entering the second part of the table with $n_1 = n_2 = 10$, we find that the critical values of R_1 for $\alpha = .01$ are 71 and 139.   In other words, taking $\alpha = .01$, an observed value of R_1 equal to or less than 71 or an observed value equal to or greater than 139 leads to rejection of the null hypothesis.   Accordingly, the observed value of R_1 in our illustrative problem, $R_1 = 64.5$, is significant at the .01 level.

The null hypothesis tested by the rank-sum test may be stated as follows: *The probability is 1/2 that a randomly selected value from Population 1 will exceed a randomly selected value from Population 2.*   In other words, in a series of experiments in each of which one value is selected at random from Population *1* and one from Population *2*, in the long run the value from Population *1* would exceed that from Population *2* exactly half the time if the above hypothesis is true.   The conditions specified by this hypothesis are satisfied by a wide variety of situations. For example, this hypothesis is satisfied by any two population distributions that are identical, regardless of their shape, whether symmetrical or asymmetrical.   Moreover, it is satisfied by any two symmetrical distributions having the same mean, whether or not they are normal, whether or not they have the same variance—indeed, whether or not they have the same shape.   It is the great generality of the hypothesis tested—the applicability of the rank-sum test to populations other than ones that are normally distributed—that makes this test a valuable statistical tool.   As our intuition might lead us to expect, the rank-sum test is chiefly sensitive to differences in central tendency, i.e., the probability of rejecting the null hypothesis is greater than α when the two populations in question differ in central tendency.

NORMAL-CURVE APPROXIMATION OF THE RANK-SUM TEST

The theoretical sampling distribution of R_1 is a discrete probability distribution similar to probability distributions considered in Chapters 4 and

6. The general formula for μ_{R_1}, the mean of this theoretical distribution, is

$$\mu_{R_1} = \frac{n_1(n_1 + n_2 + 1)}{2} \qquad (8\text{-}18)$$

The formula for the standard error of R_1 (i.e., the standard deviation of the sampling distribution of R_1) is

$$\sigma_{R_1} = \sqrt{\frac{n_1 n_2(n_1 + n_2 + 1)}{12}} \qquad (8\text{-}19)$$

When both samples are fairly large (n_1 and n_2 both greater than 10), the sampling distribution of R_1 closely approximates a normal distribution, and it is possible to test the null hypothesis described in the preceding subsection by computing

$$z = \frac{R_1 - \mu_{R_1}}{\sigma_{R_1}} \qquad (8\text{-}20)$$

For example, let us suppose that in an experiment in which $n_1 = 14$ and $n_2 = 15$ the value of R_1 was found to be 165. Substituting in Formula (8-18), we compute $\mu_{R_1} = 14(14 + 15 + 1)/2 = 210$; substituting in Formula (8-19), we compute $\sigma_{R_1} = \sqrt{14(15)(14 + 15 + 1)/12} \approx 22.91$. Finally, substituting in Formula (8-20), we compute $z \approx (165 - 210)/22.91 \approx -1.96$. Inasmuch as the critical values of z for a test at the .05 level of significance are -1.96 and 1.96, the obtained value of z results in rejection of the hypothesis that the two populations have identical distributions. On the other hand, if we refer to Table A-5 we find that a value of R_1 equal to 165 is almost (but not quite) statistically significant. The reason for the discrepancy is that the sampling distribution of R_1 is only approximately normal, and in close cases the use of the normal-distribution approximation sometimes results in rejection of the null hypothesis when the exact test does not. The approximation provided by the normal distribution may be improved by reducing the absolute value of the numerator of Formula (8-20) by .5, i.e., by computing

$$z = \frac{|R_1 - \mu_{R_1}| - .5}{\sigma_{R_1}} \qquad (8\text{-}21)$$

Regardless of its sign, the quantity between the vertical lines is treated as a positive number. Thus, although the difference $165 - 210$ is equal to -45, the value of $|165 - 210|$ is 45. Substituting in Formula (8-21), we obtain $z \approx (45 - .5)/22.91 \approx 1.94$. This value of z is not statistically significant, and the conclusion reached is the same as that reached using Table A-5.

In the preceding example values of n within the range of Table A-5 were selected so as to permit comparison of the outcome based upon the normal-curve approximation with that based upon the exact sampling distribution of R_1. However, the chief value of the approximation described in this subsection is that it permits extension of the rank-sum test to problems involving values of n greater than those included in Table A-5.

PAIRED OBSERVATIONS: THE SIGNED-RANK TEST[4]

The second nonparametric test to be described is designed for use in experiments employing paired observations. Like the t test for paired observations, the signed-rank test is based upon the differences between pairs of observations, and tests the hypothesis that μ_D, the mean of the population of differences, is zero. However, in contradistinction to the t test, which requires the assumption that the differences are distributed normally, the signed-rank test assumes only that the differences are distributed symmetrically. This assumption is not in the least restrictive, because the random assignment of experimental treatments to members of a pair insures that the differences are symmetrically distributed with a mean of zero, *unless the two experimental treatments affect the members differentially,* in which case the null hypothesis is false and should be rejected.

The computations involved in the signed-rank test will be illustrated with the data of the following hypothetical experiment.

> We shall assume that 16 subjects were available for a study of the effectiveness of a course designed to improve reading skill. On the basis of preliminary tests the subjects were grouped into pairs having similar reading ability. One member of each pair was randomly assigned to the experimental group and received the special course in reading; the remaining member of each pair was assigned to the control group and did not receive the special training. At the conclusion of the reading course all subjects were given a test of reading skill. The hypothetical scores of the two groups of subjects, arranged by pairs, are presented in the second and third columns of Table 8-8. Our problem is to determine whether performance under the two treatments differs more than might be expected merely as a result of sampling fluctuations.

The first step in performing the signed-rank test is to calculate the differences shown in the fourth column of Table 8-8. Next, ranks are assigned to the differences on the basis of their absolute value as shown in the fifth column. In other words, the sign of each difference is disregarded and ranks are assigned as if all differences were positive. Then, as shown in the last two columns, the ranks are sorted according to the signs of the corresponding differences. Finally, the sum T is computed either for the ranks assigned to negative differences or for those assigned to positive differences.[5] For the data in Table 8-8 the value of T based

---

[4] The test described in this subsection was proposed by Wilcoxon (1945, 1949).

[5] It should be noted that the symbol T, which was used in Chapter 5 to denote a normalized standard score, has an entirely different meaning in the present context.

TABLE 8-8 *Comparison of two treatments using the signed-rank test. Hypothetical scores on reading test*

PAIR	EXPERI-MENTAL SUBJECT	CONTROL SUBJECT	DIFFER-ENCE	RANK	RANKS OF NEGATIVE DIFFERENCES	RANKS OF POSITIVE DIFFERENCES
1	80	60	20	5		5
2	114	124	−10	1	1	
3	98	84	14	3		3
4	105	82	23	6		6
5	130	142	−12	2	2	
6	90	62	28	7		7
7	102	85	17	4		4
8	120	90	30	8		8
					—	—
					3	33

upon ranks assigned to negative differences is 3. Critical values of T are given in Table A-6 of Appendix A, which indicates that with eight pairs the critical values for a test at the .05 level of significance are 3 and 33. The obtained value of T is equal to the lower critical value; accordingly, the null hypothesis is rejected and it is concluded that performance on the test of reading skill is improved by the training employed in the experiment. It will be noted that if the test had been based upon the sum of the ranks of positive differences, the value of which is 33, the same conclusion would have been reached. In general, whenever the sum of ranks assigned to differences of one sign is in the lower portion of the rejection region, the sum of ranks assigned to differences of the opposite sign is in the upper portion of the rejection region; on the other hand, when one sum is in the acceptance region, so is the other.

When ties occur, the average of the tied ranks is assigned to all differences involved in the tie, as in the rank-sum test. (If the tied differences are all of the same sign, averaging the tied ranks is unnecessary: the same end result is obtained if the ranks involved are assigned to the tied differences in any arbitrary order.)

NORMAL-CURVE APPROXIMATION OF THE SIGNED-RANK TEST

When the null hypothesis described in the preceding subsection is true, the mean of the sampling distribution of T is

$$\mu_T = \frac{n(n+1)}{4} \qquad (8\text{-}22)$$

and the standard error is

$$\sigma_T = \sqrt{\frac{n(n+1)(2n+1)}{24}} \qquad (8\text{-}23)$$

As the number of differences increases, the shape of the sampling distribution approximates a normal distribution more and more closely. The approximation is very good when $n = 20$, and for samples of this size or larger the null hypothesis may be tested by computing

$$z = \frac{T - \mu_T}{\sigma_T} \tag{8-24}$$

To illustrate the use of Formula (8-24) let us suppose that in an experiment employing 20 pairs of observations the value of T was found to be 52. Using Formulae (8-22) and (8-23), we compute $\mu_T = 20(21)/4 = 105$ and $\sigma_T = \sqrt{20(21)(41)/24} \approx 26.8$. Substituting in Formula (8-24), we compute $z \approx (52 - 105)/26.8 \approx -1.98$. This value of z leads to rejection of the null hypothesis at the .05 level of significance, which is the same conclusion as that reached using Table A-6.

PROBLEMS

1. The parameters of two populations are as follows: $\mu_1 = 60$, $\mu_2 = 50$; $\sigma_1^2 = 70$, $\sigma_2^2 = 80$. Let X_1 represent a value drawn at random from Population *1*; X_2, a value drawn at random from Population 2. What are the mean and variance of the probability distribution of the difference $X_1 - X_2$?

2. Using the populations described in Problem 1, 100 students in a statistics class participated in the following sampling experiment: Each student drew a random sample of ten cases from Population *1* and a random sample of five cases from Population 2, computed the means of his two samples ($\overline{X}_1$ and $\overline{X}_2$, respectively), and determined the difference $\overline{X}_1 - \overline{X}_2$. The 100 differences obtained by the class were then summarized in a frequency distribution. (a) Of what theoretical distribution is the class's empirical distribution an approximation? (b) What is the value of the mean of the theoretical distribution? (c) What is the value of the variance of the theoretical distribution?

3. Six subjects were randomly divided into two groups, experimental and control. The scores obtained under the two treatments were as follows:

Experimental	Control
11	6
9	2
7	1

(a) Compute the value of t for testing the significance of the difference between the means of the two groups. (b) How many degrees of freedom are associated with this value of t? (c) Is the difference significant at the .05 level? (d) Would you conclude, at the .05 level, that the population means are equal or unequal?

4. Three subjects were measured twice each, once under Treatment A and once under Treatment B. The results were as follows:

Subject	Treatment A	Treatment B
1	19	8
2	14	6
3	15	10

(a) Compute the value of t for testing the significance of the difference between the two treatments. (b) How many degrees of freedom are associated with this value of t? (c) Is the difference significant at the .05 level? (d) Adopting the .05 level, would you conclude that the population means for the two treatments are equal or unequal?

5. The following are the numbers of hours spent in studying during a 24-hour period by a random sample of five freshmen: 10, 6, 4, 2, 1. The following are similar scores for a random sample of five seniors: 13, 11, 10, 9, 7. Are the population means different for freshmen and seniors?

6. An experiment was conducted to compare the effects of two drugs on the growth rate of rats. Eight rats were used in the study. Four cages were available for housing the rats, so two rats were assigned to each cage. Because of variations in light and temperature among cage locations, it was expected that the cage in which a rat lived might influence its rate of growth. Accordingly, from each cage one rat was randomly assigned to Drug 1 and the other to Drug 2. The weight gains (in grams) for the period studied were as follows: 30, 18; 35, 15; 22, 24; 26, 19. (In this listing the measures are grouped by cages, with cage groupings set off by semicolons; within each cage grouping, the first score listed is for Drug 1 and the second is for Drug 2.) Do the two drugs affect weight differentially?

7. Assume that for a given type of measure the variance of repeated determinations based on a given individual is 25, and the variance associated with individual differences (i.e., the variation among the means of the probability distributions of different individuals) is 100. (a) Sample 1 consists of ten observations obtained by measuring ten individuals once each; Sample 2 consists of ten observations obtained by measuring ten other individuals, selected independently of the individuals in Sample 1, once each. What is the value of the variance of the sampling distribution of $\overline{X}_1 - \overline{X}_2$? (b) Ten individuals are measured once each under Treatment 1 and the same individuals are measured once each under Treatment 2. For each individual, D (the difference between his score under Treatment 1 and his score under Treatment 2) is determined, then $\overline{D}$ (the mean of the ten differences) is computed. What is the value of the variance of the sampling distribution of $\overline{D}$?

8. Compute 95 per cent confidence limits for the difference $\mu_1 - \mu_2$ (a) using the data of Problem 3, (b) using the data of Problem 4, (c) using the data of Problem 5, (d) using the data of Problem 6.

9. Twelve rats were randomly divided into two groups, and the groups were tested under different experimental treatments. The scores of the rats under Treatment 1 were 8, 6, 4, 11, 5, and 12; the scores of the rats under Treatment 2 were 11, 9, 14, 19, 17, and 11. Using the appropriate nonparametric technique, test the hypothesis that the two population distributions are the same.

10. Fourteen subjects were arranged in seven pairs on the basis of similarity of score obtained in a preliminary test. One member of each pair was assigned at random to Treatment *1*; the other member, to Treatment *2*. The scores, by pairs, were as follows: 10, 8; 6, 10; 13, 10; 11, 7; 9, 4; 13, 5; 20, 10. Using the appropriate nonparametric statistic, test the significance of the difference between the two treatments.

REFERENCES

BONEAU, C. A.   The effects of violations of assumptions underlying the *t* test. *Psychol. Bull.*, 1960, **57**, 49–64.

BUGELSKI, B. R.   Presentation time, total time and mediation in paired-associate learning. *J. exp. Psychol.*, 1962, **63**, 409–412.

KURTZ, K. H. and J. PEARL.   The effects of prior fear experiences on acquired-drive learning. *J. comp. physiol. Psychol.*, 1960, **53**, 201–206.

MANN, H. B. and D. R. WHITNEY.   On a test of whether one of two random variables is stochastically larger than the other. *Ann. math. Statist.*, 1947, **18**, 50–60.

WHITE, C.   The use of ranks in a test of significance for comparing two treatments. *Biometrics*, 1952, **8**, 33–41.

WILCOXON, F.   Individual comparisons by ranking methods. *Biometrics Bull.*, 1945, **1**, 80–83.

————.   *Some rapid approximate statistical procedures.*   Stamford, Conn.: American Cyanamid Co., 1949.

ADDITIONAL READINGS

EDWARDS, A. E.   *Statistical methods for the behavioral sciences.*   New York: Rinehart, 1954.   Chap. 13 (independent samples) and Chap. 14 (paired observations).

MOSTELLER, F., R. E. K. ROURKE, and G. B. THOMAS, JR.   *Probability and statistics.*   Reading, Mass.: Addison-Wesley, 1961.   Chap. 9.   Presents a mathematical derivation of the theorems relating the mean and variance of the difference $X - Y$ to the mean and variance of X and Y.

SIEGEL, S.   *Nonparametric statistics for the behavioral sciences.*   New York: McGraw-Hill, 1956.   Chaps. 5 and 6.   Describes several nonparametric tests for use in experiments employing paired observations and independent samples.   The Mann-Whitney U Test, described in Chap. 6, is mathematically equivalent to the rank-sum test described in the present text, although the two tests differ in the mechanics by which they are performed.

SNEDECOR, G. W.   *Statistical methods applied to experiments in agriculture and biology* (5th ed.).   Ames, Iowa: Iowa State College Press, 1956.   Chaps. 3 and 4.   A detailed discussion of comparisons based upon paired observations and independent samples.

WILKS, S. S.   *Elementary statistical analysis.*   Princeton: Princeton Univ. Press, 1949.   Chap. 9.   Presents a mathematical derivation of the theorems relating the mean and variance of the difference $X - Y$ to the mean and variance of X and Y.

CHAPTER **9**

regression and correlation

THE STATISTICAL PROCEDURES DESCRIBED IN THE PRECEDING CHAPTER enable us to determine whether there is an association between two variables—i.e., whether, when there are variations in one variable (the independent variable), there are associated variations in a second (the dependent variable). Going beyond the simple fact that two variables are associated, we may seek to determine the specific mathematical equation describing the relationship between them. For example, we might wish to determine the equation relating the amplitude of a flexion (withdrawal) response to the intensity of a painful stimulus such as electric shock. As a rule, in describing the relationship between two variables by means of a mathematical equation, an equation is selected that describes the manner in which the *mean value* of the dependent variable varies with changes in the independent variable. The type of mathematical equation that best describes the relationship between a dependent and an independent variable is contingent, of course, upon the particular variables in question, and a great many different types of equation have been used for this purpose. To simplify the present discussion we shall restrict our attention to procedures that are applicable when the relationship between the variables can be described by a straight-line equation, i.e., an equation of the general form $y = a + bx$, in which x and y are variable quantities, and a and b are constants.

In addition to determining the mathematical equation describing the relationship between two variables, we may be interested in evaluating the closeness of the relationship—i.e., whether there is a high or low degree of association. For example, given that the mean flexion response of an individual varies with the intensity of the eliciting stimulus according to some particular mathematical equation, repeated determinations of the amplitude of the flexion response for a particular stimulus intensity may be highly consistent or may show a great deal of variability. In the latter case, it would appear that the amplitude of the flexion response is influenced to a considerable extent by the operation of various unknown factors, and—compared to a situation in which response amplitude is highly consistent for a given stimulus intensity—the degree of association between response amplitude and stimulus intensity would be relatively low. One of our chief concerns in this chapter will be to examine measures that may be used to assess the closeness of the relationship between two variables.

As in other problems of statistical inference, we are typically interested in drawing conclusions about distributions that are too extensive to observe in their entirety—frequently, the hypothetical distribution of all possible observations of a given kind—and we therefore base our conclusions about these distributions upon a sample of observations. Also, as in earlier problems, the sampling behavior of the statistics we employ depends upon the characteristics of the populations involved. Accordingly, the procedures that we shall consider are appropriate when dealing with certain types of populations but inappropriate when dealing with others. An idealized description of a population—or set of populations— is called a *mathematical model*. The mathematical models discussed in this chapter provide a reasonable approximation of the populations encountered in many actual research situations, but not all. When examination of a given set of data suggests that one of these models applies, the corresponding statistical procedures may be employed; otherwise, a more suitable model, and/or an alternative treatment of the data must be sought.

We shall consider two alternative research designs—i.e., two ways of collecting data—and a model appropriate to each. The first design is commonly known as a *regression design;* the second, as a *correlation design.*

REGRESSION DESIGN: FIXED VALUES OF X

The general characteristics of this type of design may be illustrated by a hypothetical study of the relationship between scores on a college entrance examination and grade-point averages (i.e., average course grades computed using an arbitrary numerical scale) at a particular college. We will assume that these measures are available for a large number of students and that we are interested in the relationship in question for entrance-examination scores in the range between a raw score of 50 and a raw score of 90. We begin by deciding, arbitrarily, to limit our attention to students having examination scores of exactly 50, 60, 70, 80, or 90. This decision serves to identify five subpopulations, each consisting of students having a certain examination score. Assuming these five populations are so large that it would not be practical to deal with every individual in each, we proceed by drawing a sample from each population and recording the grade-point averages of the individuals sampled. The characteristic on the basis of which the groups are originally distinguished (in the above example, examination score) is called the *independent variable,* values of which will be represented by the letter X; the characteristic determined after the groups have been distinguished (in the above example, grade-point average) is called the *dependent variable* and will be represented by the letter Y.

The model that we shall consider in connection with this type of

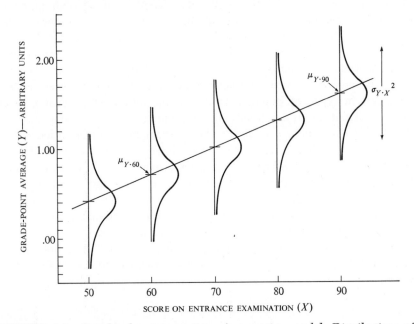

FIGURE 9-1 *Graphical representation of regression model. Distributions of grade-point averages* (Y) *are shown for five different values of X (score on entrance examination). The means of the five distributions lie on a straight line, and all distributions are normal with the same variance,* $\sigma_{Y \cdot X}^2$.

design is represented schematically in Figure 9-1. The essential characteristics of this model are as follows:

1. For each value of X (examination score) there is a distribution of Y values (grade-point averages). Several of these distributions are arbitrarily selected for consideration, and a random sample of one or more observations is drawn from each. The means of the Y measures

for the various distributions are represented by the symbol $\mu_{Y \cdot X}$. The subscript Y indicates that μ refers to the mean of Y measures; the subscript X appearing after the dot indicates that the mean referred to is for the subpopulation having a particular value of X. For example, $\mu_{Y \cdot 50}$ is the mean grade-point average for the subpopulation of students having a score of 50 on the entrance examination, $\mu_{Y \cdot 60}$ is the mean grade-point average for students having a score of 60 on the entrance examination, and so on.

2. The means, $\mu_{Y \cdot X}$, of all the subpopulations lie on a straight line described by an equation of the following general form:

$$\mu_{Y \cdot X} = A + Bx \qquad (9\text{-}1)$$

in which A and B are constants, and x represents values of X expressed as deviations from $\overline{X}$, the mean of all values of X included in the sample.[1,2] In other words, $x = (X - \overline{X})$. Substituting for x, Equation (9-1) may be written as follows: $\mu_{Y \cdot x} = A + B(X - \overline{X})$. This equation relating $\mu_{Y \cdot x}$ to x is called the *population regression equation*.

3. For each value of X the values of Y are distributed normally. It is assumed that the various Y distributions all have the same variance, represented by the symbol $\sigma_{Y \cdot x}^2$. The subscript Y indicates that σ^2 refers to the variance of Y measures; the subscript X indicates that the variance referred to is for the distribution having a particular value of X. Thus, in the above example $\sigma_{Y \cdot 50}^2$ is the variance of grade-point averages for students having a score of 50 on the entrance examination. For this particular problem, the assumption that all Y distributions have the same variance may be written as follows:

$$\sigma_{Y \cdot 50}^2 = \sigma_{Y \cdot 60}^2 = \cdots = \sigma_{Y \cdot 90}^2 = \sigma_{Y \cdot x}^2$$

The interpretation of $\sigma_{Y \cdot x}^2$ differs somewhat, depending upon whether the subpopulation of Y values corresponding to a given value of X is interpreted as consisting of (a) repeated measures of a given individual or (b) measures obtained from a series of different individuals. In the former case, $\sigma_{Y \cdot x}^2$ may be identified with the concept σ_ϵ^2 presented in Chapter 4, i.e., the variation of repeated determinations based upon a

---

[1] The symbols A and B represent characteristics of the population and, according to the convention followed in previous chapters, should therefore be represented by Greek letters. For this reason, in some texts the symbols α and β are used instead of A and B. This practice has not been followed here because the symbols α and β have already been used with a different meaning in this book.

[2] It should be noted that in using a regression design, the investigator arbitrarily decides what values of X are to be included in his sample. He might, for example, decide to include ten individuals having $X = 50$, ten having $X = 60$, and so on. Thus, in this type of design, the value of $\overline{X}$ is predetermined by the investigator and is not subject to sampling fluctuation.

given individual tested under a given set of conditions; in the latter case, $\sigma_{Y \cdot X}^2$ may be identified with the concept $\sigma^2 = \sigma_\tau^2 + \sigma_\epsilon^2$, i.e., composite variation arising from the joint action of individual differences and the various factors (errors of measurement, individual inconsistency, variations in test conditions) that produce variation among repeated determinations of a given individual. In the illustrative problem discussed above (the relation between examination score and grade-point average), each subpopulation consists of a number of distinct individuals; in the illustrative problem described in the subsection that follows, each subpopulation of the regression model consists of all possible repeated determinations that could be made of a given individual tested under a given set of conditions (i.e., using a given value of X).[3]

ESTIMATING THE POPULATION REGRESSION EQUATION

As in previous problems of statistical inference, the parameters of the actual population are unknown to the investigator, and the investigator's aim is to estimate these unknown quantities on the basis of information provided by the sample. In a regression problem the unknown quantities are A and B, the constants of the population regression equation.

TABLE 9-1 *Learning time as a function of amount of material learned. Calculation of Σx^2 and Σxy and values of x and y (hypothetical data)*

NUMBER OF STANZAS MEMORIZED X	LEARNING TIME IN MINUTES Y	x	y	xy	x^2
13	22	3	4	12	9
12	25	2	7	14	4
11	18	1	0	0	1
10	19	0	1	0	0
9	16	−1	−2	2	1
8	16	−2	−2	4	4
7	10	−3	−8	24	9
70	126			56	28

$$\overline{X} = \frac{70}{7} = 10; \quad \overline{Y} = \frac{126}{7} = 18; \quad b = \frac{\Sigma xy}{\Sigma x^2} = \frac{56}{28} = 2$$

[3] The two hypothetical studies in question also differ in another respect: the former is an example of an ex post facto investigation (values of X determined prior to the investigation and not under the direct control of the investigator); the latter is an example of an experiment in which the values of X are under the direct control of the experimenter. It should be noted that the model and the method of analyzing the data are the same for the two types of investigation.

The methods of estimating A and B will be illustrated by means of a hypothetical set of data. We will assume that an experiment has been conducted to study the relationship between amount of material to be memorized (X) and the amount of time required to memorize it (Y). More specifically, let us assume that an investigator has selected seven samples of poetry varying in length from 7 to 13 stanzas, and that he has memorized each sample, recording the time required to master each. The lengths of the various selections and the corresponding learning times are presented in the first two columns of Table 9-1; the same data are represented graphically in Figure 9-2. (A graphic representation of the

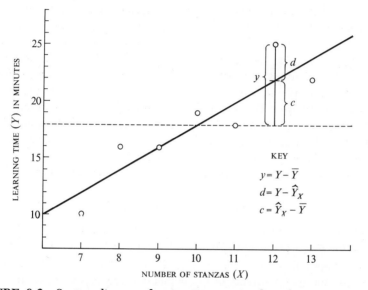

FIGURE 9-2   *Scatter diagram showing time required for learning as a function of amount of material learned. The sloping line represents the sample regression equation—i.e., gives values of $\hat{Y}_X$ for various values of X. The horizontal line represents the value of $\overline{Y}$. The circles represent observed values of Y corresponding to various values of X (hypothetical data).*

kind shown in Figure 9-2 is called a *scatter diagram*. The straight line in the figure will be explained shortly.) From both the table and the scatter diagram it is apparent that there is a positive relationship between X and Y—i.e., that small values of Y tend to be associated with small values of X, and large values of Y with large values of X. Our problem is to determine the equation of the straight line that best fits the points plotted in Figure 9-2. This equation, called the *sample regression equation*, will be taken as an estimate of the population regression equation. To determine the sample regression equation we require estimates of A and B, the two constants in the population regression equation. Our best estimate of A is simply $\overline{Y} = 18$. Our estimate of B is called the *sample regression coefficient;* this statistic is represented by the symbol b and is computed as follows:

$$b = \frac{\Sigma xy}{\Sigma x^2} \tag{9-2}$$

The denominator of the fraction on the right is familiar—it is the sum of squares of deviations from $\overline{X}$; the numerator, Σxy, requires some explanation.

The computation of Σxy is shown in Table 9-1. The third column, headed x, presents the deviation of each value of X from $\overline{X}$. Similarly, the values in the column headed y are the deviations of the Y values from $\overline{Y}$, the mean of the Y values. A novel step in the present procedure is the multiplication of each value of x by the corresponding value of y. The resulting products are recorded in the column headed xy. The sum of the products of deviations, Σxy, is the numerator of the fraction appearing on the right-hand side of Formula (9-2). It is seen that in the present problem $\Sigma xy = 56$. To obtain the denominator of the fraction on the right-hand side of Formula (9-2) values of x have been squared and summed in the last column, yielding $\Sigma x^2 = 28$. Finally, substituting in Formula (9–2), we obtain $b = \Sigma xy / \Sigma x^2 = 56/28 = 2$.

The sample regression equation may be written in general form as follows:

$$\hat{Y}_X = \overline{Y} + b(X - \overline{X}) \tag{9-3}$$

The quantity on the left, $\hat{Y}_X$, is an estimate of the mean value of Y in the population for a given value of X. In other words, $\hat{Y}_X$ is an estimate of $\mu_{Y \cdot X}$. As pointed out above, $\overline{Y}$ and b are estimates of A and B, respectively, the two constants in the population regression equation. Substituting the data of the present problem in Equation (9-3), we obtain the following sample regression equation for the data presented in Table 9-1:

$$\hat{Y}_X = 18 + 2(X - 10)$$

This equation is represented graphically by the sloping line in Figure 9-2.

To estimate $\mu_{Y \cdot x}$ for any given value of X we simply substitute in the above equation the appropriate value of X. For example, to estimate the population mean for $X = 8$ we compute $\hat{Y}_8 = 18 + 2(8 - 10) = 18 + 2(-2) = 14$. The same value may be obtained graphically by reading the height (ordinate) of the straight line above $X = 8$ in Figure 9-2.

The line described by the sample regression equation is the "best fitting" line in two senses. First, it is based upon unbiased estimates of A and B, the constants of the population regression equation, and provides an unbiased estimate of $\mu_{Y \cdot x}$ for any given value of X. Second, the sum of squares of deviations from this line is the least possible for the data in the sample. That is to say, if we were to determine the vertical distance of each point from the line, then squared each distance and summed the squares for all the points, the sum obtained would be less than for any other line that could be fitted to the data. The latter criterion is called the "least-squares" criterion of goodness of fit.

A COMPUTATIONAL FORMULA FOR Σxy

We saw in Chapter 3 that computation of Σx^2 by the above method (subtracting $\overline{X}$ from every score) can be quite laborious when the deviations are decimal values rather than whole numbers. Accordingly, the following computational formula was developed for obtaining the sum of squares of deviations:

$$\Sigma x^2 = \frac{n\Sigma X^2 - (\Sigma X)^2}{n} \qquad (3\text{-}10)$$

The same considerations apply to the computation of Σxy, and computational formulae are available for obtaining this quantity. One computational formula for the sum of products of deviations is the following:

$$\Sigma xy = \frac{n\Sigma XY - (\Sigma X)(\Sigma Y)}{n} \qquad (9\text{-}4)$$

TABLE 9-2 *Calculation of Σxy using computational formula*

X	Y	XY
13	22	286
12	25	300
11	18	198
10	19	190
9	16	144
8	16	128
7	10	70
70	126	1,316

$$\Sigma xy = \frac{n\Sigma XY - (\Sigma X)(\Sigma Y)}{n}$$

$$= \frac{7(1,316) - (70)(126)}{7}$$

$$= \frac{9,212 - 8,820}{7}$$

$$= \frac{392}{7} = 56$$

This formula is seen to be completely analogous to the above formula for Σx^2, with products substituted for corresponding squares throughout.

The computation of Σxy using Formula (9-4) is illustrated in Table 9-2. The first two columns list the raw values of X and Y; the third presents the products of the raw scores, i.e., the product of each value of X multiplied by the corresponding value of Y. The sum of this column gives the quantity ΣXY appearing in the first part of the numerator of Formula (9-4). The second part of the numerator, $(\Sigma X)(\Sigma Y)$, is simply the sum of the X values multiplied by the sum of the Y values. The computations are shown in the bottom part of the table. It will be noted that the value of Σxy obtained by this method is the same as that obtained in Table 9-1 by computing deviations from $\overline{X}$ and $\overline{Y}$.

PARTITIONING Σy^2

In this section we shall see how Σy^2, the sum of squares of deviations of the dependent variable, can be divided into two parts, one part associated with variation in X, and the other unrelated to X. First, however, we will have to lay some groundwork.

We begin with the following definition of y:

$$y = (Y - \overline{Y})$$

In Figure 9-2 the value of $\overline{Y}$ is indicated by the dashed horizontal line, and y, shown for the point at $X = 12$, is represented by the distance between the dashed line and the point representing the observed value of Y.

We may think of y as consisting of two parts: (1) the distance from $\overline{Y}$ to $\hat{Y}_X$ (the height of the sample regression line for a given value of X) and (2) the distance from $\hat{Y}_X$ to the observed value of Y, i.e., the deviation of the observed value of Y from the sample regression line. We shall represent these two components by the symbols c and d, respectively, and define them as follows:

$$c = \hat{Y}_X - \overline{Y}, \qquad d = Y - \hat{Y}_X$$

It is apparent from the definitions of the quantities involved and from inspection of Figure 9-2 that the following relationship obtains among the quantities under consideration:

$$y = c + d \qquad (9\text{-}5)$$

Although it will not be proved mathematically, an analogous relationship holds among the sums of squares of these quantities, i.e.,

$$\Sigma y^2 = \Sigma c^2 + \Sigma d^2 \qquad (9\text{-}6)$$

The meaning of the quantities in the above formulae may be clarified by reference to Table 9-3 and Figure 9-3.

TABLE 9-3 *Components of y and Σy^2*

Y	$\hat{Y}_x$	y	c	d	y^2	c^2	d^2
22	24	4	6	−2	16	36	4
25	22	7	4	3	49	16	9
18	20	0	2	−2	0	4	4
19	18	1	0	1	1	0	1
16	16	−2	−2	0	4	4	0
16	14	−2	−4	2	4	16	4
10	12	−8	−6	−2	64	36	4
					138	112	26

Y—observed value of Y (learning time in minutes)
$\hat{Y}_x$—estimate of $\mu_Y \cdot x$; height of regression line for value of X in question
$y = Y - \overline{Y}$; deviation of observed value of Y from $\overline{Y}$
$c = \hat{Y}_x - \overline{Y}$; deviation of regression line from $\overline{Y}$
$d = Y - \hat{Y}_x$; deviation of observed value of Y from regression line

The first column of the table presents observed values of Y, shown by the plotted points (open circles) in the figure. The second column of the table presents values of $\hat{Y}_x$ (i.e., estimates of values of $\mu_Y \cdot x$ for the values of X included in the experiment), represented in the figure by the height of the sample regression line at the respective values of X. The y column of the table gives the deviations of the observed values of Y from Y; these deviations are represented by the heavy vertical lines in the top part of Figure 9-3. The c column of the table gives the deviations of $\hat{Y}_x$ values from $\overline{Y}$; the values of c are represented by the heavy vertical lines in the middle part of Figure 9-3. The d column gives the deviations of values of Y from corresponding values of $\hat{Y}_x$—in other words, deviations of observed values of Y about the sample regression line; these deviations are represented by the heavy vertical lines in the bottom part of Figure 9-3. It will be noted that, in agreement with Formula (9-5), in each row of Table 9-3 y is equal to the sum of c and d.

The last three columns of Table 9-3 present the squares of y, c, and d, respectively. The sums recorded at the bottom of these columns are Σy^2, Σc^2, and Σd^2, respectively. Note that in agreement with Formula (9-6), $\Sigma y^2 = 112 + 26 = 138$.

We have thus seen how Σy^2, which reflects the total variation in Y, may be divided into two component sums of squares, one (Σc^2) associated with variation in X, and the other (Σd^2) unrelated to X. These two components of Σy^2 will be designated as the *sum of squares due to regression,* and the *residual sum of squares,* respectively.

The quantities discussed above provide an indication of the closeness of relationship between X and Y. When there is a very close relationship,

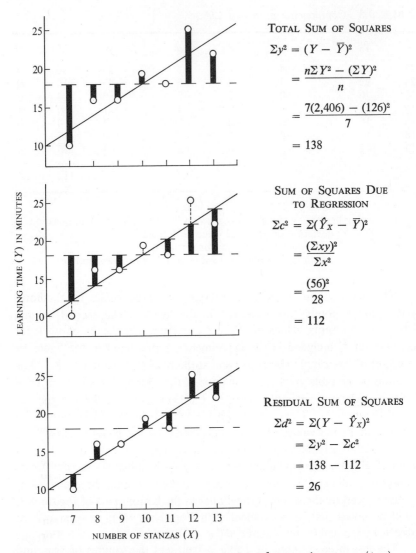

Total Sum of Squares

$$\Sigma y^2 = (Y - \bar{Y})^2$$

$$= \frac{n\Sigma Y^2 - (\Sigma Y)^2}{n}$$

$$= \frac{7(2,406) - (126)^2}{7}$$

$$= 138$$

Sum of Squares Due to Regression

$$\Sigma c^2 = \Sigma(\hat{Y}_X - \bar{Y})^2$$

$$= \frac{(\Sigma xy)^2}{\Sigma x^2}$$

$$= \frac{(56)^2}{28}$$

$$= 112$$

Residual Sum of Squares

$$\Sigma d^2 = \Sigma(Y - \hat{Y}_X)^2$$

$$= \Sigma y^2 - \Sigma c^2$$

$$= 138 - 112$$

$$= 26$$

FIGURE 9-3 *Graphical representation of total sum of squares (top), sum of squares due to regression (middle), and residual sum of squares (bottom). Based on hypothetical data presented in Table 9-1.*

the observed points (Y values) lie close to the sample regression line.   In other words, the deviations from the regression line are very small, and Σd^2 constitutes only a small fraction of Σy^2.   On the other hand, if Y is not closely related to X, the points are scattered widely above and below the regression line, and Σd^2 constitutes a major portion of Σy^2.   In the extreme case in which there is no relationship between X and Y, the regression line is a horizontal line at the level of $\overline{Y}$, Σc^2 is zero, and Formula (9-6) reduces to $\Sigma y^2 = \Sigma d^2$.

To assess the degree of relationship between X and Y it is useful to express Σd^2 and Σc^2 as proportions of Σy^2, i.e., to compute $\Sigma c^2 / \Sigma y^2$ (the proportion of Σy^2 due to regression) and $\Sigma d^2 / \Sigma y^2$ (the residual proportion). In the illustrative problem relating learning time to amount of material learned, the proportion due to regression is $112/138 \approx .81$; the residual proportion is $26/138 \approx .19$. Thus, as inspection of the plotted points suggests, a substantial proportion of the variation in Y is associated with variation in X.

EFFICIENT COMPUTATION OF Σy^2, Σc^2, AND Σd^2

In the foregoing account, sums of squares were obtained by determining individual deviations, squaring the deviations, and summing the squares. In the present subsection more efficient methods of computing these quantities are described.

Σy^2 is obtained in the same manner as Σx^2. The computation of Σy^2 for the illustrative problem above is shown in the top part of Figure 9-3. (The calculation of ΣY^2 ($=2,406$), which appears in the computational formula for Σy^2, is not shown.)

Σc^2 may be obtained by the following formula: $\Sigma c^2 = (\Sigma xy)^2 / \Sigma x^2$. The computation of Σc^2 is illustrated in the middle part of Figure 9-3.

Inasmuch as Σc^2 and Σd^2 add up to Σy^2, Σd^2 may be computed simply by subtracting Σc^2 from Σy^2, as shown in the bottom part of Figure 9-3.

ESTIMATING $\sigma_{Y \cdot x}^2$

The deviations of observations in the sample about the sample regression line arise from the fact that in the subpopulation of observations corresponding to any given value of X there is some variation of Y values. It will be recalled that in the regression model described earlier this variation is represented by the symbol $\sigma_{Y \cdot x}^2$. In the same way that in a single-sample problem deviations from a sample mean provide a basis for estimating the variance of the population sampled, in a regression problem deviations from the regression line provide a basis for estimating $\sigma_{Y \cdot x}^2$— i.e., in a regression problem the values of $\hat{Y}_X$ serve a function analogous to that of the sample mean in a single-sample problem.

The estimate, $s_{Y \cdot x}^2$, of $\sigma_{Y \cdot x}^2$ is given by the following formula:

$$s_{Y \cdot x}^2 = \frac{\Sigma d^2}{n - 2} \tag{9-7}$$

In the denominator 2, rather than 1, is subtracted from n for mathematical reasons related to the fact that it is necessary to estimate two parameters

(A and B) rather than one (μ) before computing the sum of squares of deviations. The term n in Formula (9-7) refers to the number of observations of Y that are available. In the study relating learning time to amount of material learned, $s_{Y \cdot x}^2$ is computed as follows: $s_{Y \cdot x}^2 = 26/(7 - 2) = 26/5 = 5.2$.

TESTING THE HYPOTHESIS THAT $B = 0$

In Chapter 4 two variables, X and Y, were said to be *independent* if the value of one is in no way dependent upon the value of the other. Within the context of the concepts developed in the present chapter, the concept of *independence* may be explained somewhat more technically as follows: Two variables, X and Y, are independent (unrelated) if Y has the same distribution—that is, the same mean, variance, and shape—for all values of X. When X and Y are independent, B, the population regression coefficient, is equal to zero, and the population regression line is horizontal, i.e., has zero slope.

We have noted that the sample regression coefficient, b, is an unbiased estimate of B. Like other statistics, b varies from sample to sample. Thus, when $B = 0$ (i.e., when Y is unrelated to X), b will sometimes be greater than zero and sometimes less, depending on sampling fluctuations. Therefore, to determine whether a given value of b is significantly different from zero—i.e., large enough to cause us to reject the hypothesis that $B = 0$—the discrepancy from zero of an obtained value of b must be evaluated against the estimated standard error of b. An estimate of s_b^2, the variance of b, is

$$s_b^2 = \frac{s_{Y \cdot x}^2}{\Sigma x^2} \tag{9-8}$$

An estimate of the standard error of b is obtained by taking the square root of s_b^2.

A hypothesis about B is tested by means of t computed as follows:

$$t = \frac{b - B_0}{s_b} \tag{9-9}$$

in which B_0 is the hypothetical value of B. The number of degrees of freedom associated with this value of t is $n - 2$, the number of degrees of freedom available for estimating $s_{Y \cdot x}^2$ and s_b^2. In testing the hypothesis that X and Y are independent, i.e., that $B = 0$, Formula (9-9) reduces to the following:

$$t = \frac{b}{s_b} \tag{9-10}$$

To test this hypothesis using the value of b obtained in the illustrative problem above, we first compute s_b^2, making use of our previous calculation of $s_{Y \cdot x}^2$, as follows: $s_b^2 = 5.2/28 \approx .186$. Taking the square root, we obtain $s_b \approx .431$. Solving for t, we obtain $t \approx 2/.431 \approx 4.64$. With five degrees of freedom, this value of t is significant at the .01 level, causing us to reject the hypothesis that X and Y are independent and to conclude instead that they are positively related.

CORRELATION DESIGN: RANDOM VALUES OF X AND Y

Using the regression design described above, certain values of X are fixed by the investigator and values of Y are selected at random from the populations so defined. Using a *correlation design,* on the other hand, neither the values of X nor of Y are fixed by the investigator, but are taken as they come, so to speak. In the latter type of design the two variables have the same status—either may be regarded as the dependent or independent variable. In the model we shall consider in connection with correlation designs, the relationships of the regression model are assumed to work both ways: it is assumed that for every value of X there is a distribution of Y values and, conversely, for every value of Y there is a distribution of X values. Just as the values of $\mu_{Y \cdot x}$ (the Y means for various values of X) are assumed to lie on a straight line, so are the values of $\mu_{X \cdot Y}$ (the X means for various values of Y) assumed to lie on a (different) straight line. Further details of the correlation model will be described after first examining an illustrative problem.

COMPUTATION OF THE SAMPLE REGRESSION EQUATIONS

For purposes of illustration, we shall assume that nine subjects are tested on a task in which speed is achieved at the expense of errors, i.e., a task on which errors may be reduced by taking more time, or time saved by incurring more errors. Hypothetical time and error scores for the nine subjects are presented in Table 9-4 and in Figure 9-4. The negative relationship between time and errors is apparent from the downward trend of the data points plotted in the figure: as the number of errors committed goes up, the time required goes down.

The basic quantities required, $\overline{X}$, $\overline{Y}$, Σx^2, Σxy, and Σy^2, are computed in the lower part of Table 9-4. (It will be noted that because of the negative relationship between X and Y, the sum of products, Σxy, has a negative sign.) In the present problem we must distinguish two regression coefficients, one for estimating $\mu_{Y \cdot x}$ on the basis of X, the other for estimating $\mu_{X \cdot Y}$ on the basis of Y. It is customary to identify these two coefficients by distinct verbal labels and, when they are written symbolically, by distinct subscripts. The former (that used in estimating $\mu_{Y \cdot x}$) is

TABLE 9-4   *Errors and time scores of nine subjects (hypothetical data)*

ERRORS X	TIME IN SECONDS Y	X^2	XY	Y^2
11	144	121	1,584	20,736
16	108	256	1,728	11,664
5	192	25	960	36,864
3	240	9	720	57,600
12	96	144	1,152	9,216
8	156	64	1,248	24,336
15	144	225	2,160	20,736
18	60	324	1,080	3,600
11	192	121	2,112	36,864
99	1,332	1,289	12,744	221,616

$$\overline{X} = \frac{99}{9} = 11; \quad \overline{Y} = \frac{1,332}{9} = 148$$

$$\Sigma x^2 = \frac{9(1,289) - (99)^2}{9} = 200$$

$$\Sigma y^2 = \frac{9(221,616) - (1,332)^2}{9} = 24,480$$

$$\Sigma xy = \frac{9(12,744) - (99)(1,332)}{9} = -1,908$$

called the *coefficient of regression of Y on X* and is represented by the symbol $b_{Y \cdot X}$; the latter (that used in estimating $\mu_{X \cdot Y}$) is called the *coefficient of regression of X on Y* and is represented by the symbol $b_{X \cdot Y}$. The formulae for the two regression coefficients are as follows:

$$b_{Y \cdot X} = \frac{\Sigma xy}{\Sigma x^2}, \quad b_{X \cdot Y} = \frac{\Sigma xy}{\Sigma y^2} \qquad \text{(9-11), (9-12)}$$

Substituting, we obtain the following numerical values for the two coefficients: $b_{Y \cdot X} = -1,908/200 = -9.54$; $b_{X \cdot Y} = -1,908/24,480 \approx -.078$.

Expressed in general terms, the formulae for the two sample regression equations are as follows:

$$\hat{Y}_X = \overline{Y} + b_{Y \cdot X}(X - \overline{X})$$
$$\hat{X}_Y = \overline{X} + b_{X \cdot Y}(Y - \overline{Y})$$

It will be noted that the second equation (that for estimating $\mu_{X \cdot Y}$) is of the same general form as the first (that for estimating $\mu_{Y \cdot X}$), with the difference that X is substituted for Y, and vice versa, throughout. Inserting the appropriate numerical values, the two regression equations for the present problem are as follows:

$$\hat{Y}_X = 148 - 9.54(X - 11)$$
$$\hat{X}_Y = 11 - .078(Y - 148)$$

The sample regression lines described by these equations are represented graphically in Figure 9-4. The downward slopes of these lines correspond to the negative signs of the regression coefficients.

PARTITIONING SUMS OF SQUARES

Σy^2, the sum of squares of deviations around $\overline{Y}$, may be partitioned into a portion due to regression and a residual portion (i.e., a portion consisting of deviations around regression), as in the regression problem considered earlier. Similarly, Σx^2, the sum of squares of deviations around $\overline{X}$, may be partitioned into two components. In order to distinguish the components of Σy^2 from those of Σx^2 the two sets of components will be identified by appropriate subscripts when there is danger of ambiguity: the two components of Σy^2 will be indicated by the symbols Σc_Y^2 and Σd_Y^2; those of Σx^2, by Σc_X^2 and Σd_X^2.

The two components of Σy^2 are computed as follows: $\Sigma c_Y^2 = (\Sigma xy)^2/\Sigma x^2 = (-1,908)^2/200 \approx 18,202;$ $\Sigma d_Y^2 = \Sigma y^2 - \Sigma c_Y^2 \approx 6,278.$ Expressing these values as proportions of Σy^2, we obtain $\Sigma c_Y^2/\Sigma y^2 \approx 18,202/24,480 \approx .74$, the proportion due to regression; and $\Sigma d_Y^2/\Sigma y^2 \approx 6,278/24,480 \approx .26$, the residual proportion.

We consider next the partitioning of Σx^2, the sum of squares of deviations around $\overline{X}$. In Figure 9-4, $\overline{X}$ is represented by the vertical dashed

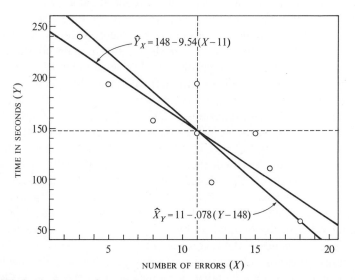

FIGURE 9-4 *Scatter diagram of error and time measures presented in Table 9-4 (hypothetical data).*

line constructed at $X = 11$; deviations from $\overline{X}$ correspond to the horizontal distances of the plotted points from this line. The portion of Σx^2 due to regression may be computed as follows: $\Sigma c_x^2 = (\Sigma xy)^2/\Sigma y^2 = (-1,908)^2/24,480 \approx 148.7$. The residual sum of squares, obtained by subtraction, is as follows: $\Sigma d_x^2 \approx 200 - 148.7 = 51.3$. Expressing the values of these two components as proportions of Σx^2, we obtain $\Sigma c_x^2/\Sigma x^2 \approx 148.7/200 \approx .74$ and $\Sigma d_x^2/\Sigma x^2 \approx 51.3/200 \approx .26$. It will be noted that the proportion of Σx^2 due to regression and the residual proportion are the same as the corresponding proportions of Σy^2. This identity always holds: in a given problem the proportion of the sum of squares due to regression is the same for both variables.

CHANGING THE UNITS OF MEASUREMENT: THE EFFECTS ON $b_{Y \cdot X}$ AND $b_{X \cdot Y}$

In the experiment discussed above, time scores were recorded to the nearest second. Let us inquire how the computations would be affected if time were recorded in minutes rather than seconds. In order to study the changes involved, the data of Table 9-4 have been reproduced in Table 9-5 with the time scores expressed in minutes. It will be noted that the change in units of measurement is accomplished by dividing each of the original time scores by 60. We saw in Chapter 3 that dividing every score in a distribution by a constant has the effect of reducing the variance of that distribution. This change is apparent from the reduced range of time scores—a range from 1.0 to 4.0 compared to a range from 60 to 240 in the original data—and is reflected in the reduced value of Σy^2. We feel intuitively that in some sense the relationship between time and errors is the same despite the change in the units of measurement; therefore we shall seek to determine whether there are any measures that remain constant in the face of this change and that might thus qualify as an index of the degree of relationship between X and Y. In particular, we shall examine the effects of the change on two types of measure: (1) the sample regression coefficients and (2) the proportion of Σx^2 and Σy^2 due to regression.

First we compute $b_{Y \cdot X}$, the coefficient of regression of Y on X, as follows: $b_{Y \cdot X} = \Sigma xy/\Sigma x^2 = -31.8/200 = -.159$. We note that this value is substantially less than the value obtained originally; it is, in fact, exactly one-sixtieth of the original value, -9.54. Turning now to the coefficient of regression of X on Y, we compute $b_{X \cdot Y} = \Sigma xy/\Sigma y^2 = -31.8/6.8 \approx -4.68$. We note that this value is sixty times the corresponding value in the original problem. We thus arrive at an important conclusion: the values of the regression coefficients, $b_{Y \cdot X}$ and $b_{X \cdot Y}$, are dependent upon the units of measurement employed; therefore the magnitudes of these quantities cannot be taken as an indication of the closeness of relationship between X and Y.

TABLE 9-5 *Errors and time scores of nine subjects. Same data as Table 9-4 using different units of time*

Errors X	Time in Minutes Y	X^2	XY	Y^2
11	2.4	121	26.4	5.76
16	1.8	256	28.8	3.24
5	3.2	25	16.0	10.24
3	4.0	9	12.0	16.00
12	1.6	144	19.2	2.56
8	2.6	64	20.8	6.76
15	2.4	225	36.0	5.76
18	1.0	324	18.0	1.00
11	3.2	121	35.2	10.24
99	22.2	1,289	212.4	61.56

$$\overline{X} = \frac{99}{9} = 11; \ \overline{Y} = \frac{22.2}{9} \approx 2.47$$

$$\Sigma x^2 = \frac{9(1,289) - (99)^2}{9} = 200$$

$$\Sigma y^2 = \frac{9(61.56) - (22.2)^2}{9} = 6.8$$

$$\Sigma xy = \frac{9(212.4) - (99)(22.2)}{9} = -31.8$$

Let us now determine the proportion of Σy^2 due to regression and the residual proportion. We compute $\Sigma c_Y^2 = (\Sigma xy)^2/\Sigma x^2 = (-31.8)^2/200 \approx 5.06$. Expressing this value as a proportion of Σy^2, we obtain $\Sigma c_Y^2/\Sigma y^2 \approx 5.06/6.8 \approx .74$. It will be noted that this proportion is the same as the corresponding proportion computed on the basis of the original data. The balance of Σy^2, the proportion .26, is, of course, also the same as for the original data. (We have seen that in a given problem the proportion of Σx^2 due to regression is the same as the proportion of Σy^2 due to regression, so there is no need to compute the proportion of Σx^2 in the present case.) The above findings lead to the conclusion that the proportion of Σx^2 and Σy^2 due to regression is independent of the units of measurement employed. This observation reinforces our earlier view that the proportion of Σx^2 and Σy^2 due to regression may be taken as an indication of the degree of relationship between two variables.

THE COEFFICIENT OF CORRELATION, r

We have seen that the two regression coefficients for a given set of data vary depending upon the units of measurement chosen, and for this reason these coefficients were considered unsuitable as measures of the degree of association between X and Y. However, using a transformation described in Chapter 3, it is possible to transform values of X and Y so as to obtain a set of values that are independent of the original units of measurement employed. We shall represent transformed values of X by the letter U; transformed values of Y, by the letter V. The transformations in which we are interested may be described as follows:

$$U = \frac{X - \overline{X}}{s_X}, \qquad V = \frac{Y - \overline{Y}}{s_Y} \qquad \text{(9-13), (9-14)}$$

In other words, the value of U corresponding to any given value of X is obtained by subtracting $\overline{X}$ from the value of X in question and dividing the difference by s_X, the standard deviation of the X distribution; values of V are computed from values of Y in an analogous manner. Regardless of the original units of measurement used to record X, values of U are distributed with a mean of zero and a standard deviation of 1; similarly, regardless of the units of measurement used to record Y, values of V are distributed with a mean of zero and a standard deviation of 1. In other words, the distributions of U and V are unique in the sense that, for a given set of data, the end result is independent of the original units of measurement employed—whatever the original units used to record X and Y, the resulting values of U and of V are the same. Because the values of U and V are unique for a given set of data, regression coefficients based upon the values of U and V are likewise unique, i.e., have the same value regardless of the units of measurement originally used to record X and Y. As a consequence of their unique status, regression coefficients obtained in this manner are of special interest as measures of the degree of association between X and Y.

The general procedure described above will be illustrated using the data presented in Table 9-4. First we compute the variances of the two distributions as follows: $s_X{}^2 = \Sigma x^2/(n - 1) = 200/8 = 25$; $s_Y{}^2 = \Sigma y^2/(n - 1) = 24,480/8 = 3,060$. Taking the square roots, we obtain the two standard deviations, $s_X = 5$ and $s_Y \approx 55.3$. Next, using these standard deviations and the values of $\overline{X}$ and $\overline{Y}$ given in the lower portion of Table 9-4, and substituting in Formulae (9-13) and (9-14), we obtain the values of U and V recorded in the first two columns of Table 9-6. The lower portion of the table shows the computation of the sums of squares and products (Σu^2, Σv^2, and Σuv) based upon the transformed values.

We next compute the regression coefficients based upon the transformed values. The coefficient of regression of V on U is computed as follows: $b_{V \cdot U} = \Sigma uv/\Sigma u^2 = -6.89/8.00 \approx -.86$. The other regression coefficient, $b_{U \cdot V} = \Sigma uv/\Sigma v^2 = -6.89/8.00 \approx -.86$, is identical to the first. The equality of the two regression coefficients is a result of the

TABLE 9-6   *Transformed error and time measures. Based on data presented in Table 9-4*

ERRORS U	TIME V	U^2	UV	V^2
0.0	−.07	.00	.000	.005
1.0	−.72	1.00	−.720	.518
−1.2	.80	1.44	−.960	.640
−1.6	1.66	2.56	−2.656	2.756
0.2	−.94	.04	−.188	.884
−0.6	.14	.36	−.084	.020
0.8	−.07	.64	−.056	.005
1.4	−1.59	1.96	−2.226	2.528
0.0	.80	.00	.000	.640
0.0	.00*	8.00	−6.890	8.000*

$$\Sigma u^2 = \frac{9(8.00) - (0.0)^2}{9} = 8.00$$

$$\Sigma v^2 = \frac{9(8.000) - (.00)^2}{9} = 8.00$$

$$\Sigma uv = \frac{9(-6.890) - (0.0)(.00)}{9} = -6.89$$

* Because of rounding errors, the sum of the recorded values of V is actually .01, and the sum of the recorded values of V^2 is actually 7.996. However, for clarity of exposition, these sums have been recorded as .00 and 8.000, respectively—the exact values that would be obtained if rounding errors did not occur.

equality of Σu^2 and Σv^2, the denominators of the respective coefficients. Since s_U is always equal to s_V (both are always equal to 1), it is clear that Σu^2 is always equal to Σv^2; it follows that $b_{V \cdot U}$ is always equal to $b_{U \cdot V}$.

The regression coefficient computed on the basis of transformed values as described above is called the *coefficient of correlation* and is represented by the symbol r. The statistic r may be defined as follows:

$$r = b_{V \cdot U} = b_{U \cdot V}$$

in which U and V are transformed scores computed as indicated in Formulae (9-13) and (9-14). In honor of its originator, Karl Pearson, this statistic is commonly referred to as *Pearson's r*—or, more fully, as the *Pearson product-moment coefficient of correlation*. Because the coefficient of correlation—unlike the regression coefficients $b_{Y \cdot X}$ and $b_{X \cdot Y}$ computed directly from values of X and Y—is independent of the units of measurement used in recording the original data, it is useful as an indication of the degree of association between X and Y.

The statistic r varies between the limits -1 and 1. A coefficient of 1 indicates a perfect positive relationship between X and Y—i.e., a relationship in which Y increases as X increases, and all the plotted points lie exactly on a straight line. A coefficient of -1 indicates a perfect negative relationship, one in which Y decreases as X increases, and all the plotted points lie exactly on a straight line. A coefficient of zero indicates no systematic relationship between X and Y for the data in question. Values of r between these reference points indicate less than a perfect positive relationship (r between zero and 1) or less than a perfect negative rela-

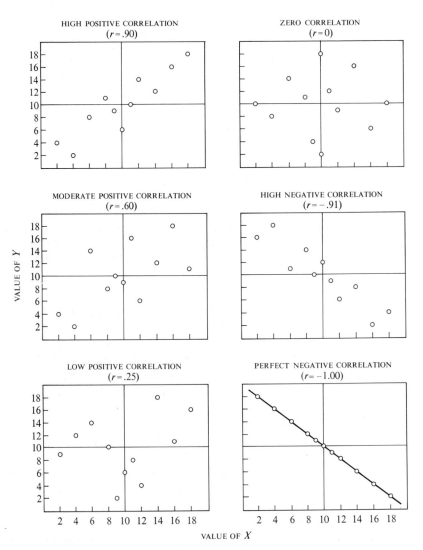

FIGURE 9-5 *Scatter diagrams illustrating selected values of r.*

tionship (*r* between zero and −1). Scatter diagrams illustrating several representative values of *r* are presented in Figure 9-5.

The three diagrams on the left-hand side of the figure represent varying degrees of positive correlation. In the upper left diagram there is a fairly high degree of association between X and Y ($r = .90$). It will be noted that the data points lie fairly close to a straight line (not shown) running from the lower left corner to the upper right corner, and that almost all of the points lie either in the upper right or lower left quadrants. The scatter diagram immediately below shows a set of data in which there is a moderate degree of association between X and Y ($r = .60$). Here, as in the diagram above, most of the data points lie in the upper right and lower left quadrants, but the points do not lie as close to a straight line as in the upper diagram. In the lower left diagram there is only a slight positive relationship between X and Y ($r = .25$), and in the upper right diagram there is no relationship at all ($r = 0$). In the latter diagram the data points are distributed more or less evenly among the four quadrants, and there is no systematic tendency for large values of Y to be associated with large values of X, or small values of Y with small values of X. The middle and lower diagrams on the right represent a high negative relationship and a perfect negative relationship, respectively. The arrangement of points in the middle right diagram ($r = -.91$) is very similar to that shown in the upper left diagram ($r = .90$), except that the trend in Y is downward, rather than upward, with increasing values of X. In the lower right diagram ($r = -1.00$) the data points are seen to lie exactly on a straight line.

A useful interpretation of *r* derives from the fact that r^2 is equal to the proportion of Σy^2 (and of Σx^2) due to regression. Stated symbolically,

$$r^2 = \frac{\Sigma c_Y^2}{\Sigma y^2} = \frac{\Sigma c_X^2}{\Sigma x^2}$$

In the present problem, $r^2 \approx (-.86)^2 \approx .74$, and this value is seen to be in agreement with the proportion $\Sigma c_Y^2/\Sigma y^2$ computed earlier. On the basis of this relationship, we see that a value of *r* equal to .50 indicates that one-quarter of the variation in Y may be accounted for in terms of regression, i.e., associated variation in X; a value of *r* equal to .70 indicates that roughly half the variation of Y may be accounted for in terms of regression on X.

It should be noted that the interpretation of *r* in terms of the proportion of Σy^2 due to regression is purely descriptive. That is, r^2 indicates how, *for the data in a particular sample,* the variation of observed values of Y may be divided into two components—(1) the variation of values of $\hat{Y}_X$ (values computed from the *sample* regression equation) around $\overline{Y}$ (the *sample* mean) and (2) variation of values of Y around values of $\hat{Y}_X$. Because no inferences concerning characteristics of the population from which the data were drawn are involved, this interpretation of *r* is legitimate whether or not the population conforms to the correlation model briefly described earlier in the chapter and described in greater detail in a later subsection.

A COMPUTATIONAL FORMULA FOR *r*

The computation of *r* by the procedures described above, although serving to indicate the meaning of *r*, is unnecessarily laborious. The calculation of *r* is considerably simplified by means of the following computational formula:

$$r = \frac{\Sigma xy}{\sqrt{(\Sigma x^2)(\Sigma y^2)}}$$ (9-15)

It will be noted that this formula makes use of sums of squares and products, Σx^2, Σy^2, and Σxy, computed directly from original values of *X* and *Y*. Applying Formula (9-15) to the original data presented in Table 9-4, and using the values of Σx^2, Σy^2, and Σxy computed in the lower portion of the table, *r* is computed as follows: $r = -1,908/\sqrt{(200)(24,480)} \approx -1,908/2,213 \approx -.86$. The reader may wish to satisfy himself, by computing *r* for the data in Table 9-5, that changing the units of measurement has no effect on *r*.

THE POPULATION CORRELATION COEFFICIENT, ρ

The correlation coefficient, *r*, is a statistic based upon the observations in a sample. We may imagine performing the same computations on a population of observations—for example, the entrance-examination scores and grade-point averages of all students attending a given school. The parameter obtained in this manner, called the *population correlation coefficient,* is represented by the symbol ρ (the Greek letter *rho*).

Under certain conditions the sample coefficient of correlation, *r*, is an unbiased estimate of ρ and may be used for testing hypotheses about ρ. However, the population must satisfy the following, rather stringent, conditions if inferences about ρ are to be made on the basis of *r*: First, the means of the *Y* distributions for various values of *X* must lie on a straight line in the manner indicated in Figure 9-1. Similarly, the means of the *X* distributions for various values of *Y* must lie on a straight line. Second, all the *Y* distributions must be distributed normally with the same variance, $\sigma_{Y \cdot X}^2$. In a like manner, all the *X* distributions must be distributed with the same variance, $\sigma_{X \cdot Y}^2$, although this variance need not be the same as that of the *Y* distributions. A population having these characteristics is said to have a *bivariate normal distribution.* The name derives from the fact that two normally distributed variables are involved.

When sampling is from a bivariate normal population, r may be used to test hypotheses about ρ. The hypothesis most commonly tested is that ρ equals zero, i.e., that there is no relationship between X and Y in the population. This hypothesis may be tested using the t statistic computed as follows:

$$t = \sqrt{\frac{(n - 2)r^2}{1 - r^2}}, \qquad df = n - 2 \qquad (9\text{-}16)$$

By means of some simple algebraic manipulations, Formula (9-16) may be shown to be a variation of Formula (9-10). Like the value of t computed using Formula (9-10), the value of t computed using Formula (9-16) is based upon $n - 2$ degrees of freedom—i.e., two less than the number of Y observations (which is the same, of course, as the number of X observations). Using Formula (9-16), the correlation coefficient for the data in Table 9-4 may be tested for significance by computing t as follows: $t = \sqrt{7(-.86)^2/[1 - (-.86)^2]} \approx 4.46$. With seven degrees of freedom, critical values of t for the .01 level of significance are -3.499 and 3.499. Accordingly, the hypothesis that $\rho = 0$ is rejected, and it is concluded that in the population there is a correlation between X and Y.

REGRESSION AND CAUSATION

An investigation using a correlation design is a variety of *ex post facto* investigation, and interpretation of the results of such a study is subject to the limitations discussed in Chapter 1 in connection with *ex post facto* investigations. From the fact that there is a significant relationship between two variables it does not necessarily follow that variation in one causes variation in the other. As was pointed out in Chapter 1, an observed relationship between two variables in this type of study may be the result of their common relationship to some third factor. An impressive illustration of this point, cited by Snedecor (1956), is the nearly perfect negative correlation, $r = -.98$, observed between the birth rate in Great Britain and the production of pig iron in the United States during the period from 1875 to 1920. Surely neither of these two variables affected the other directly; the relationship apparently came about because these two quantities both varied as a function of time during the period in question, one increasing, the other decreasing.

RELIABILITY

It has been emphasized in earlier chapters that repeated measures of the same individual typically exhibit some variation from one measurement to the next. Thus, when considering a particular score of a particular individual (e.g., a measure of his reaction time or of his IQ), a question arises concerning the stability or reliability of that score—i.e., there is a question concerning the extent to which a second determination of the same measure would agree with the first.   Putting the matter somewhat differently, when we encounter a distribution of observations consisting of one score for each of several individuals, it is not apparent to what extent the variation observed among the scores reflects true differences among individuals and how much is due to individual inconsistency.   (We have noted previously that, even if all individuals should exhibit similar performance on the average, there is typically fluctuation among observations as a consequence of individual inconsistency.)   If we have but a single measurement for each individual, there is no way of assessing the relative contribution of these two general sources of variation; on the other hand, with two or more measurements based on each individual, it is possible to evaluate the contribution of each source.   In this subsection we shall consider the use of the correlation coefficient for making an evaluation of this kind.

As background for this procedure, we shall first consider a measure for describing the reliability, in a given population, of a given type of measure.   The necessary concepts may be illustrated with reference to the model population represented in Table 4-4, which summarizes the probability distribution of X for each of the several individuals comprising the population.   In analyzing the distribution of X in this model, we distinguished three measures of variation: σ_ϵ^2 (the variation of repeated determinations based upon a given individual), σ_τ^2 (the variation associated with individual differences), and σ^2 (the overall variation in X).   Using these concepts, the *reliability* of X, which will here be represented by the symbol R, may be defined as follows:

$$R = \frac{\sigma_\tau^2}{\sigma^2} = \frac{\sigma_\tau^2}{\sigma_\tau^2 + \sigma_\epsilon^2} \qquad (9\text{-}17)$$

In other words, R is defined as the proportion of the total variation in X $(\sigma_\tau^2 + \sigma_\epsilon^2)$ that may be attributed to individual differences (σ_τ^2).   Substituting the numerical values of σ_τ^2 and σ_ϵ^2, we find for the model described in Table 4-4 that $R = 1{,}197/(1{,}197 + 2^{11}\!/_{12}) \approx .998$—a higher value than is characteristic of most actual behavior measures.   From the above definition of R, it is a matter of simple algebra to show that the complement of R (i.e., $1 - R$) is equal to $\sigma_\epsilon^2/(\sigma_\tau^2 + \sigma_\epsilon^2)$—that is, the proportion of σ^2 due to variation of repeated determinations.   For the model described in Table 4-4, $\sigma_\epsilon^2/(\sigma_\tau^2 + \sigma_\epsilon^2) \approx 1 - .998 = .002$.

The value of R for a given measure in a population may be estimated as follows: A sample of individuals is drawn from the population in question, and two determinations of the measure of interest (e.g., reaction time) are obtained for each individual.   The coefficient of correlation, r, based upon the two sets of measures provides an estimate of R. A value of r obtained in this manner is commonly called a *reliability coefficient*.

TABLE 9-7 *Calculation of reliability coefficient. Simulated data: two determinations on each of ten individuals*

INDIVIDUAL NUMBER	FIRST DETERMINATION X	SECOND DETERMINATION Y	X^2	XY	Y^2
4	23	19	529	437	361
5	27	28	729	756	784
8	44	48	1,936	2,112	2,304
9	53	52	2,809	2,756	2,704
11	63	66	3,969	4,158	4,356
14	81	83	6,561	6,723	6,889
16	95	92	9,025	8,740	8,464
17	100	98	10,000	9,800	9,604
19	114	109	12,996	12,426	11,881
20	120	115	14,400	13,800	13,225
	720	710	62,954	61,708	60,572

$$\Sigma x^2 = \frac{10(62,954) - (720)^2}{10} = 11,114$$

$$\Sigma y^2 = \frac{10(60,572) - (710)^2}{10} = 10,162$$

$$\Sigma xy = \frac{10(61,708) - (720)(710)}{10} = 10,588$$

$$r = \frac{\Sigma xy}{\sqrt{(\Sigma x^2)(\Sigma y^2)}} = \frac{10,588}{\sqrt{(11,114)(10,162)}} \approx .996$$

This procedure may be illustrated using the data of Table 9-7. These data were obtained by drawing a sample of ten individuals (represented by dice) from the model population described in Table 4-4 and randomly determining two values of X for each individual (simulated by rolling each die twice). Extending to the present situation the terminology employed earlier in this chapter, the first determination for each individual has been designated X; the second, Y. The calculation of Σx^2, Σy^2, Σxy, and r is shown in the lower part of the table. It will be noted that the value of r based upon this sample is .996—a fairly good approximation of the population value, $R \approx .998$, that we computed above.

CORRELATION AND PAIRED OBSERVATIONS

In Chapter 8 we considered an experimental design in which the observations of one sample are paired in some manner with the observations of the other sample.   One outcome of this procedure, if pairing is successful, is to establish a correlation between the observations of the two samples, i.e., low values in one sample tend to be associated with low values in the other, and so on.   Another outcome is that the means of the two samples tend to differ less than they would have without pairing: if Sample *1* includes an unusual number of high-scoring individuals, with the result that $\overline{X}_1$ exceeds μ_1, then Sample *2* will have a comparable number of high-scoring individuals, and $\overline{X}_2$ will usually exceed μ_2.   Now let us imagine a number of repetitions of an experiment employing paired observations, in each of which we compute $\overline{X}_1$ and $\overline{X}_2$.   When the value of $\overline{X}_1$ for a given experiment is relatively high, the associated value of $\overline{X}_2$ will also tend to be relatively high; conversely, when one mean is relatively low, the other will tend to be low also.   In other words, over a series of such experiments, $\overline{X}_1$ and $\overline{X}_2$ will be positively correlated.   Moreover, the correlation, $\rho_{\overline{X}_1,\overline{X}_2}$, between X_1 and X_2 over an indefinitely long series of experiments has the same numerical value as ρ, the correlation between X_1 and X_2 (the individual measures in the two populations).

Equipped with the concept of $\rho_{\overline{X}_1,\overline{X}_2}$ the correlation between $\overline{X}_1$ and $\overline{X}_2$, we may gain further understanding of the variance of the difference $\overline{X}_1 - \overline{X}_2$.   The general formula for the variance of such a difference, applicable both to experiments employing independent observations and to those employing paired observations, is the following:

$$\sigma_{\overline{X}_1-\overline{X}_2}{}^2 = \sigma_{\overline{X}_1}{}^2 + \sigma_{\overline{X}_2}{}^2 - 2\rho_{\overline{X}_1,\overline{X}_2}\sigma_{\overline{X}_1}\sigma_{\overline{X}_2} \qquad (9\text{-}18)$$

In an experiment employing independent observations there is no correlation between $\overline{X}_1$ and $\overline{X}_2$—i.e., $\rho_{\overline{X}_1,\overline{X}_2} = 0$—and Formula (9-18) reduces to

$$\sigma_{\overline{X}_1-\overline{X}_2}{}^2 = \sigma_{\overline{X}_1}{}^2 + \sigma_{\overline{X}_2}{}^2 \qquad (8\text{-}2)$$

Thus, Formula (8-2) for the variance of the difference between the means of independent groups is seen to be a special case of Formula (9-18).

Next consider the implications of Formula (9-18) for experiments involving paired observations.   It will be recalled that in this type of experiment $\overline{D}$, the mean of the differences, is equal to $\overline{X}_1 - \overline{X}_2$; accordingly, the two expressions—$\overline{D}$ or $\overline{X}_1 - \overline{X}_2$—may be used interchangeably.   Formula (9-18) indicates that, in an experiment employing paired observations, the variance of $\overline{X}_1 - \overline{X}_2$ depends upon $\rho_{\overline{X}_1,\overline{X}_2}$ (the correlation between $\overline{X}_1$ and $\overline{X}_2$), which, as we have noted above, is the same as ρ (the correlation between X_1 and X_2, the individual observations obtained under the two treatments). At one extreme, if pairing is completely ineffective ($\rho = \rho_{\bar{X}_1,\bar{X}_2} = 0$), the variance of $\bar{X}_1 - \bar{X}_2$ is equal to $\sigma_{\bar{X}_1}^2 + \sigma_{\bar{X}_2}^2$; in other words, the variance of the difference is the same as if pairing had not been employed. However, when pairing is effective—i.e., when members of a pair tend to be alike, and ρ is greater than zero—the variance of the difference is decreased by the amount of the last term in Formula (9-18), $2\rho_{\bar{X}_1,\bar{X}_2}\sigma_{\bar{X}_1}\sigma_{\bar{X}_2}$; the greater the correlation established between the two sets of observations by pairing, the greater is the reduction of the variance of the difference. In the special case in which $\sigma_{\bar{X}_1}^2 = \sigma_{\bar{X}_2}^2 = \sigma_{\bar{X}}^2$ and $\rho = 1$, the variance of $\bar{X}_1 - \bar{X}_2$ is zero. Thus, the advantage of pairing is seen to depend upon the closeness of the relationship established between the two sets of observations as a result of pairing. If a sufficiently high relationship is established, the reduction of the variance of the difference more than compensates for the degrees of freedom lost as a result of pairing; if only a low correlation is established, the gains resulting from reduction of the variance of the difference may be more than offset by the loss of degrees of fredom.

RANK CORRELATION

In a previous subsection a method was described for testing the hypothesis that $\rho = 0$ (Formula (9-16)). A limitation of this method is that it is applicable only when the data in question are drawn from a bivariate normal distribution. In the present subsection we shall consider a measure of correlation that, whatever the shape of the population distribution, may be used to test the hypothesis that X and Y are independent. The statistic in question is the *rank correlation coefficient,* commonly designated r_S. The subscript S stands for the name of the originator, Charles Spearman.

The computation of r_S is illustrated in Table 9-8 using data previously presented in Table 9-4. The first two columns of Table 9-8 present the raw data—error and time scores of nine individuals. The first step in computing r_S is to rank separately the nine values of X and the nine values of Y. Ranks assigned to the values of X are recorded in the third column of the table; ranks assigned to the values of Y, in the fourth. (It will be noted that tied ranks are handled in the same manner as in the ranking procedures discussed in Chapter 8—the mean of the tied ranks is assigned to all measures involved in the tie.) Next, as shown in column five, the difference D is determined for each pair of ranks. In the last column, the differences are squared and summed. The rank correlation coefficient is computed from ΣD^2 using the following formula:

$$r_S = 1 - \frac{6\Sigma D^2}{n(n^2 - 1)} \qquad (9\text{-}19)$$

TABLE 9-8   *Computation of* r_s, *the rank correlation coefficient. Based on hypothetical errors and time scores presented in Table 9-4*

Errors X	Time in Seconds Y	Rank of X	Rank of Y	D	D²
11	144	4.5	4.5	0	.00
16	108	8	3	5	25.00
5	192	2	7.5	−5.5	30.25
3	240	1	9	−8	64.00
12	96	6	2	4	16.00
8	156	3	6	−3	9.00
15	144	7	4.5	2.5	6.25
18	60	9	1	8	64.00
11	192	4.5	7.5	−3	9.00
					223.50

$$r_s = 1 - \frac{6\Sigma D^2}{n(n^2 - 1)} = 1 - \frac{6(223.50)}{9(81 - 1)} = 1 - \frac{1,341}{720} \approx -.86$$

The calculations are shown in the bottom part of Table 9-8. The value obtained, −.86, is seen to be identical to the value of r computed earlier for the same data. This identity is exceptional: the two statistics, r and r_s, are usually similar in value but not equal.

Instead of determining the sum of squares of differences between ranks and computing r_s using Formula (9-19), r_s may be obtained by applying Formula (9-15) for r directly to the ranks of X and Y; in other words, r_s is simply Pearson's product-moment correlation coefficient applied to ranks. Like r, the statistic r_s varies between the limits −1 (one set of ranks exactly the reverse of the other) and 1 (both sets of ranks exactly the same), and—except for sampling fluctuations—is equal to zero when there is no relationship between X and Y.

As noted earlier, r_s is especially useful because it can be used, regardless of the shape of the population distribution, to test the hypothesis that X and Y are independent—i.e., the hypothesis that there is no association in the population between X and Y. Critical values of r_s for testing this hypothesis at the .10, .05, .02, and .01 levels of significance are given in Table A-7 of Appendix A. The hypothesis that X and Y are independent is rejected if the observed value of r_s is equal to or greater than the appropriate critical value given in the table, or if r_s is equal to or less than a like value of negative sign. For example, with nine pairs of observations, any value of r_s greater than .833 or less than −.833 results in rejection, at the .01 level of significance, of the hypothesis that X and Y are independent. Accordingly, on the basis of the value computed in Table 9-8 ($r_s \approx -.86$), we would reject the hypothesis that X and Y

are independent and conclude that in the population these two measures are negatively related. For values of n exceeding those listed in Table A-7, an approximate test of the hypothesis that X and Y are independent may be performed using Formula (9-16), substituting r_s for r in the formula.

PROBLEMS

The following are the data for Problems 1, 3, 12, and 20.

PROBLEM 1		PROBLEM 3		PROBLEM 12		PROBLEM 20	
Grams	Responses	X	Y	Test Score	Yards Swum	First Testing	Second Testing
24	92	6	5	13	7	103	100
23	80	5	3	12	7	102	102
22	84	4	6	9	6	99	97
21	100	3	3	6	4	96	97
20	102	2	4	5	4		
19	96	1	0	3	2		
18	124	0	2				
17	116						
16	106						

1. Nine rats were trained to press a bar in a Skinner box and were then extinguished (i.e., allowed to press the bar, but with the feeder disconnected) with different amounts of pressure required to operate the bar. The number of grams pressure required to operate the bar and the number of responses during the first 20 minutes of extinction are given above. Plot a scatter diagram of these data.

2. Using the data of Problem 1, determine the deviation of each X value from $\overline{X}$ and the deviation of each Y value from $\overline{Y}$. (a) Using these deviations, compute Σx^2, Σy^2, and Σxy. (b) Determine the sample regression equation. (c) Estimate $\mu_{Y \cdot X}$ for $X = 17$ and for $X = 22$.

3. Plot a scatter diagram of the data given above for Problem 3.

4. (a) Compute Σx^2, Σy^2, and Σxy for the data of Problem 3, using the appropriate computational formulae. (b) Determine the sample regression equation for these data. (c) Estimate $\mu_{Y \cdot X}$ for $X = 1$ and for $X = 4$.

5. Using the data of Problem 1, compute $c = \hat{Y}_X - \overline{Y}$ and $d = Y - \hat{Y}_X$ corresponding to each value of X. Verify that in each case $y = c + d$. Also verify that $\Sigma d = 0$. (a) Square each value of c and determine Σc^2. Similarly, square each value of d and determine Σd^2. Verify that $\Sigma y^2 = \Sigma c^2 + \Sigma d^2$. (b) Determine the proportion of Σy^2 due to regression and the residual proportion.

6. Starting with the quantities Σx^2, Σy^2, and Σxy computed in Problem 2, use the appropriate computational methods to verify the values of Σc^2 and Σd^2 computed by direct methods in Problem 5.

7. Starting with the quantities Σx^2, Σy^2, and Σxy obtained in Problem 4, partition Σy^2 for the data of Problem 3 into a portion due to regression and a residual portion. Express both these parts as a proportion of Σy^2.

8. Estimate $\sigma_{Y \cdot X}^2$ for the population of Problem 1.

9. Estimate $\sigma_{Y \cdot X}^2$ for the population of Problem 3.

10. Test the hypothesis that $B = 0$ for the population of Problem 1.

11. Test the hypothesis that $B = 0$ for the population of Problem 3.

12. At a summer camp six boys were given a physical fitness test (X). The same boys were later tested to determine how far they could swim (Y). The data are given at the beginning of this section with distances swum recorded to the nearest yard. (a) Determine the two regression coefficients for these data. (b) Determine the proportion of Σy^2 due to regression. Similarly, compute the proportion of Σx^2 due to regression. How do the two proportions compare?

13. Suppose the distances swum (Problem 12) had been recorded to the nearest foot rather than the nearest yard. How would the regression coefficients be affected? (a) Change the distances from yards to feet and compute the regression coefficients for the new units of measurement. Compare your results with those obtained in Problem 12. (b) Determine the proportion of Σy^2 due to regression. How does this compare with the corresponding proportion in Problem 12? Which is a better indication of degree of association, the regression coefficients or the proportion of Σy^2 due to regression?

14. Compute the means and standard deviations of the X and Y distributions of Problem 12. Using these quantities, compute transformed scores as indicated in Formulae (9-13) and (9-14). Using these transformed scores, compute the two regression coefficients, $b_{Y \cdot U}$ and $b_{U \cdot V}$. How do the two coefficients compare?

15. Using the appropriate *computational* formula, compute the coefficient of correlation for the data of Problem 12. Compare your result with the results of Problem 14.

16. Using the data of Problem 12, compute the proportion of Σy^2 due to regression by squaring r. Compare your result with that of Problem 12, Part (b).

17. Test the hypothesis that, in the population sampled in Problem 12, $\rho = 0$.

18. A day's production of bearings at a factory are measured to the nearest thousandth of an inch. The variance of the true sizes, σ_τ^2, is 18 units. However, because of errors of measurement, repeated measurements of a given bearing have a variance, σ_ϵ^2, of two units. (a) What is the variance of the observed measures? (b) What is the reliability, R, of the measurements under these conditions?

19. What is the reliability, R, of the test described in Problem 7 of Chapter 4?

20. Four subjects were given the same test on two different occasions. The scores for the two testings are given at the beginning of this section. Estimate R, the reliability of the test in question.

21. Using the data of Problem 12, compute r_s, the rank correlation coefficient. Using this statistic, test the hypothesis that X and Y are independent.

REFERENCE

SNEDECOR, G. W. *Statistical methods applied to experiments in agriculture and biology* (5th ed.). Ames, Iowa: Iowa State College Press, 1956. Chaps. 6 and 7. A very thorough discussion, at an intermediate level of difficulty, of the concepts of regression and correlation.

ADDITIONAL READINGS

EDWARDS, A. L. *Statistical methods for the behavioral sciences.* New York: Rinehart, 1954. Chaps. 7 (regression), 8 (Pearson's *r*), 9 (reliability), and 10 (measures of correlation other than Pearson's *r*).

GUILFORD, J. P. *Fundamental statistics in psychology and education* (3d ed.). New York: McGraw-Hill, 1956. Chap. 8 (a general discussion of the correlation coefficient as a measure of association) and Chap. 17 (a discussion of the theory of reliability).

LI, J. C. R. *Introduction to statistical inference.* Ann Arbor: Edwards Brothers, 1957. Chaps. 16 and 17. A detailed discussion of linear regression.

UNDERWOOD, B. J., C. P. DUNCAN, JANET A. TAYLOR, and J. W. COTTON. *Elementary statistics.* New York: Appleton-Century-Crofts, 1954. Chap. 10.

WEINBERG, G. H. and J. A. SCHUMAKER. *Statistics: an intuitive approach.* Belmont, Calif.: Wadsworth, 1962. Chaps. 16–18. Presents a nontechnical discussion of the basic concepts underlying regression and correlation. This reference is especially recommended for readers with limited mathematical background.

CHAPTER 10

analysis of qualitative data

THE STATISTICAL PROCEDURES CONSIDERED THUS FAR ARE DESIGNED FOR use with quantitative variables, i.e., data that are expressed in numerical form. Frequently, however, the variables with which an investigation is concerned are of a qualitative kind. For example, an investigator might inquire whether the frequency with which a given multiple-choice test item is passed or failed differs between the two sexes. The two variables of interest in such an investigation—(*a*) sex and (*b*) performance on the item in question—are both qualitative. In other words, any given individual would be classified either as male or female and as passing or failing the test item, but it would not be possible to distinguish gradations of either variable. In this chapter statistical procedures for testing hypotheses concerning qualitative variables of this kind are described.

TESTING AN A PRIORI HYPOTHESIS
CONCERNING RELATIVE FREQUENCIES

The first type of problem we consider is one in which the investigator wishes to determine whether the relative frequency with which a given characteristic (or given type of event) is observed to occur conforms to some a priori hypothesis, i.e., a hypothesis based upon theoretical considerations rather than experimental observations. This type of problem is illustrated by the following study of psychokinesis—a purported psychic phenomenon in which physical events are influenced by the will of the individuals participating. To study this phenomenon 30 subjects were tested as follows: For each subject an experimenter tossed an ordinary coin 100 times, and on each toss the subject attempted, through mental concentration, to influence the coin to land head side up. Altogether, 3,000 tosses of a coin were observed in this experiment. Of these 3,000 trials, 1,544 were successes (i.e., the coin landed head side up) and 1,456 were failures (i.e., the coin landed head side down). The null hypothesis to be tested in this experiment is that the efforts of the subjects to influence the coin psychokinetically were without effect and, hence, that the frequency with which the coin landed heads or tails was determined purely by chance. Representing the probability of success on any given trial by p and the probability of failure by q, the null hypothesis may be stated as follows: $p = q = .5$. Representing the total number of trials by n and the theoretical frequency of success (i.e., the expected frequency of success according to the null hypothesis) by F_1, the formula for computing the value of F_1 may be written as follows:

$$F_1 = np \qquad (10\text{-}1)$$

Thus, $F_1 = 3,000(.5) = 1,500$. Similarly, F_2, the theoretical frequency of failure, is equal to $nq = 3,000(.5) = 1,500$. The observed and theoretical frequencies for this experiment—the latter in parentheses—are summarized in Table 10-1.

TABLE 10-1 *Frequency of success in attempting to influence the fall of a coin psychokinetically*

OUTCOME	OBSERVED AND THEORETICAL FREQUENCIES	
Success	1,544	(1,500)
Failure	1,456	(1,500)
TOTAL	3,000	

$$\chi^2 \approx 2.58$$

Theoretical frequencies are given in parentheses.

It will be noted that the observed frequency of success, 1,544, is somewhat greater than the corresponding theoretical frequency, and the observed frequency of failure, 1,456, is somewhat less than the theoretical frequency for that category. (It should be noted that when only two categories are employed in classifying data—in the present instance, success or failure—it is always the case that one observed frequency falls short of its theoretical value by exactly the same amount as the other exceeds its theoretical value.) The discrepancy obtained in this experiment between the observed and theoretical frequencies is in the direction that would be expected if the attempts of the subjects to influence the coin psychokinetically were partially successful. However, even if the null hypothesis should be true—i.e., the efforts of the subjects without effect—we would expect some discrepancy between the theoretical and observed frequencies as a consequence of sampling error. The problem with which we are faced in any given experiment is to evaluate whether the discrepancy observed is within the limits we might reasonably expect on the basis of sampling error (in which case we would accept the null hypothesis) or is greater than would usually occur by chance (in which case we would reject the null hypothesis).

The statistic used to evaluate the discrepancy between observed and theoretical frequencies is represented by the symbol χ^2 (the Greek letter *chi* with the exponent 2) and is called *chi square*. To compute χ^2 we first determine, for each category used in classifying the data, the difference between the observed and theoretical frequency, square this difference, divide the squared difference by the theoretical frequency for that category, then sum the results for all categories. If we let f_1 and f_2 represent the observed frequency of success and failure, respectively, for the experiment summarized in Table 10-1, the computation of χ^2 may be represented as follows:

$$\chi^2 = \frac{(f_1 - F_1)^2}{F_1} + \frac{(f_2 - F_2)^2}{F_2}$$

$$= \frac{(1{,}544 - 1{,}500)^2}{1{,}500} + \frac{(1{,}456 - 1{,}500)^2}{1{,}500}$$

$$= \frac{(44)^2}{1{,}500} + \frac{(-44)^2}{1{,}500} \approx 2.58$$

More generally, the computation of χ^2 may be represented as follows:

$$\chi^2 = \Sigma \frac{(f - F)^2}{F} \tag{10-2}$$

in which the fraction $(f - F)^2/F$ following the summation sign is computed separately for each category and then summed for all categories. It is readily apparent that the value of χ^2 is either zero or—since the numerator of each fraction is squared—some positive number. The smaller the difference between the observed and theoretical frequencies, the smaller is the value of χ^2; the greater the difference, the greater the value of χ^2. Thus, a small value of χ^2 leads to acceptance of the null hypothesis; a large value, to rejection. On the basis of the theoretical sampling distribution of χ^2, it is possible to specify critical values of χ^2 corresponding to various values of α. Thus, for a test at the .05 level of significance, the critical value would be selected so that a value of χ^2 equal to or greater than the critical value would have only a .05 probability of occurrence when the null hypothesis is true. The theoretical sampling distribution of χ^2, like the distribution of t, differs depending upon the number of degrees of freedom involved. In problems of the type described in the present section (testing an a priori hypothesis), the number of degrees of freedom is one less than the number of categories used in classifying observations—i.e., $k - 1$, in which k represents the number of categories. In the psychokinesis problem described above, there are two categories (success and failure), so the number of degrees of freedom is $2 - 1 = 1$.

Critical values of χ^2 for selected values of α are given in Table A-8 of Appendix A. As in the table of critical values of t (Table A-4), each row of Table A-8 gives critical values for a different number of degrees of freedom. We note that for $df = 1$ the critical value of χ^2 for a test at the .05 level of significance is 3.841. Accordingly, the value of χ^2 computed for the data of Table 10-1 ($\chi^2 \approx 2.58$) leads to acceptance of the null hypothesis—in other words, the experiment fails to provide evidence of a psychokinetic influence upon the fall of the coin.

The procedure described above affords a two-sided test of the hypothesis that $p = .5$; i.e., following the above procedure, the null hypothesis would have been rejected if the observed frequency of success had been either sufficiently greater or sufficiently less than the theoretical frequency of success. However, the nature of the phenomenon under investigation in our illustrative problem is such that an investigator might be interested in rejecting the null hypothesis only if the observed frequency of success exceeded the theoretical frequency by a sufficient amount (but not if the observed frequency fell short of the theoretical frequency). In effect, an investigator conducting his test in this manner would be testing the one-sided hypothesis $p \leq .5$. To perform such a test at the .05 level of significance the critical value of χ^2 would be taken from the column headed .10 in Table A-8. In the present problem the critical value of χ^2 for a one-sided test at the .05 level of significance is seen to be 2.706, and the observed value of χ^2 ($\chi^2 \approx 2.58$) is not statistically significant. More generally, the value of α for a one-sided test is half the value specified in the heading of any given column of Table A-8. It should be noted that the method described here for performing a one-sided test is applicable only for experiments in which χ^2 is based upon one degree of freedom, i.e., experiments in which only two patterns of outcome are possible. (For example, in our illustrative experiment above, the two possible patterns are (*a*) observed frequency of success greater—and observed frequency of failure less—than the corresponding theoretical frequencies or (*b*) the reverse.) When χ^2 is based upon a greater number of degrees of freedom, many patterns of outcome are possible, and the concept of one-sided test is not applicable.

A COMPUTATIONAL FORMULA

FOR TESTING THE HYPOTHESIS THAT $p = q = .5$

As will become evident in subsequent sections of this chapter, Formula (10-2) is a general formula that can be used in every type of problem that we shall consider. There are also available a number of special formulae—each applicable to one specific type of problem—that permit the computation of χ^2 with somewhat less arithmetic labor than Formula (10-2).

In two-category problems of the kind illustrated in the preceding subsection, the hypothesis that $p = q = .5$ may be tested by computing χ^2 as follows:

$$\chi^2 = \frac{(f_1 - f_2)^2}{f_1 + f_2} \tag{10-3}$$

Substituting the data of Table 10-1 in Formula (10-3), χ^2 is computed as follows: $\chi^2 = (1{,}544 - 1{,}456)^2/(1{,}544 + 1{,}456) = (88)^2/3{,}000 \approx 2.58$. This value of χ^2 is seen to be the same as that computed previously using Formula (10-2).

It is emphasized that Formula (10-3) is applicable only when the hypothesis being tested is that $p = q = .5$; when other values of p and q are specified by the hypothesis being tested, Formula (10-2) should be used. (For an example of a problem of the latter kind, see Problem 2 at the end of the chapter.)

CORRECTION FOR CONTINUITY

When χ^2 is computed from discrete sample frequencies—as is the case in all the problems that we shall consider—the sampling distribution of χ^2 is discrete. That is to say, only certain isolated values of χ^2 are possible, each of which has a certain probability of occurrence when the null hypothesis is true. While it is theoretically possible to compute critical values based upon this distribution, the actual computations are so complex as to be unfeasible from a practical point of view, except in problems involving relatively small samples. Fortunately, the sampling distribution of the χ^2 statistic is closely approximated by a theoretical continuous distribution, the areas of which may be determined with relative ease.[1]   The

---

[1] Strictly speaking, the designation χ^2 *distribution* is appropriate to the latter distribution and not to the sampling distribution of the statistic defined by Formula (10-2). However, because the discrete sampling distribution of the statistic defined by Formula (10-2) closely approximates the continuous χ^2 distribution, the distinction between the two distributions is commonly disregarded in practice. In order to distinguish the two distributions and thus lessen the likelihood of confusion Cochran (1954) uses the symbol X^2 to designate the statistic defined by Formula (10-2), reserving the designation χ^2 for the continuous distribution. The less rigorous practice of using χ^2 to refer to both distributions—and, hence, in two slightly different senses—is followed here because it has gained widespread use.

critical values given in Table A-8 are based upon the latter (continuous) distribution; consequently, when these critical values are used for tests based upon the χ^2 statistic defined by Formula (10-2), the values of α given in Table A-8 are approximate only, the actual value of α being somewhat greater than the nominal value (the value indicated in the table). The larger the value of n (the total number of observations), the more nearly does the actual value of α approximate the nominal value of α for the critical value in question. As a rule of thumb, the approximation is generally deemed satisfactory for practical purposes when all theoretical frequencies are equal to or greater than 5. This rule of thumb works well for problems in which χ^2 is based upon a single degree of freedom, but, as we shall note below, may be somewhat relaxed when the number of degrees of freedom is greater than one.[2]

In problems involving one degree of freedom, it is possible to modify the computation of χ^2 in such a way that the actual (discrete) sampling distribution of χ^2 more closely approximates the theoretical (continuous) distribution upon which critical values are based, or, putting the matter somewhat differently, so that the actual value of α more nearly coincides with the nominal value indicated in Table A-8. This modification is known as the *correction for continuity* and, using Formula (10-2), is made by reducing the absolute value of each difference between an observed and theoretical frequency by .5 before squaring the difference— i.e., by treating each difference, regardless of sign, as a positive number and subtracting .5 from this value. So modified, Formula (10-2) may be written as follows:

$$\chi_c^2 = \Sigma \frac{(|f - F| - .5)^2}{F} \tag{10-4}$$

Applying this formula to the data presented in Table 10-1, we have

$$\chi_c^2 = \frac{(44 - .5)^2}{1,500} + \frac{(44 - .5)^2}{1,500} = \frac{(43.5)^2}{1,500} + \frac{(43.5)^2}{1,500} \approx 2.52$$

The subscript c in χ_c^2 stands for "corrected." It will be noted that the corrected value of chi square is slightly less than the uncorrected value computed previously for the same data.

When χ^2 is computed using Formula (10-3), the correction for continuity is made by subtracting 1 from the absolute value of the difference in the numerator before squaring, as follows:

$$\chi_c^2 = \frac{(|f_1 - f_2| - 1)^2}{f_1 + f_2} \tag{10-5}$$

[2] In two-category problems involving theoretical frequencies less than 5, an exact test based upon the binomial distribution (a discrete probability distribution) may be used. This test is described by Dixon and Massey (1957, Chap. 13) and by Siegel (1956, Chap. 4).

Using this formula, χ_c^2 may be computed for the data presented in Table 10-1 as follows: $\chi_c^2 = (88 - 1)^2/3,000 \approx 2.52$. This value of χ_c^2 is seen to be the same as that obtained using Formula (10-4).

TESTING AN A PRIORI HYPOTHESIS—PROBLEMS INVOLVING MORE THAN ONE DEGREE OF FREEDOM

In the illustrative problem considered above, two categories (success and failure) were used to classify observations, and χ^2 was therefore based upon one degree of freedom. We next consider a problem in which more than two categories are used to classify observations, and χ^2 is based upon more than one degree of freedom.

For purposes of illustration we will examine the data of the following experiment: A subject was instructed to recite a series of digits, simulating as nearly as possible a random series such as might be obtained by means of a lottery. A total of 200 responses (spoken digits) were recorded; the frequencies with which the ten possible responses (*zero, one, two,* · · · , *nine*) occurred are shown in Table 10-2.

TABLE 10-2 *Distribution of responses by subject instructed to simulate a random series of digits*

RESPONSE	zero	one	two	three	four	five	six	seven	eight	nine
FREQUENCY	21	19	22	29	18	13	21	16	19	22

$$\chi^2 = \frac{(21 - 20)^2}{20} + \frac{(19 - 20)^2}{20} + \cdots + \frac{(22 - 20)^2}{20} = 8.1$$

The question we shall consider in analyzing these data is whether this subject exhibits any response biases such that certain responses systematically tend to occur with a greater frequency than others. The null hypothesis to be tested is that in the population of all possible responses, from which the 200 responses observed are a sample, all ten responses have the same probability. Letting p_0, p_1, p_2, · · · represent the probabilities of the verbal responses *zero, one, two,* · · · , respectively, the null hypothesis may be stated as follows: $p_0 = p_1 = p_2 = \cdots = p_9 = .10$. According to this hypothesis, F_0, the theoretical frequency for the response *zero*, is $np_0 = 200(.10) = 20$. Similarly, the theoretical frequency of each of the other possible responses is 20. Examination of Table 10-2 indicates that the observed frequency of certain responses (e.g., *three*) is considerably greater than 20, whereas the observed frequency of other responses (e.g., *five*) is considerably less. Our problem is to determine whether these discrepancies are greater than might reasonably be expected on the basis of sampling fluctuations.   To reach a decision concerning this question we compute χ^2 using Formula (10-2), as shown beneath Table 10-2.   Since ten categories are used to classify the data, the number of degrees of freedom associated with this value of χ^2 is $10 - 1 = 9$.   Consulting Table A-8, we find that for a test at the .05 level of significance the critical value of χ^2 is 16.919.   Thus, the computed value of χ^2 ($\chi^2 = 8.1$) is not significant at the .05 level, and the null hypothesis is accepted—the present data fail to provide clear evidence of a response bias.

Several points of comparison of the present problem with the previous problem, in which $df = 1$, are worth noting.   First, the correction for continuity made in the previous problem is not applicable to the data of the present problem: no simple correction is available that is suitable for problems involving more than one degree of freedom.   Second, Formula (10-3) cannot be used to compute χ^2 in the present problem: this formula is applicable only to problems in which two categories are used in classifying data.   Third, the distinction between a "one-sided" and "two-sided" test is not applicable in the present problem: in contrast to a two-category problem (in which, as we noted earlier, the results can differ from theoretical expectation in only two ways), in the present problem there is a great variety of ways in which the pattern of observed frequencies can differ from the theoretical pattern.   The whole rationale of one-sided tests depends upon there being but two possible kinds of outcome to an experiment; consequently, the notion of one sided test cannot be extended to experiments having a great variety of possible outcomes.

In problems involving more than one degree of freedom, the value of n (the total number of observations) should be large enough to provide that at least 80 per cent of the theoretical frequencies are equal to or greater than 5, and none of the theoretical frequencies is less than 1 (Cochran, 1954).   When this rule of thumb is observed, the actual value of α will be reasonably close to the nominal value of α indicated in Table A-8.

CONTINGENCY TESTS: THE COMPARISON OF PROPORTIONS BASED UPON TWO OR MORE INDEPENDENT SAMPLES

2×2 TABLES

The statistical procedure considered next may be illustrated with reference to the following investigation (R. G. Hunt, unpublished material): One hundred and six mental patients diagnosed as having a manic-depressive psychosis were classified on the basis of two characteristics: (*a*) sex and (*b*) the type of symptom (manic or depressive) predominating in their behavior. The results of this classification are shown in Table 10-3.

TABLE 10-3 *Dominant symptoms—male, female manic-depressive patients*

| DOMINANT SYMPTOMS | SEX | | TOTAL |
	Male	Female	
Manic	23	25	48
Depressed	16	42	58
TOTAL	39	67	106

Based on unpublished data provided by R. G. Hunt.

It will be noted that of the 106 patients, 39 were men and 67 were women. Whereas 59 per cent of the men (23/39) exhibited predominantly manic symptoms, only 37 per cent of the women (25/67) exhibited a similar pattern of behavior. The question we shall consider is whether these two sample proportions (59 per cent of men versus 37 per cent of women) are significantly different—i.e., differ more than might be expected if the proportion of manic individuals in the population of male patients is the same as the proportion of such individuals in the population of female patients. The null hypothesis to be tested is that these two population proportions are the same. If the null hypothesis is true, the two variables in question (sex and dominant symptom) are independent; otherwise, they are correlated, or, as is more commonly said in connection with qualitative variables of this kind, the distribution of one is contingent upon the value of the other. For this reason, the procedure with which we are concerned is commonly called a *test of contingency;* it might with equal justification be called a *test of independence* (for contingency is the converse of independence), but the latter designation is less commonly used.

In order to compute χ^2 using Formula (10-2) we must determine the theoretical frequency, according to the null hypothesis, for each of the four cells of Table 10-3. Assuming the null hypothesis to be true, our best estimate of the proportion of manic-depressive patients in whom manic symptoms are dominant is 48/106, the proportion of such individuals in our combined sample of men and women. Multiplying this fraction by the number of men in our sample, we obtain $39(48)/106 \approx 17.7$ as the theoretical frequency for male patients with manic symptoms dominant. More generally, the theoretical frequency for any given cell of the table is obtained by multiplying the total for the row in which that cell appears by the total for the column in which that cell appears and dividing this product by n, the total number of cases. Thus, the theoretical frequency for male patients with depressed symptoms is $58(39)/106 \approx$ 21.3, the theoretical frequency for female patients with manic symptoms is $48(67)/106 \approx 30.3$, and that for female patients with depressed symptoms is $58(67)/106 \approx 36.7$. These theoretical frequencies, together with the observed frequencies, have been summarized in Table 10-4.

TABLE 10-4 *Dominant symptoms: observed and theoretical frequencies*

| DOMINANT SYMPTOMS | SEX | | TOTAL |
	Male	Female	
Manic	23 (17.7)	25 (30.3)	48
Depressed	16 (21.3)	42 (36.7)	58
TOTAL	39	67	106

$$\chi^2 = \frac{(23 - 17.7)^2}{17.7} + \frac{(25 - 30.3)^2}{30.3} + \frac{(16 - 21.3)^2}{21.3} + \frac{(42 - 36.7)^2}{36.7} \approx 4.60$$

Theoretical frequencies are given in parentheses.

Since the sum of the theoretical frequencies for any given row is always equal to the total of observed frequencies for that row, and the sum of theoretical frequencies for any given column is equal to the total of observed frequencies for that column, it is possible in a 2×2 table, once any one of the theoretical frequencies has been computed, to obtain all of the remaining theoretical frequencies by subtraction from appropriate row or column totals.   Thus, for example, the theoretical frequency for female patients with manic symptoms (30.3) may be obtained by subtracting 17.7 (the theoretical frequency for male patients with manic symptoms) from 48 (the total number of patients with manic symptoms), and so on.

In accordance with our earlier observation that the proportion of male patients with predominantly manic symptoms is greater than the proportion of women with similar symptoms, we note that the observed frequency of males with manic symptoms is in excess of the corresponding theoretical frequency, whereas the observed frequency of women having manic symptoms falls short of the theoretical frequency for that cell of the table.   The frequencies for the remaining cells are complementary to those referred to above and, of course, are consistent with the pattern of results just described.

The computation of χ^2 using Formula (10-2) is shown at the bottom of the table.

The number of degrees of freedom associated with χ^2 based on a contingency table depends upon the number of rows and columns in the table. Representing the number of rows by r and the number of columns by c, the general rule giving the number of degrees of freedom in a contingency table may be written as follows: $df = (r - 1)(c - 1)$.   Thus, in a 2×2 contingency table, the number of degrees of freedom is $(2 - 1)(2 - 1) = 1$.   Consulting Table A-8, we find that the critical value of χ^2 for a test at the .05 level of significance is 3.841; accordingly, the computed value of χ^2 ($\chi^2 \approx 4.60$) is significant at the .05 level.   The null hypothesis is therefore rejected, and it is concluded that the relative frequency of the two types of symptoms is different for male and female patients.

As in all chi-square problems involving one degree of freedom, the value of chi square corrected for continuity (i.e., χ_c^2) may be computed for a 2×2 contingency table using Formula (10-4).   For the data presented in Table 10-4, the computation of χ_c^2 is as follows: $\chi_c^2 = (4.8)^2/17.7 + (4.8)^2/30.3 + (4.8)^2/21.3 + (4.8)^2/36.7 \approx 3.77$.   In this instance the corrected value of chi square falls slightly short of the critical value for the .05 level of significance; accordingly, we must revise the conclusion reached above on the basis of the uncorrected value of chi square.   It might be added, however. that these data are sufficiently suggestive to warrant further investigation of the relationship between sex and the symptoms of manic-depressive psychoses.

The rule of thumb described earlier concerning sample size in problems involving one degree of freedom may be used as a guide in connection with 2×2 contingency tables: using χ_c^2, the actual value of α in a 2×2 contingency test will be sufficiently close to the nominal value of α indicated in Table A-8 if all theoretical frequencies involved in the test are equal to or greater than 5.   When theoretical frequencies smaller than 5 are involved, an exact test designed by Fisher (1958) may be used. The latter test is described by Siegel (1956, Chap. 6) and by Walker and Lev (1953, Chap. 4).   (Unless necessitated by the occurrence of small theoretical frequencies, Fisher's exact test is not usually used for testing contingency in a 2×2 table, because the arithmetic labor it entails is often quite formidable.)

A COMPUTATIONAL FORMULA FOR 2×2 TABLES

The observed frequencies of a 2×2 contingency table are shown schematically in Table 10-5.   The frequencies for the four cells of the table are

TABLE 10-5 *Schematic representation of frequencies in a 2×2 table*

a	b	$a + b$
c	d	$c + d$
$a + c$	$b + d$	n

represented by the letters a, b, c, and d; the row totals, by the sums $a + b$ and $c + d$; the column totals, by the sums $a + c$ and $b + d$; the total number of cases, by n. In terms of this notation, the corrected value of chi square for a 2×2 contingency table may be obtained using the following computational formula:

$$\chi_c^2 = \frac{n(|ad - bc| - n/2)^2}{(a + b)(c + d)(a + c)(b + d)} \qquad (10\text{-}6)$$

Using the data of Table 10-4, χ_c^2 is computed as follows:

$$\chi_c^2 = \frac{106[|(23)(42) - (25)(16)| - 53]^2}{(48)(58)(39)(67)} = \frac{106(|966 - 400| - 53)^2}{7{,}274{,}592}$$

$$= \frac{106(513)^2}{7{,}274{,}592} \approx 3.83$$

The reason for the slight discrepancy between the value of χ_c^2 computed using Formula (10-4) and that computed using Formula (10-6) is that the former value of χ_c^2 is somewhat in error as a consequence of rounding errors in the calculation of theoretical frequencies. Were it not for such rounding errors, the values of χ_c^2 computed by the two formulae would be identical.

CONTINGENCY TABLES INVOLVING MORE THAN ONE DEGREE OF FREEDOM

The contingency test described above for 2×2 tables can be extended to problems in which one or both of the variables under investigation involves more than two categories. The computation of χ^2 in problems of this kind may be illustrated with reference to the data presented in Table 10-6. This table gives the frequencies obtained when 100 manic-depressive patients were classified by dominant symptom (two categories) and by religion (three categories). The problem with which this analysis is concerned is whether the relative frequency of the two types of symptoms differs among patients of different religions; the null hypothesis to be tested is that these relative frequencies (the proportion of patients with manic symptoms dominant and the proportion with depressed symptoms dominant) are the same for all three religions.

The rationale and computational procedure for obtaining theoretical frequencies, which are indicated in parentheses in Table 10-6, are essentially the same as described above in connection with 2×2 tables. For example, the theoretical frequency 19.3 appearing in the upper left cell of the table is obtained by multiplying 46 (the total for that row) by 42 (the total for that column) and dividing the result by 100 (the total number of cases).

The computation of χ^2 using Formula (10-2) is shown in the lower part of the table. (Note that because the number of degrees of freedom

TABLE 10-6 *Dominant symptoms in manic-depressive patients of different religions*

| DOMINANT SYMPTOMS | RELIGION | | | TOTAL |
	Protestant	Roman Catholic	Jewish	
Manic	22 (19.3)	19 (23.0)	5 (3.7)	46
Depressed	20 (22.7)	31 (27.0)	3 (4.3)	54
TOTAL	42	50	8	100

$$\chi^2 = \frac{(22 - 19.3)^2}{19.3} + \frac{(19 - 23.0)^2}{23.0} + \cdots + \frac{(3 - 4.3)^2}{4.3} \approx 2.84$$

Based on unpublished data provided by R. G. Hunt.

This table is based upon the same individuals as Table 10-3. Because information concerning the religious affiliation of three individuals was unavailable, those individuals have been omitted in the present analysis. To simplify calculation of theoretical frequencies, three additional cases were discarded, bringing the total number of cases to 100. (The three cases discarded were individuals of the Roman Catholic religion—one manic, two depressed.) Inclusion of the latter individuals does not materially change the value of χ^2.

is greater than one, no correction is made for continuity.) The number of degrees of freedom associated with this value of χ^2 is $(r - 1)(c - 1) = (2 - 1)(3 - 1) = 2$. Consulting Table A-8, we find that with two degrees of freedom the critical value of χ^2 for a test at the .05 level of significance is 5.991. Thus, the obtained value of χ^2 is not significant at the .05 level—these data provide no clear evidence that the dominant symptom of manic-depressive patients is related to religion.

COMPARISON OF PROPORTIONS BASED UPON PAIRED OBSERVATIONS

As in dealing with quantitative variables, it is possible in investigations concerned with qualitative variables to collect observations in such a way that every observation in one group is matched or paired with a corresponding observation in the other group. The methods of matching observations in the case of qualitative data are the same as described in Chapter 8 in connection with quantitative data. For purposes of illustration, we shall consider a hypothetical example in which the change in voters' preferences between a poll in August and one in October is analyzed. We will suppose that a random sample of 20 voters was polled in August concerning which candidate—*A* or *B*—they then favored, and that in October the same group of individuals was questioned as to which candidate they favored at that time. Hypothetical results are presented in Table 10-7.

TABLE 10-7   *Voter preferences in two successive polls* (*hypothetical data*)

VOTER	CANDIDATE PREFERRED		DIRECTION OF CHANGE
	August	October	
1	A	A	0
2	A	A	0
3	A	A	0
4	A	A	0
5	A	B	−
6	A	B	−
7	A	B	−
8	A	B	−
9	A	B	−
10	A	B	−
11	A	B	−
12	A	B	−
13	B	A	+
14	B	A	+
15	B	B	0
16	B	B	0
17	B	B	0
18	B	B	0
19	B	B	0
20	B	B	0

The question we seek to answer is whether there is any difference between the proportion of voters favoring Candidate *A* in August and the proportion favoring him in October; in other words, we wish to determine whether there is a trend over time in favor of either candidate. As in dealing with paired observations involving quantitative variables, we base our analysis upon the differences—in the present example, changes—within pairs. Examining Table 10-7, we note that some voters who preferred Candidate *A* in August still preferred him in October; these voters exhibit no change (indicated by a zero in the last column of the table). Other voters originally preferred Candidate *A*, but switched to Candidate *B* in the second poll; these voters displayed changes away from *A* (indicated by a minus sign in the last column). Still other voters initially preferred *B* but switched to *A* (indicated by a plus sign). Finally, some voters preferred *B* originally and did not change (indicated by a zero). Clearly, if there is any net difference between the proportion of voters preferring *A* in August and the proportion favoring *A* in October, this difference is an outcome of the changes in preference—voters who did not change did not contribute to any difference that may be observed. Accordingly, we may ignore the pairs in which there was no change and base our analysis upon those in which there was a change one way or the other. The basic logic of the test is as follows: If there is any net change in the population in favor of either candidate—i.e., a difference between the August and October proportions—this difference must arise because of a preponderance of changes in one direction over changes in the opposite direction; if the two types of change are equally numerous, then they will cancel one another and there will be no net change over time.   Therefore, the test we wish to make may be construed as a test of whether, in the population, the changes are equally numerous in both directions—that is, whether 50 per cent of the changes are positive in sign and 50 per cent negative.   The test thus reduces to a test of the a priori hypothesis that in the population of differences $p = q = .5$, in which p represents the relative frequency of positive differences and q represents the relative frequency of negative differences.   In our illustrative problem, f_1 and f_2, the observed frequencies of positive and negative differences, are 2 and 8, respectively.   Substituting in Formula (10-5), we compute $\chi_c^2 = (|2 - 8| - 1)^2/(2 + 8) = (5)^2/10 = 2.5$.   This value of chi square falls short of the critical value for a test at the .05 level of significance with one degree of freedom; thus, the data presented in Table 10-7 do not afford statistically significant evidence of a trend over time in favor of either candidate.

Data such as the voter preference data that were presented in Table 10-7 may be conveniently summarized in the manner shown in Table 10-8.

TABLE 10-8 *Summary of preferences in two successive polls*

Candidate Preferred—First Poll	Candidate Preferred—Second Poll		Total
	A	B	
B	B-A Pattern 2	B-B Pattern 6	8
A	A-A Pattern 4	A-B Pattern 8	12
Total	6	14	20

In this table the rows represent a classification of individuals on the basis of their preferences in the first poll; the columns, a classification on the basis of their preferences in the second poll.   The proportion of individuals favoring Candidate A on the first poll, 12/20, is readily computed from the row totals; the proportion favoring Candidate A on the second poll, 6/20, is computed from the column totals.   It will be noted that these two proportions, unlike the proportions compared in a 2×2 contingency test, are both based upon the same 20 individuals, each of whom was questioned twice.[3]   The frequency presented in the upper left cell of the table is a count of the number of individuals who first favored Candidate B and then switched to Candidate A (positive changes).   The frequency in the upper right cell is a count of the individuals who preferred Candidate B in both polls (zero change).   The frequency presented in the lower left cell is a count of individuals who preferred Candidate A both times (also zero change).   And the frequency presented in the lower right cell is a count of individuals who switched from A to B (negative changes).   Thus, the two frequencies on which our test is based are those in the upper left and lower right cells; the other two frequencies are ignored in computing chi square.   Using the notation described in Table 10-5 and substituting in Formula (10-5), the formula for chi square used to test a hypothesis concerning proportions based upon paired observations may be written as follows:

$$\chi_c^2 = \frac{(|a - d| - 1)^2}{a + d} \qquad (10\text{-}7)$$

Substituting the data of Table 10-8, we obtain

$$\chi_c^2 = \frac{(|2 - 8| - 1)^2}{2 + 8} = \frac{(5)^2}{10} = 2.5$$

which is, of course, the same value as computed using Formula (10-5).

EQUIVALENT TESTS BASED UPON THE z STATISTIC
AND THE NORMAL DISTRIBUTION

For each of the chi-square problems described above involving one degree of freedom, an equivalent test based upon the z statistic and the normal distribution is available.   In this section we shall examine the normal-distribution equivalent of the chi-square test of a priori hypotheses (two-category problems) and of the chi-square contingency test for a 2×2 table.   Because the chi-square test comparing proportions based upon paired observations reduces to a test of an a priori hypothesis, this test will not be considered separately in this section.

---

[3] The distinction between a contingency test and a test involving proportions based upon paired observations may be further clarified by expressing the proportions compared in each type of test in terms of the notation of Table 10-5.   In a contingency test based upon a 2×2 table, the proportion $a/(a + c)$ is compared with the proportion $b/(b + d)$; in a test concerning proportions based on paired observations, the two proportions compared are $(a + c)/n$ and $(c + d)/n$.

TESTS OF A PRIORI HYPOTHESES

In problems in which two categories are employed in classifying qualitative data, the concept of sample proportion is equivalent to the concept of sample mean if, for purposes of computing the mean, a score of *zero* is assigned to one category and a score of *one* is assigned to the other. The equivalence of proportion and mean can be illustrated using the data presented in Table 10-1. Of the 3,000 tosses of a coin summarized in this table, the proportion of successful trials is $1,544/3000 \approx .5147$. The computation of $\overline{X}$, the sample mean of these data, is shown in Table

TABLE 10-9 *Computation of sample mean using scores of zero and one*

Outcome	X	f	fX
Success	1	1,544	1,544
Failure	0	1,456	0
			1,544

$$\overline{X} = \frac{\Sigma fX}{n} = \frac{1,544}{3,000} \approx .5147$$

10-9. A score of *one* is arbitrarily assigned to the success category and a score of *zero* to the failure category. The class frequencies are given in the column headed f; the fX products are given in the last column; and the computation of $\overline{X}$ is shown at the bottom of the table. It will be noted that the value of $\overline{X}$ is the same as the proportion of successes. (If scores had been assigned the other way around—i.e., a score of *one* assigned to the failure category and a score of *zero* to the success category—the value of $\overline{X}$ would have been .4853, the proportion of failures in the sample.)

Similarly, by assigning *zero* and *one* scores as described above, the concept of population mean can be related to the a priori probability of success. Recalling that according to the null hypothesis $p = q = .5$, and substituting in Formula (4-6), we obtain $\mu = .5(1) + .5(0) = .5$. More generally, $\mu = p(1) + q(0) = p$.

The value of σ^2, the population variance based upon scores of *zero* and *one,* may also be derived from the values of p and q. Substituting in Formula (4-7), we obtain $\sigma^2 = p(1 - \mu)^2 + q(0 - \mu)^2$. Since $\mu = p$, this result may be written as follows: $\sigma^2 = p(1 - p)^2 + q(0 - p)^2$. Since $p + q = 1$, the quantity $1 - p$ is equal to q, and the first term on the right of the last equation for σ^2 may be written pq^2; since $0 - p$ is simply $-p$, and since $(-p)^2$ is the same as p^2, the second term on the right of the last equation for σ^2 may be written qp^2. Thus, we may write $\sigma^2 = pq^2 + qp^2$. Factoring out pq on the right-hand side of this equation, we obtain $\sigma^2 = pq(q + p)$. Finally, since $q + p = 1$, this last equation simplifies to

$$\sigma^2 = pq \qquad (10\text{-}8)$$

For our illustrative problem in which $p = q = .5$, the value of σ^2 is $.5(.5) = .25$.

Thus, the 3,000 tosses of a coin summarized in Tables 10-1 and 10-9 may be regarded as a sample from a population in which $\mu = p = .5$ and $\sigma^2 = pq = .25$. On the basis of this information, it follows from Formulae (6-1) and (6-2) that, according to the null hypothesis, the sampling distribution of $\overline{X}$ has the following mean and variance:

$$\mu_{\overline{X}} = \mu = p = .5$$

$$\sigma_{\overline{X}}^2 = \frac{\sigma^2}{n} = \frac{pq}{n} = \frac{.25}{3,000} \approx .0000833$$

Taking the square root of $\sigma_{\overline{X}}^2$, we obtain the standard error of the mean, $\sigma_{\overline{X}} \approx .00913$. Because of the large sample size in this study, the sampling distribution of $\overline{X}$ closely approximates a normal distribution.

Following procedures described in Chapter 7, the null hypothesis that $\mu = .5$ may be tested by computing z as follows: $z = (\overline{X} - \mu_0)/\sigma_{\overline{X}} \approx (.5147 - .5000)/.00913 = .0147/.00913 \approx 1.61$. This value of z falls short of the critical value of z for a test at the .05 level of significance; accordingly, the null hypothesis is accepted.

Although different in form, the test performed above is mathematically equivalent to the chi-square test performed previously using the same data. The equivalence of the two tests may be made more apparent by noting that for problems involving one degree of freedom, $\chi^2 = z^2$, and critical values of χ^2 are equal to the squares of critical values of z. Thus, for example, with one degree of freedom, the critical value of χ^2 for a test at the .05 level of significance is 3.841; the critical value of z for the same level of significance is 1.960; and $(1.960)^2 \approx 3.842$—which, within the limits permitted by rounding errors, is the same as the critical value of χ^2. Similarly, the uncorrected value of χ^2 based on the data of Table 10-1 is 2.58, and z^2 is $(1.61)^2 \approx 2.59$—which, within the limits of rounding errors, is the same as the value of χ^2.

COMPARISON OF PROPORTIONS BASED UPON INDEPENDENT SAMPLES

As already noted previously, the chi-square contingency test based on a 2×2 table amounts to a comparison of proportions based upon two independent samples. For example, the contingency test based upon the data of Table 10-3 compares the proportion of manic individuals in a sample of 39 men with the corresponding proportion in a sample of 67 women. Interpreted as sample means, the two proportions in question may be designated $\overline{X}_1$ (the mean for the sample of men) and $\overline{X}_2$ (the mean for the sample of women). The values of these two means, to three decimal places, are as follows: $\overline{X}_1 = 23/39 \approx .590$; $\overline{X}_2 = 25/67 \approx .373$. Using the notation introduced in Chapter 8, the mean of the sampling distribution of the difference $\overline{X}_1 - \overline{X}_2$ will be designated $\mu_{\overline{X}_1 - \overline{X}_2}$ and the standard error of this distribution will be designated $\sigma_{\overline{X}_1 - \overline{X}_2}$. The sampling distribution of $\overline{X}_1 - \overline{X}_2$ is approximately normal in shape; accordingly, the hypothesis that $\mu_1 = \mu_2$ may be tested by computing

$$z = \frac{(\overline{X}_1 - \overline{X}_2) - \mu_{\overline{X}_1 - \overline{X}_2}}{\sigma_{\overline{X}_1 - \overline{X}_2}} \qquad (10\text{-}9)$$

in which the value of $\mu_{\overline{X}_1 - \overline{X}_2}$ implied by the null hypothesis is $\mu_1 - \mu_2 = 0$.

In order to determine the value of $\sigma_{\overline{X}_1 - \overline{X}_2}$ we need to know the values of σ_1^2 and σ_2^2, the variances of Populations 1 and 2 (male and female patients), respectively. Letting p represent the proportion of male patients with manic symptoms predominating and q the proportion of male patients with depressed symptoms predominating, σ_1^2 is given by Formula (10-8), i.e., $\sigma_1^2 = pq$. Since, according to the null hypothesis, the values of p and q are the same for both populations, σ_1^2 and σ_2^2 are equal; accordingly, we may omit the distinguishing subscripts and simply write $\sigma^2 = pq$ for both populations. Substituting pq for σ^2 (the common variance of Populations 1 and 2) in Formula (8-6), we obtain the following formula for the standard error of the difference $\overline{X}_1 - \overline{X}_2$:

$$\sigma_{\overline{X}_1 - \overline{X}_2} = \sqrt{pq\left(\frac{1}{n_1} + \frac{1}{n_2}\right)} \qquad (10\text{-}10)$$

As we noted previously in connection with the chi-square analysis of these data, the values of p and q are unknown and must be estimated from the data provided by the sample. Here, as in the previous analysis, we base our estimate on the combined data of the two groups: our estimate of p is 48/106 (the appropriate row total divided by the total number of cases), and our estimate of q is 58/106. These two estimates will be designated $p_{(est.)}$ and $q_{(est.)}$, respectively.

At this point in our discussion it will be useful to rewrite Formula (10-9), making the following changes: (a) omitting $\mu_{\overline{X}_1 - \overline{X}_2}$—which, as we have previously noted, has a value of zero according to the null hypothesis—and (b) entering in the denominator the value of $\sigma_{\overline{X}_1 - \overline{X}_2}$ given by Formula (10-10), substituting $p_{(est.)}$ for p and $q_{(est.)}$ for q. Thus modified, Formula (10-9) becomes

$$z = \frac{\overline{X}_1 - \overline{X}_2}{\sqrt{p_{(\text{est.})} q_{(\text{est.})} \left(\dfrac{1}{n_1} + \dfrac{1}{n_2}\right)}} \qquad (10\text{-}11)$$

(Formula (10-11) for z is seen to be similar in form to Formula (8-10) for t; the difference resides in the nature of the estimate of σ^2, the common variance of Populations *1* and *2*.) Substituting the data of Table 10-3 in Formula (10-11), we obtain

$$z = \frac{\dfrac{23}{39} - \dfrac{25}{67}}{\sqrt{\left(\dfrac{48}{106}\right)\left(\dfrac{58}{106}\right)\left(\dfrac{1}{39} + \dfrac{1}{67}\right)}} \approx \frac{.590 - .373}{\sqrt{.453(.547)(.0256 + .0149)}}$$

$$\approx \frac{.217}{\sqrt{.01}} = 2.17$$

This value of z, like the uncorrected value of χ^2 based on Table 10-3, is significant at the .05 level. The value of z^2, to two decimal places, is 4.71. The slight discrepancy between the value of z^2 and the value of χ^2 in Table 10-4 is due to rounding errors; using a sufficient number of decimal places to eliminate rounding errors in the first two decimal places, both χ^2 and z^2 are found to have a value of 4.67.

PROBLEMS

1. An individual claims he can distinguish two brands of margarine by taste. To test his claim he is given a series of 20 pieces of bread, some spread with Brand *A* and some with Brand *B*. (Whether *A* or *B* is used on a given piece of bread is determined randomly.) He identifies the margarine on 14 pieces of bread correctly; that on six, incorrectly. Using a one-sided test, would you reject at the .05 level of significance the hypothesis that he cannot distinguish between Brands *A* and *B*?

2. There are 80 questions on a multiple-choice examination. On each question there are four choices, one of which is correct. Thus, the probability that an individual would answer any given question correctly if he guessed on that question is .25. Tom answered 30 items correctly. Would you reject at the .05 level of significance the hypothesis that Tom was guessing on all the items?

3. To promote sales of a children's cereal the manufacturer plans to include in the package an inexpensive toy. Four toys are under consideration for this purpose. In order to determine which of the four toys has the most appeal for children, 200 children are each given a choice among the four toys, with the following results: 40 selected Toy *A*; 70, Toy *B*; 55, Toy *C*; 35, Toy *D*. Test the hypothesis that in the population, preferences are evenly divided among the four choices.

4. The frequency distribution of 600 rolls of a die was as follows:

Value Obtained	1	2	3	4	5	6
Frequency	98	97	92	130	96	87

Test the hypothesis that this was a fair die, fairly rolled.

5. One thousand volunteers were randomly divided into two groups of 500 subjects each. The subjects in one group were innoculated with a vaccine designed to give immunity against influenza; those in the other group were given an injection of saline solution. During the year following the injection, 60 subjects receiving the vaccine and 140 subjects receiving the saline solution contracted influenza. Test at the .01 level the hypothesis that the vaccine afforded no protection against influenza.

6. Eight hundred individuals were asked in a poll whether they regularly watched a certain television program and whether they had ever used the product advertised on that program. One hundred respondents indicated that they regularly watched the program in question. Of these, 27 said they had tried the sponsor's product. Of the 700 individuals who did not regularly watch the show, 133 said they had tried the product. Determine at the .05 level whether use of the sponsor's product is contingent upon viewing habits.

7. The *median test,* a nonparametric test of the hypothesis that two populations are identically distributed, is a special case of the chi-square test of contingency in a 2×2 table. This test may be illustrated using the data presented in Table 8-7. (For purposes of the present illustration, the value 48 in the control group, modified in Table 8-7 to demonstrate the handling of tied observations, will be restored to 47, the actual value.) Making the above change in Table 8-7, the overall median of the two groups combined is 47.5 jumps. If the two sets of observations (experimental and control) are classified according to location above or below the overall median, the results are as follows:

| | GROUP | | TOTAL |
	Control	Experimental	
Number of Observations Above Overall Median	1	9	10
Number of Observations Below Overall Median	9	1	10
TOTAL	10	10	20

A test of the hypothesis that the two treatment populations have identical distributions is equivalent to a test of whether the proportion of cases above the combined median is contingent upon experimental treatment. Compute the corrected value of chi square for this test.

8. The following are the distributions of grades given by three instructors teaching three sections of the same course.

	A	B	C	D	F	TOTAL
Instructor X	15	27	36	15	7	100
Instructor Y	4	8	20	11	7	50
Instructor Z	6	15	44	24	11	100
TOTAL	25	50	100	50	25	250

Are the grade distributions of the three instructors significantly different at the .05 level?

9. Fifty students took a multiple-choice test at the beginning of a course and the same test again at the end of the semester. For one of the test items, a classification of the 50 students according to their performance on the two testings yielded the following results:

		SECOND TESTING		TOTAL
		Fail	Pass	
FIRST TESTING	Pass	5	19	24
	Fail	11	15	26
	TOTAL	16	34	50

Using chi square corrected for continuity, determine whether there was a statistically significant change from the first testing to the second in the proportion of students passing this item.

10. In order to determine whether two multiple-choice test items differ in difficulty the performance of 100 students on both items was analyzed. A classification of the 100 students according to their performance on the two items yielded the following results:

		ITEM B		TOTAL
		Fail	Pass	
ITEM A	Pass	10	45	55
	Fail	15	30	45
	TOTAL	25	75	100

Compute χ_c^2 to determine whether the proportion passing Item A (55/100) is significantly different from the proportion passing Item B (75/100).

11. A population consists of 200,000 individuals—160,000 in favor of Candidate A and 40,000 in favor of Candidate B. If we assign a score of *one* to those in favor of A and a score of *zero* to those in favor of B, what are μ and σ^2 of the distribution?

12. What are the mean and variance of the theoretical sampling distribution of $\bar{X}$ for samples of 40 cases from the population described in the preceding question?

13. Compute the value of z for testing the hypotheses indicated in Problems 1, 2, 5, and 6.

REFERENCES

COCHRAN, W. G.   Some methods for strengthening the common χ^2 tests. *Biometrics,* 1954, **10,** 417–451.

DIXON, W. J. and F. J. MASSEY, JR.   *Introduction to statistical analysis* (2d ed.). New York: McGraw-Hill, 1957.

FISHER, R. A.   *Statistical methods for research workers* (13th ed.).   New York: Hafner, 1958.

SIEGEL, S. *Nonparametric statistics for the behavioral sciences.* New York: McGraw-Hill, 1956.

WALKER, HELEN M. and J. LEV. *Statistical inference.* New York: Holt, 1953.

ADDITIONAL READINGS

EDWARDS, A. L. *Statistical methods for the behavioral sciences.* New York: Rinehart, 1954. Chap. 18.

LEWIS, D. and C. J. BURKE. The use and misuse of the chi-square test. *Psychol. Bull,* 1949, **46,** 433–489. This article calls attention to a number of errors to be avoided in the use of chi square.

UNDERWOOD, B. J., C. P. DUNCAN, JANET A. TAYLOR, and J. W. COTTON. *Elementary statistics.* New York: Appleton-Century-Crofts, 1954. Chap. 13.

scientific method

applied to the study of behavior

The techniques of statistical inference considered in Part II play an important role in establishing facts (empirical generalizations) based upon experimental observations. However, there is more to the scientific understanding of any set of phenomena than the simple amassing of experimental facts: just as a building is more than a pile of bricks, scientific knowledge ideally is more than a hodgepodge of disconnected facts. Within any field, the aim of science is to establish relationships among facts, to develop an organized scheme in which the interrelationships among otherwise disparate facts become evident. It is with these broad aspects of scientific knowledge—its structure and organization—that Part III is concerned.

Essentially, scientific knowledge evolves through an interplay between observation and the formulation of general explanatory principles that unify the facts of observation. Experimental (or other) observations lead to the development of hypotheses concerning the general principles underlying observed phenomena. In turn, these hypotheses suggest further observations by which they can be tested, and confirmed or disconfirmed. New observations frequently result *in modification of the original hypotheses, which then suggests further observations—and so on.*

The two chapters that follow deal with these two broad phases of the scientific enterprise.   Chapter 11 examines certain general characteristics of observation in science and considers in some detail a related issue of special concern to the field of psychology—namely, whether conscious experience should be construed as an observable phenomenon.   Chapter 12 is concerned with the nature of explanation in science, i.e., with the formulation of general principles that explain and unify the facts of observation.

CHAPTER 11

observation and verbal report

ALTHOUGH PSYCHOLOGISTS DIFFER AMONG THEMSELVES WITH RESPECT TO many methodological issues, most contemporary psychologists subscribe to the general point of view that the methods that have proved fruitful in other scientific areas, such as physics, chemistry, and physiology, may be applied successfully to the study of behavior.   According to this view, psychology is distinguished from other natural sciences only by the kinds of phenomena in which it is interested.   Whereas physics, for example, studies such questions as how the motions of objects are related to their masses and the forces acting upon them, psychology seeks to determine the variables that affect the behavior of living organisms.   Although the questions are different, the general manner in which problems are investigated and answers formulated is held to be similar in all branches of science.   In this chapter and the next we shall examine certain general principles of scientific method with special attention to the application of these principles to the study of behavior.

A common misconception concerning the purpose of studying scientific method should be dispelled at the outset.   Such analysis does not, as has sometimes been assumed, provide a set of how-to-do-it rules automatically leading to the development of scientific knowledge.   Indeed, no such rules exist: designing fruitful experiments and formulating useful scientific laws and theories are creative processes that defy reduction to any simple set of rules.   It is more accurate to view the analysis of scientific method as an explication of the objectives of science and the manner in which they are achieved, and as a guide to what we may, and what we should not, expect of the scientific investigation of any phenomenon.   Such an analysis provides a frame of reference that orients the scientist toward his task and lays down broad guidelines for assessing specific procedures and proposed explanations within science.   History indicates that misconceptions concerning scientific method may cause confusion and the wasting of energy on fruitless issues, and that the elimination of such misconceptions often enables scientists to turn misdirected efforts toward more profitable channels.

THE OBJECTIVES OF SCIENCE—
EXPLANATION, PREDICTION, AND CONTROL

In undertaking an analysis of scientific method, it will be well to have at the outset a clear understanding of the objectives of science.   In brief, science seeks to develop general principles (theories and laws) that enable us to explain, predict, and control observable phenomena.   Explanation, prediction, and control are similar in that each is based upon our understanding of the relationship of the event in question to other observable events or conditions.   Thus, a given event is explained by showing that, in accordance with established principles, it is a consequence of concomitant or prior events.   For example, the occurrence of a given personality trait (e.g., compulsiveness) in an individual might be explained by showing that it is a consequence of certain experiences in his past history. Prediction is similar to explanation, except that the outcome of a given set of circumstances is anticipated, i.e., specified before it actually occurs. For example, knowing the positions and relative motions of the sun, earth, and moon, it is possible for astronomers to predict eclipses of the sun with great accuracy.   (Although equally spectacular examples of the prediction of behavior are rare, there are some areas in which our ability to predict behavior has developed to a degree that is of practical value.   For example, an individual's performance on an intelligence test enables us to make rough predictions concerning his progress in school.)   In controlling an event, we not only anticipate that a given set of circumstances will have a specified outcome, but also manipulate the relevant conditions so as to bring about the outcome in question.   For example, all training—of animals, children, or adults—has as its aim the modification (and, hence, the control) of behavior.

OBSERVATION AND DESCRIPTION IN SCIENCE

Many characteristics of scientific method derive from the fact that science is a social enterprise involving the combined efforts of a community of individuals and thus an undertaking in which effective communication is essential. It is inconceivable that science as we know it today could have developed were it not for the fact that scientific knowledge can be communicated from one individual to another and from one generation to the next. Largely because of the central importance of communication in science, scientific knowledge is formulated as a set of verbal statements. Indeed, the analysis of scientific method may be construed as an analysis of the way scientists use language.

The verbal statements that constitute scientific knowledge refer, of course, to events in the real world. The point at which correspondence is established between these verbal statements and the phenomena to which they refer is the observation process. In performing observations, the task of the scientist is to produce verbal statements (or other symbolic records) that correspond to observable events in a manner established by the conventions of the language being used. Thus, the observation process consists of more than just observing; it consists of observing and recording. We shall refer to the recorded results of observation as *observation statements,* or, as Bergmann (1957) calls them, *descriptions of individual facts.* Examples of observation statements are such statements as "The rat turned right at the choice point of the maze," "The subject completed the puzzle in two minutes," and "The dog secreted ten drops of saliva when the buzzer sounded." In the three subsections that follow we shall examine a number of considerations pertaining to statements of this kind.

THE REQUIREMENTS OF CONSISTENCY AND UNIFORMITY OF USAGE

It is obvious that there can be no effective communication among observers unless there is agreement among them concerning the way in which descriptive terms are to be used. A necessary condition for attaining uniformity of usage among individuals is, of course, that an individual be consistent in the way he uses a given term: if he does not agree with himself on different occasions, he cannot be expected to agree with others.

A lack of uniformity among observers in the usage of terms employed in the description of behavior frequently constitutes a major problem in psychological research. The difficulties involved are illustrated by some findings reported by Azrin, Holz, Ulrich, and Goldiamond (1961). These investigators employed a procedure in which the task of the observer was to listen to a conversation and count the number of opinions expressed by one of the speakers. To determine the uniformity with which different observers identified statements of opinion, a tape recording of one conversation was scored independently by four observers. After hearing the same five-minute segment of the tape, the four observers reported the following counts: 9, 15, 16, and 18 opinions. A fifth observer, who scored the same conversation twice (once during the original taping and once during playback), reported 8 and 11 opinions on two scorings of the same five-minute segment. It is apparent from these data that the seemingly simple task of identifying statements of opinion is one that was not performed consistently by a given observer or uniformly by different observers.

To the extent that a given descriptive category or term is used differently by different observers, the meaning of that term is ambiguous, and its usefulness for purposes of communicating observations is correspondingly limited. An important function of many of the procedures and much of the apparatus used in the laboratory study of behavior is to restrict the ways in which the behavior under study can vary, thus simplifying the problem of describing that behavior and maximizing the uniformity with which the behavior is described by different observers.

THE DESCRIPTIVE VOCABULARY OF SCIENCE: PRIMITIVE AND DEFINED TERMS

To a large extent the development of a scientific discipline consists in the development of a specialized language for describing and summarizing the observations of that field. Of course, the language used in science has its origins in a natural language, i.e., the language used by a community of individuals in their everyday affairs. Frequently, however, the scientist finds it useful to make certain distinctions not made in everyday speech and to ignore others that are; it then becomes useful to introduce technical terms that are not a part of the everyday language. Often the words that the scientist uses are taken from everyday speech, but these words are assigned new and specialized meanings corresponding only roughly to their meaning in the vernacular. (Here we shall ignore the complication arising from the fact that scientists of different nationalities use different languages; whatever the language in question, the principles involved are the same.)

In discussing technical terms used in science, it will be useful to distinguish two major classes of terms: descriptive and theoretical. Descriptive terms, also referred to as *empirical concepts,* are words used in describing particular observations (e.g., "This *liquid* is *sour-tasting*") or in formulating general statements based upon observation (e.g., "All *acids* are *sour-tasting*"). Theoretical terms, on the other hand, may be roughly characterized as referring to hypothetical entities or processes that are not subject to direct observation; more precisely, a term is classified as theoretical if it is introduced as part of a theory and its meaning is established by the theory in which it occurs. Familiar examples are the terms "proton" and "electron," two of the many terms used to refer to hypothetical particles at a subatomic level. (In some instances there may be difficulty in classifying a given term as descriptive or theoretical because the meaning of that term is not firmly established, i.e., it is used in different senses by different writers. The term "response tendency" is a case in point—certain uses of this term appear to be descriptive, others theoretical.)   In this subsection we shall examine the manner in which the meaning of descriptive terms is established; a corresponding analysis of theoretical terms will be undertaken in the following chapter.

It was noted above that the scientist frequently introduces new terms or assigns new and specialized meanings to words taken from everyday speech.   In effect, this amounts to the reconstruction of a natural language along lines better suited to scientific purposes.   In actual practice the reconstruction of a natural language proceeds in a piecemeal, informal fashion: typically, the process is carried only far enough to serve the practical needs of the scientist, and a detailed analysis of the entire language structure is rarely, if ever, undertaken.   However, it is useful to consider the structure that such a language would have if a thoroughgoing reconstruction were actually performed.   Such an analysis provides a model exemplifying certain general features of the (partially) reconstructed language of science and serving as an ideal approximated by that language.

The meaning of many words in the scientist's descriptive vocabulary is established by definition.   For example, "intelligence quotient" may be defined as "the ratio of an individual's mental age to his chronological age."   The words used in defining a given term may in turn be defined themselves—for example, definitions could be provided of the terms "mental age" and "chronological age" used in the above definition.   However, this procedure cannot be continued indefinitely; if the process of definition is to serve any useful function, it must eventually lead to a point at which all the words used in a definition are understood and there is no need for further definition.   Thus, any language must contain certain words that are understood without being defined and that serve as a basis for defining other words.   Such undefined words are called the *primitive terms* of a language.

The primitive and defined terms of a language constitute a hierarchy with the primitive terms at the base; words defined by means of the primitive terms may in turn be used in the definition of further words, and so on.   This hierarchical arrangement of words may be illustrated by the definition of terms used for describing family relationships.[1]   Taking as our primitive terms the words "male," "female," and "child of" (which designates a relationship between two individuals, as in "*x* is the child of *y*"), we may define the concepts "father," "mother," "siblings," and "first cousins" as follows:

[1] The example is adapted from Hempel (1952).   In order to simplify the present discussion some of the logical rigor of Hempel's presentation is sacrificed here.

x is the father of y = x is male; y is the child of x

x is the mother of y = x is female; y is the child of x

x and y are siblings = u is the father of x and of y; v is the mother of x and of y

x and y are first cousins = x is the child of u; y is the child of v; u and v are siblings

In each of the above definitions the equal sign is used to indicate that the statement on the left is synonymous with the (compound) statement on the right, so that one may be substituted for the other in any context with no change of meaning.   It is apparent that further relationship terms (e.g., "grandfather," "brother," "half-brother," "second cousin") can be introduced by an extension of the above procedure.   The hierarchical arrangement of the terms presented in the above series of definitions is clearly evident.   The terms "father" and "mother," which are defined using primitive terms only, are used in the definition of "sibling," which in turn is used in the definition of "first cousins."   By an appropriate series of substitutions the defined terms in any definition (or in any other statement) can be eliminated and replaced entirely by primitive terms. However, the resulting statements would be prohibitively complex and virtually unintelligible.   For example, although it would be possible to describe all family relationships using statements containing only the primitive terms "male," "female," and "child of," to do so would be impracticably cumbersome.   Thus, while defined terms are expendable from a purely logical point of view, they are indispensable for purposes of practical communication.

The terms of a natural language cannot be readily classified as primitive or defined—natural languages simply are not constructed in such a systematic fashion.   However, it is of interest to consider the question of what words would function as primitive terms in the reconstruction of a natural language for use in science.   To state the matter somewhat differently, we may seek to determine the types of words that scientists regard—implicitly, if not explicitly—as primitive terms for purposes of defining other descriptive terms.   Analysis of the descriptive vocabulary used in science suggests that the primitive terms of this vocabulary consist of words used to record the results of simple observation, terms such as "blue," "sour-tasting," "solid," "hard," "coincident with," and so on. We shall call such words *primitive observation terms* and shall refer to them collectively as the *basic observation vocabulary*.   It will be noted that observation terms of the sort described above are especially suited for use as primitive terms because their meaning can be established by direct experience or, as is sometimes said, by "pointing definitions."   For example, to teach an individual to use the term "sour-tasting"—in other words, to establish the meaning of this term—we could assemble a group of sour substances, have him taste each, and remark, "This, this, and this are sour-tasting." Indeed, it is hard to imagine any other way in which we could teach an individual to use the term "sour-tasting" in agreement with other users of the language; in particular, it does not seem possible to formulate a verbal definition of this term that would clearly establish its meaning. It therefore appears that the only way of introducing many observation terms into a language is to include them as primitive terms.

Most of the descriptive terms used in science are not primitive observation terms but can be defined by means of the latter. The terms used in defining a given descriptive term may be either primitive observation terms or defined terms. However, as we have already noted above, by a series of suitable substitutions defined terms can be eliminated and replaced by primitive terms. Thus, in an ideally reconstructed language it would be possible (though unnecessary for many purposes) to state the meaning of any descriptive term using only primitive observation terms. In such a language it is assured, provided the primitive terms are used uniformly by all speakers, that there is no ambiguity concerning the meanings of defined terms.

A form of definition used to establish the meaning of many of the descriptive terms employed in science is illustrated in the following definition of the term "soluble."

$$x \text{ is soluble} = \textbf{if } x \text{ is placed in water, } \textbf{then } x \text{ dissolves}$$

This type of definition is called an *operational definition* because it specifies the operations that must be performed in order to determine whether the term being defined is applicable in a given case.[2,3] In order to determine whether a given substance is soluble we must first do something—we must place it in water—and then, depending upon what we observe to occur (whether or not it dissolves), we say that it is or is not soluble. Many terms defined in this manner are referred to as *disposition terms* because they refer to the disposition of something to react in a certain way (or produce a certain effect) under specified test conditions. Examples from the physical sciences are the terms "explosive," "volatile," "combustible," and "rigid," to name a few; examples from the field of psychology include such terms as "aggressive," "authoritarian," "passive," and "neurotic," each of which refers to a disposition to react in a certain way—or in one

---

[2] The designation "operational definition" has sometimes been used in a broader sense to refer to any definition of an empirical concept in terms of observable variables. However, the explication given here, proposed by Bergmann (1957), corresponds more closely to the meaning originally proposed by Bridgman (1928).

[3] Certain technical issues may be raised concerning the most appropriate logical schema for formulating operational definitions, and certain alternatives to the schema presented here have been proposed. These issues are discussed by Bergmann (1957) and by Hempel (1952). Because the issues involved concern matters of logical detail rather than general principle, they are not presented here.

of several alternative ways—under specified conditions. Many terms that we do not ordinarily think of as dispositional may also be defined operationally, as "soluble" was. Consider, for example, the term "aversive," a descriptive term applied to a certain class of stimuli. Roughly speaking, aversive stimuli are those that would be characterized as unpleasant, i.e., stimuli such as electric shock, unpleasant odors, disturbing noises, and so on, that we normally try to escape from or rid ourselves of. Whether or not a given stimulus is aversive may be ascertained by determining the effects upon behavior of terminating that stimulus: if the termination of a stimulus immediately following some response results in learning (e.g., as indicated by a decrease in the latency of that response on subsequent presentations of the stimulus in question), then that stimulus is said to be aversive. Thus, the term "aversive" may be defined operationally as follows:

x (a stimulus) is aversive $=$ **if** x (1) is terminated immediately following the occurrence of some response and (2) is presented again on another occasion, **then** the response in question occurs with decreased latency relative to its latency on previous occurrences of x.

The value of operational definitions, as of any definition, is that they remove ambiguities concerning the meanings of terms and, hence, make possible more effective communication. Moreover, since operational definitions make explicit reference to certain types of observations—i.e., they specify the types of observations upon which the use of a particular term is contingent—they insure that the concepts so defined have direct and explicit reference to observation. However, the limits within which operational definitions are useful have not always been fully appreciated, and some writers have mistakenly contended that with the exception of primitive terms, every term used in science must be operationally defined. This point of view fails to distinguish between the manner in which terms of the descriptive vocabulary of science are introduced and the manner in which theoretical terms are introduced. The meaning of terms belonging to the descriptive vocabulary is established by definition, often of the operational variety; theoretical terms, as we shall see in the following chapter, are introduced in a different manner.

While the definition of a concept fixes its meaning, it does not necessarily confer upon that concept what Bergmann (1957) has called *significance*. By the significance of a concept is meant its usefulness, i.e., the extent to which it is lawfully related to other concepts and therefore useful in the formulation of empirical laws. (For a detailed discussion of empirical laws, see the following chapter.) For example, we have already noted that the concept of intelligence quotient is useful because, among other things, it is one of the factors related to success in school and can therefore be used in the prediction of school success.   On the other hand, consider the concept *brow/nose quotient,* defined as the ratio of the height of one's brow to the length of one's nose.   Although the meaning of this concept is as clear and unambiguous as the meaning of intelligence quotient, on the basis of existing knowledge it seems doubtful that this concept will be found to enter into any important biological or psychological laws.   The reason for introducing (defining) a new concept is that we have reason to believe the concept will possess significance in the sense defined above; however, the mere fact that a concept is carefully defined is no guarantee that this aim will be realized.

In concluding this discussion of definition, the reader is reminded that the notion of a hierarchy of interlocking, rigorously defined concepts built upon a base of primitive observation terms is an ideal rather than a fully accomplished fact.   As a scientific discipline matures, this ideal may be fairly closely approximated.   But in the early stages of the development of a discipline the definition of many concepts tends to be sketchy, and the terms used in defining a given concept are themselves often poorly defined.   Needless to say, at such a stage of development the meaning of many concepts is hazy at best.   Although many of the concepts pertaining to behavior have been considerably refined in meaning since the inception of psychology as an experimental discipline, it is probably fair to say that as yet relatively few concepts possessing a high degree of significance have emerged in this field.   Judged in relation to the more mature physical sciences, psychology, though surely past its infancy, seems still a fledgling discipline.

THE SELECTIVE NATURE OF DESCRIPTION

If any event is considered in sufficient detail, it is unique, i.e., different in some way from all other similar events.   To take a commonplace example, the way an individual ties his shoes on two occasions, although similar, is never exactly the same.   But in order to achieve prediction it is necessary to deal with events that are recurrent rather than one-of-a-kind.   Consequently, no attempt is made in scientific description to describe any event in all its detail; rather, events are described with respect to certain general properties of special interest.

The selective nature of scientific description may be illustrated by considering a type of behavior widely used in psychological research—the bar-pressing behavior of a rat in a Skinner box.   The essential features of the apparatus employed in studying this behavior are shown in Figure 11-1. This apparatus consists of a box through one wall of which projects a lever that can be depressed by a light pressure.   Mounted on the wall, usually in the vicinity of the lever, is a food receptacle.   A vending device located outside the box drops a small pellet of food into the receptacle each time the lever is depressed.   Given suitable training under these conditions, a hungry rat will press the bar at a fairly steady rate, pausing to eat each pellet of food as it is delivered.

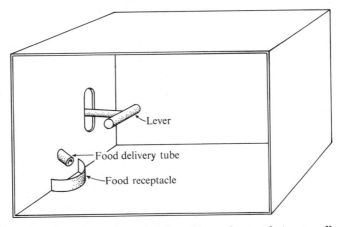

FIGURE 11-1   *Schematic diagram of a Skinner box with front wall removed to show interior.*

If we watch the behavior of a rat in this situation, we observe a continuous process in which a complex series of coordinated movements blend into a smoothly flowing sequence.   How is this fluid process to be broken down into parts, i.e., analyzed?   Of the infinitely complex pattern of movements we observe, what are we to record?   Our basic problem is to identify some recurrent part of the behavior in question.   If the unit chosen is to be recurrent, our definition of this unit must permit some variation of detail, for, as noted above, no behavioral sequence is ever repeated exactly in all its details.

As a first approximation, let us adopt depression of the lever as the unit to be studied.   Even this specification allows considerable latitude: shall we count a response if the lever barely moves, or shall we require that it be depressed all the way?   Shall we count it only if the rat uses both paws, or will one paw do?   Skinner (1938) suggests our records will show the greatest regularity if we count those lever presses that are adequate to operate the feeding device and result in the delivery of a food pellet.   He points out that in defining a response in this way we are dealing with an abstraction.   The class of events that we count as responses are alike in one respect—that they all result in operation of the feeder—but otherwise differ in detail: the bar may be pressed vigorously or gently, with the right paw or the left one, and so on.   Of course, for certain purposes our interest may go beyond simply recording whether or not a response occurs.   We may wish to record the force of a response, its latency, or other characteristics.   Nonetheless, our description is never complete; it always deals with selected properties.

CONSCIOUS EXPERIENCE AND VERBAL REPORT

A longstanding methodological issue within the field of psychology concerns the status of conscious experience.   One point of view—that which perhaps most nearly corresponds to common sense—may be formulated as follows: Just as we observe and describe events occurring in the external development, we can observe and describe our own conscious experience.   (The process of "observing" and "describing" conscious experience is called *introspection* or *phenomenal description* and is sometimes regarded as a special form of observation peculiar to the field of psychology.)   An alternative point of view—one associated with the behavioristic tradition in psychology—holds that the events of conscious experience are not observable in the same sense as events occurring in the external environment.   This position regards conscious experience as a theoretical construct that is inferred from observable behavior.   The construct "conscious experience"—or some construct like it—seems to be necessary to account for certain facts of behavior, but is held, like the theoretical construct "atom" in physics, to be inaccessible to direct observation.   Proponents of the behavioristic view refer to verbal statements purporting to be descriptions of conscious experience (e.g., "I am having a blue sensation") as *verbal reports*.   According to this view, a verbal report is not to be construed as description in the usual sense, but as an observable bit of behavior having the same status as any other overt behavior.[4]

In examining this view further, it will be useful to make a distinction between two classes of receptors—(1) those that are sensitive to stimulus conditions in the external environment (e.g., light, sound, temperature) and (2) those that are sensitive to conditions inside the organism, i.e., receptors located in the internal organs and in the muscles, tendons, and joints.   Corresponding to the distinction between these two major classes of receptors, we may distinguish two classes of stimuli—public and private. Public stimuli are events in the external environment that are capable of affecting the receptors of any normal individual; private stimuli, on the other hand, are conditions within the body of a given individual and

---

[4] It is, of course, unusual for a statement such as "I am having a blue sensation" to occur in the course of everyday affairs.   Such a statement, or some variant of it, would be made only when one intends to refer to processes occurring within oneself, as opposed to describing things or events external to oneself.   This statement might be made by an individual participating in a psychological experiment—e.g., one involving electrical stimulation of the brain—when he knows (or believes) that his experience is illusory and that no blue object is present.

accessible only to the internal receptors of that individual.   In the discussion that follows we shall consider separately verbal reports occasioned by public stimuli and those occasioned by private stimuli.

VERBAL REPORTS OCCASIONED BY PUBLIC STIMULI

As a basis for further discussion we shall begin by examining two representative phenomena suggesting the need for a theoretical construct such as conscious experience.

We consider first the phenomenon known as *color contrast,* in which the apparent color of a surface is affected by the color of adjacent areas. This phenomenon may be demonstrated using disks of colored paper arranged in the manner schematically represented in Figure 11-2.   In Ar-

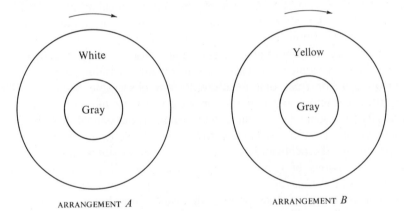

ARRANGEMENT *A*   ARRANGEMENT *B*

FIGURE 11-2 *Schematic representation of materials for demonstrating color contrast. In Arrangement A a small gray circle is mounted in front of a large white circle; Arrangement B is similar except that the large circle is yellow. In both arrangements the circles can be rapidly rotated in the direction indicated by the arrows so as to blur the boundary between the small circle and its background.*

rangement *A* a large white disk and a smaller gray disk are mounted on a motor shaft (not shown) so that they can be rotated rapidly in the direction shown by the arrow.   The gray disk is mounted slightly off-center so that when the circles are rotated the boundary separating the gray and the white areas is blurred.   Arrangement *B* is similar except that the larger circle is yellow rather than white.   If both sets of disks are illuminated with white light and an observer is asked to describe the color of each of the smaller circles, he will report that in Arrangement *A* the smaller disk is gray and that in Arrangement *B* it is blue.   (More generally, if the color of the larger disk in Arrangement *B* is varied, the subject will describe the smaller disk as having the color complementary to the larger disk: if the larger disk is red, the smaller disk will be described as blue-green; if the larger disk is violet, the smaller disk will be described as yellow-green; and so on.)   Here we have a case in which two identical objects, gray disks, are described differently depending upon the background against which they are viewed.   It is natural to assume that the processes occurring within the organism (i.e., conscious experiences) are different in the two cases.

In the example considered above, the observer's description of a physical stimulus varies depending upon the context in which that stimulus is presented.   In another type of situation the observer's description of a stimulus object may vary spontaneously even though the stimulus and its context remain unchanged.   The latter type of phenomenon is illustrated by the drawing in Figure 11-3, an example of reversible perspective.

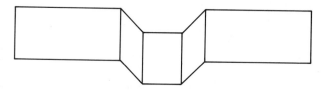

FIGURE 11-3   *An example of reversible perspective. The middle section of the figure may be seen either as protruding toward the observer or as receding from him.*

A subject viewing this drawing may at first report that he perceives the middle section of the figure as protruding toward him; later, as receding from him.   With continued viewing, the subject may alternate between these two descriptions several times.   Again, since the stimulus remains unchanged, it is natural to assume that the changes in the verbal report reflect changes occurring within the observer.

Findings such as those summarized above suggest that certain processes occurring within the observer intervene between the objective stimulus and the ultimate verbal report of the observer and that, although these intervening processes are largely determined by the objective stimulus situation, they do not always bear a one-to-one correspondence to the physical stimulus.   The everyday name for such internal processes is *conscious experience*.   However, because the designation *conscious experience* has acquired certain connotations that it is preferable to avoid in the present discussion, here the designation *sensory-perceptual event* will be used instead.   We shall conceive of a sensory-perceptual event as being—at least in part—a pattern of neural activity in the central nervous system.   Because of our meager knowledge of the neurophysiological processes underlying perception, little can be said concerning the details of sensory-perceptual events. However, the facts of perception suggest that the characteristics of a given sensory-perceptual event are determined largely (but not wholly) by receptor activity (e.g., by the pattern of activity of neural fibers originating in the retina of the eye). The term *sensory* in the designation of this construct is selected to imply dependence on receptor activity; the term *perceptual,* to imply less than complete dependence upon such activity. (Identification of the factors other than receptor activity that affect sensory-perceptual events is the concern of the field of perception. We shall not go into this question here, for to do so would take us too far afield.) The presumed relationships between physical stimuli, sensory-perceptual events, and verbal responses are represented schematically in Figure 11-4.

$$S_y \longrightarrow P_y \dashrightarrow R_{\text{``yellow''}}$$

$$S_b \longrightarrow P_b \dashrightarrow R_{\text{``blue''}}$$

$$S_g \longrightarrow P_g \dashrightarrow R_{\text{``green''}}$$

FIGURE 11-4   *Schematic representation of the relationship between physical stimuli (first column), hypothetical sensory-perceptual events (second column), and verbal responses (third column). Solid arrows represent connections that depend largely upon the structure of receptors and of the nervous system; dashed arrows represent learned connections.*

Here the symbols S_y, S_b, and S_g represent three physical objects differing in color; the symbols P_y, P_b, and P_g represent the corresponding sensory-perceptual events; and the symbols $R_{\text{``yellow''}}$, $R_{\text{``blue''}}$, and $R_{\text{``green''}}$ represent corresponding verbal responses. The solid arrows between physical objects and the corresponding sensory-perceptual events represent connections that depend primarily upon the structure of the receptors and nervous system of the observer; the dashed arrows between sensory-perceptual events and the corresponding verbal responses represent learned connections.

In proceeding with our analysis of the experimental situations described above, it will be helpful to distinguish between standard conditions of presenting stimulus objects and certain special conditions that may be investigated in the laboratory. For example, standard conditions for viewing colored objects are (1) that the objects are illuminated by white light, (2) that the objects are viewed against a neutral (white, gray, or black) background, and (3) that the boundaries separating the objects in question from their background are sharp and distinct. It is assumed that under these standard conditions yellow objects always produce one type of sensory-perceptual event (P_y), blue objects always produce another type of sensory-perceptual event (P_b), and so on for the remaining colors.   It is further assumed that when we, as children, learn color names, objects are presented under standard conditions, or at least under conditions that closely approximate standard conditions.   In order to account for the results of experiments on color contrast we must assume that under certain special conditions of viewing, a given physical object does not produce the same type of sensory-perceptual event as under standard conditions.   For example, in Arrangement *B* of Figure 11-2 the conditions under which the gray disk is viewed depart from standard conditions in two respects—the background is not neutral, but colored, and the boundaries separating the gray disk from its background are not distinct.   Apparently, under these special conditions the gray disk produces the type of sensory-perceptual event that is produced by a blue object under standard conditions.   Inasmuch as the observer has learned to make the verbal response "blue" to this type of sensory-perceptual event, the gray disk is described as blue under the conditions of Arrangement *B*.

A similar analysis may be made of the observer's verbal behavior when presented with an ambiguous figure such as shown in Figure 11-3. Standard conditions for teaching individuals to describe the surfaces of solid objects provide sufficient cues concerning the distances of different parts of the surfaces in question to make the shape of any given surface unambiguous—for example, a protruding portion of a surface gives rise to one type of sensory-perceptual event, a recessed portion to another. Apparently, the stimulus configuration shown in Figure 11-3 may give rise alternately to these two types of sensory-perceptual events, and these two sensory-perceptual events spontaneously fluctuate with continued viewing of this configuration, with the result that the observer makes corresponding changes in his verbal report.

It is apparent that on the basis of an observer's verbal report we can make certain inferences concerning the sensory-perceptual events leading to the report in question, and assuming standard conditions of observation, we can also make certain inferences concerning the physical object under observation.   For example, if an observer reports that a certain object is black, we may infer that a certain type of sensory-perceptual event occurred when he looked at the object, and assuming the observation was made under standard conditions, we may infer that the object has certain physical characteristics.   Which type of inference is of interest will depend upon the purposes for which the observation was made. Usually we are interested in the physical characteristics of the object being observed, and the sensory-perceptual events of the observer are of no particular concern; however, in a psychological investigation of perceptual processes the characteristics of the physical objects (stimuli) are known to the experimenter, and the subject's verbal report is of interest because of what it indicates about his sensory-perceptual events. The interest of the experimenter may be conveyed to the subject in the instructions he is given. That is, the subject may be told that he is to describe the way the object *appears to him* or (what amounts to the same thing) he may be told to describe his *perception* of the object.

Our instructions to the subject notwithstanding, a question may be raised concerning the manner in which his verbal report should be construed. As noted earlier, one point of view is that the subject *observes* his sensory-perceptual events and *describes* them. Upon closer examination, however, it appears that this manner of speaking uses the terms "observe" and "describe" in a sense that is entirely different from their customary meaning. Whether an observation is performed under standard conditions or under the special conditions of a psychological experiment, the subject looks at (or in some other manner directs his attention toward) some physical object, and the resulting receptor activity gives rise to certain sensory-perceptual events, on the basis of which a verbal report is made. It seems purely arbitrary and somewhat misleading to say in one case (i.e., under standard conditions) that the subject is observing and describing a physical object, but that in the other case (in an investigation of perceptual processes) he is observing and describing his own sensory-perceptual events. The position taken here is that in both cases what is being observed and described (sometimes erroneously) is a physical object. If it should ever become possible to specify the details of sensory-perceptual events—i.e., to describe them—such descriptions will presumably be in terms of patterns of neural firing or other physiological concepts, not in the terms used in the verbal reports of subjects in psychological investigations of perception. For example, the color names "blue," "red," etc., used in the verbal reports of subjects participating in studies of color contrast, are descriptive of observable physical objects but not of sensory-perceptual events.

The above argument does not deny that sensory-perceptual events (conscious experiences) are part of the subject matter of psychology; it only asserts that sensory-perceptual events should be construed as being among the theoretical constructs of psychology rather than as constituting part of the observable events with which psychology is concerned. It is a corollary of this position that there is no special method of observation —one peculiar to the field of psychology—for observing sensory-perceptual events. Although the specific techniques (special equipment, etc.) used by the various branches of science differ somewhat depending upon the types of phenomena under investigation, the fundamental characteristics of the observation process are the same in all sciences, psychology included.

VERBAL REPORTS OCCASIONED BY PRIVATE STIMULI

It is readily apparent that we can communicate to others a certain degree of information concerning our private stimuli. In a rough way at least, we can indicate when we are fatigued, hungry, or anxious; when we are experiencing an internal pain such as stomach cramps or a headache; or when we are engaging in covert behavior such as thinking or silent counting. However, because we do not have access to one another's private stimuli, it is not as a rule possible to establish a high degree of uniformity among individuals in the relationships between private stimuli and the verbal responses employed to report them. For example, let us contrast the problems involved in teaching a child to say "There is a dog" and those involved in teaching him to say "I have a headache." The stimulus to which the first response is appropriate (i.e., the presence of a dog) is public and is accessible to both the child and the parent. If the child says "There is a dog" when a dog is actually present, the parent will assent; on the other hand, if the child says "There is a dog" in response to a cat or some other animal, the parent will correct him. In this way we may insure that eventually the child comes to make the response "There is a dog" under exactly—or nearly exactly—the same conditions as the parent, who, as a result of similar training when he was a child, has learned to make this response in agreement with other individuals speaking the same language. In teaching the child to make the response "I have a headache," the situation is quite different. The child cannot experience the parent's private stimuli, nor can the parent experience the child's. It is therefore not possible to check on the child and correct him if he makes the response in the presence of the "wrong" private stimuli. Consequently, we cannot expect verbal reports pertaining to private stimuli to be used with the same degree of uniformity as can be achieved in the case of certain public stimuli. Nonetheless, it appears that there is at least some agreement among individuals in the way private stimuli are reported. In this subsection we shall consider some of the techniques that are available for teaching individuals to report their private stimuli in accordance with established conventions. A major question with which we shall be concerned is the extent to which these techniques enable us to achieve consistency and uniformity of usage in verbal reports of this kind.[5]

For purposes of illustration, let us consider the verbal response "I am anxious" (or the roughly equivalent responses "I am afraid" or "I am frightened"). Presumably this response refers to certain feelings, i.e., the presence of certain private stimuli. Because a parent teaching

[5] The main ideas presented in this subsection derive from the writings of Skinner (1945; 1953, Chap. XVII; 1957, pp. 130 ff.).

a child to make this response does not have direct access to the private stimuli of the child, he must be guided in the teaching process by certain public accompaniments of those stimuli. He might, for example, infer the presence of a state of anxiety on the basis of the external stimulus situation, the responses of the child, or both. For example, if a child is observed to cry and run to the parent in response to a sudden loud noise, the parent may comfort the child by saying, "Don't be afraid. It won't hurt you." However, the parent has no way of knowing if the private stimuli that the child experiences in situations of this type are the same as experienced by the parent (or other individuals) in similar situations. Indeed, clinical and experimental evidence (e.g., Lacey, Bateman, and Van Lehn, 1953; Schnore, 1959) suggests that the pattern of physiological activity—and presumably, the associated private stimuli—that occurs in response to stressful situations differs markedly from one individual to another. For example, in one individual the predominant private stimuli occurring during stress may be those arising from increased heart rate, changes in the digestive system, and increased sweating; in another individual the predominant stimuli may be those associated with increased muscle tension and disturbances of breathing. Thus, two individuals who report that they are anxious may in fact have very different feelings.

Skinner (1957) has called attention to another reason that verbal responses that ostensibly refer to private stimuli may be used inconsistently by a given individual and nonuniformly by different individuals. Because in teaching a response to a given private stimulus the teacher must be guided by public accompaniments of the private stimulus in question, and because those public accompaniments may also be accessible to the learner, the verbal responses in question may become associated with the public accompaniments instead of, or in addition to, the private stimulus. For example, a child may learn to say "I am afraid" not only in response to certain private stimuli but also in response to his own overt behavior of cringing or running away from something. Consequently, a given verbal response may have different implications on different occasions. To borrow an example from Skinner, the response "I am hungry" may mean that the subject is experiencing certain private stimuli (e.g., it may mean that his stomach is churning), or it may be based upon certain public events (e.g., it may simply mean that the subject has not eaten for a long time or that he is now eating voraciously). While it is true that the various states of affairs described above may often occur concomitantly (i.e., after a long fast an individual may experience churning sensations in his stomach and may eat voraciously), one does not necessarily imply the others. For example, an individual may eat to escape boredom— and hence say "I am hungry"—even though it has not been long since his last meal and he is not experiencing the private stimuli characteristically produced by a period of fasting.

VERBAL REPORTS BASED UPON METAPHORICAL EXTENSION

A verbal label that has been learned to one stimulus may also occur in response to some other stimulus that is similar in certain respects to the first. (Speaking in theoretical terms, we would say that the sensory-perceptual events produced by the one stimulus are in some manner similar to those produced by the other.) For example, wine experts describe some wines as "rough," others as "smooth." Inasmuch as the literal meanings of the terms "rough" and "smooth" do not apply to liquids, it appears that these terms are used in connection with wines because of similarities between the sensory-perceptual events produced by drinking certain wines and those produced, say, by running one's finger over a rough or smooth surface. Similarly, when a pain arising from internal conditions (private stimuli) is characterized as "sharp," the use of this term is presumably based upon similarities between the sensory-perceptual events produced by the internal conditions in question and those produced by contact with a sharp object such as a pin. Because the extension of a verbal response from one stimulus to another in this manner resembles the literary device known as *metaphor,* Skinner (1957) has named this phenomenon *metaphorical extension.*

When a verbal response is made to a private stimulus on the basis of metaphorical extension, it may be assumed that the private stimulus in question somehow resembles the stimulus to which that response is appropriate in a literal sense. Such information, however, is not very specific, for we usually have no way of knowing in what respects the two stimuli are similar and in what ways they are different. Thus, verbal responses based upon metaphorical extension are at best an ambiguous guide to the nature of the private events that they purport to describe. Moreover, there is a tendency to lose sight of the metaphorical nature of such responses and to interpret them literally; to do so can lead to serious conceptual errors, as will be shown in the following discussion.

The difficulties involved in the interpretation of verbal responses based upon metaphorical extension—and the conceptual errors that may arise if such responses are interpreted literally—may be illustrated with reference to verbal reports concerning visual imagery. In describing an object or array of objects from memory—for example, in describing the arrangement of furniture in one's living room—some individuals report that they experience visual images of the objects in question. This use of the term "image" appears to be a metaphorical extension of the term from public stimuli to which it is applicable in a literal sense—for example, images seen in mirrors or photographic images projected on a screen by a slide projector. In reporting that he is experiencing a visual image, an individual implies there is a similarity between the internal processes he is experiencing and the processes that occur when looking at an actual (public) image. Implicit in this metaphor is the notion that, just as an individual can describe an array of objects by looking at and describing a pictorial representation of the array, he may also describe the array by "looking at" a memory image (in some metaphorical sense) and responding to his image. However, it may readily be shown that there are important differences between the two situations. For example, after memorizing a set of letters presented in the form of a letter square such as shown in Figure 11-5, many subjects will report having a very clear

G   Q   A   X

J   C   M   B

T   F   L   N

Y   H   R   P

FIGURE 11-5 *A letter square. After memorizing the arrangement of letters, subjects are tested for their ability to recite the letters in different orders.*

visual image of the square. However, if required to recite the letters by columns (i.e., in the order *G, J, T, Y*, and so on), almost all subjects take substantially longer than if the letters are recited by rows (i.e., in the order *G, Q, A, X*, and so on). On the other hand, if the subject reads the letters directly from the square (rather than reciting them from memory), there is very little difference, if any, between the times required for the two orders of naming. Such results make it clear that the internal processes that give rise to verbal reports of visual images differ in important respects from the processes to which they are likened in the metaphorical use of the term "image." Because we have no way of knowing what properties of the internal processes in question the term "image" is based upon, the precise import of the term is not at all clear. Indeed, although we ordinarily think of the term "image" as indicating something about the characteristics of internal processes occurring during recall, as used by some individuals this term may connote nothing more than the fact that the individual can describe the objects in question from memory.

Since we have no way of determining precisely what internal conditions lead a given individual to use the term "image" in a metaphorical sense, we have no way of knowing whether different individuals use the term in the same way. In any given situation involving recall of stimuli not present, we find that some individuals report having clear images, others report having none. On the one hand, it is possible that such differences in verbal reports reflect differences among subjects in the internal processes occurring; on the other hand, the differences in verbal report may simply be a consequence of the lack of uniformity with which the term is used, i.e., differences in the way different subjects understand the term "image."

The foregoing considerations serve to underscore the behavioristic thesis that verbal reports concerning internal processes cannot be taken at their face value. Since it cannot be established that the verbal responses employed in reporting internal processes are used uniformly by different individuals, these responses cannot reasonably be accorded the same status as descriptive terms referring to public stimuli. On the other hand, verbal responses used in reporting internal processes may be treated on a par with other observable behavior. An analysis of the general principles governing the occurrence of such responses may constitute a useful basis for drawing inferences concerning events occurring within the individual.

REFERENCES

AZRIN, N. H., W. HOLZ, R. ULRICH, and I. GOLDIAMOND. The control of the content of conversation through reinforcement. *J. exp. anal. Behav.,* 1961, **4,** 25–30.

BERGMANN, G. *Philosophy of science.* Madison, Wis.: Univ. of Wisconsin Press, 1957.

BRIDGMAN, P. W. *The logic of modern physics.* New York: Macmillan, 1928.

HEMPEL, C. G. *Fundamentals of concept formation in empirical science. Int. Encycl. Unified Sci.,* Vol. 2, No. 7, Chicago: Univ. of Chicago Press, 1952.

LACEY, J. I., DOROTHY E. BATEMAN, and RUTH VAN LEHN. Autonomic response specificity: an experimental study. *Psychosom. Med.,* 1953, **15,** 8–21.

SCHNORE, M. M. Individual patterns of physiological activity as a function of task differences and degree of arousal. *J. exp. Psychol.,* 1959, **58,** 117–128.

SKINNER, B. F. *The behavior of organisms.* New York: Appleton-Century-Crofts, 1938.

———. The operational analysis of psychological terms. *Psychol. Rev.,* 1945, **52,** 270–277.

———. *Science and human behavior.* New York: Macmillan, 1953.

———. *Verbal behavior.* New York: Appleton-Century-Crofts, 1957.

ADDITIONAL READINGS

GRAHAM, C. H. Sensation and perception in an objective psychology. *Psychol. Rev.,* 1958, **65,** 65–76.

MANDLER, G. and W. KESSEN. *The language of psychology.* New York: Wiley, 1959. Chaps. 1–4. A detailed analysis of the problems of description in psychology.

SKINNER, B. F. Behaviorism at fifty. *Science,* 1963, **140,** 951–958.

SPENCE, K. W.   The empirical basis and theoretical structure of psychology. *Phil. Sci.,* 1957, **24,** 97–108.   A summary of the behavioristic point of view at mid-century.   Reprinted in K. W. Spence, *Behavior theory and learning.*   Englewood Cliffs, N.J.: Prentice-Hall, 1960.   Pp. 71–88.

WATSON, J. B.   Psychology as the behaviorist views it. *Psychol. Rev.,* 1913, **20,** 158–177.   An early article in which the behavioristic point of view is stated with clarity and vigor.

ZENER, K. and MERCEDES GAFFRON.   Perceptual experience: an analysis of its relations to the external world through internal processings.   In S. Koch (ed.), *Psychology: a study of a science.*   Vol. 4.   New York: McGraw-Hill, 1962.   Pp. 515–618, especially pp. 516–562.   A detailed discussion, from the phenomenological point of view, of verbal reports of conscious experience.

CHAPTER 12

prediction and explanation

EXPLANATION OF EVENTS THAT HAVE ALREADY OCCURRED AND PREDICTION of events that have not yet occurred have the same logical form: both consist in logically deducing a statement of individual fact (observation statement) from certain other statements. Because of the central role of logical deduction in scientific explanation and prediction, our discussion of prediction and explanation will be prefaced by some brief remarks concerning the nature of logical deduction.

Deduction is a procedure in which, from one or more initial statements called *premises,* a new statement is derived in accordance with the rules of logic. The new statement, the *conclusion,* is said to be *logically implied* by the premises. For present purposes it is not necessary to examine the rules of logic in detail; it is sufficient to note that adherence to these rules assures that if the premises employed are true, the conclusion obtained will also be true. The most familiar example of the deduction of a conclusion from a set of premises is the syllogism. In this form of deduction, two premises are employed and a single conclusion is drawn, as in the following example.

(*A*) All blondes are highly susceptible to sunburn.
(*B*) Jane is a blonde.

(*C*) Jane is highly susceptible to sunburn.

In this example, statements *A* and *B* are premises and statement *C* is the conclusion. The deduction is valid (i.e., follows the rules of logic), so if the premises are true, the conclusion must also be true.

The deduction of conclusions from premises is analogous to the solution of equations in mathematics. For example, given the equation $x + y = 10$ and the equation $x = 6$, we may, by applying the rules of algebra, derive the new equation $y = 4$. The first two equations are analogous to the premises of a syllogism; the third, to the conclusion. Since we have correctly applied the rules of algebra in deriving the third equation from the first two, we are assured that if the first two are true, so is the third.

EMPIRICAL LAWS

An empirical law is a general statement describing regularities among observable phenomena. An example is the Law of Classical Conditioning, based upon the work of Pavlov. As is well known, Pavlov observed that if a neutral stimulus (e.g., a musical tone) is repeatedly presented to a hungry animal, and each presentation is followed closely in time by the presentation of food—a stimulus that regularly elicits the response of salivation—then the neutral stimulus will eventually acquire the capacity to elicit salivation by itself. Similar findings have been obtained with a wide variety of responses other than salivation. For example, if a neutral stimulus is repeatedly paired with a puff of air to the surface of the eye—a stimulus that regularly elicits blinking—the neutral stimulus will acquire the capacity to elicit the response of blinking. Stated in general terms, the Law of Classical Conditioning may be written as follows: If each presentation of a neutral stimulus is closely followed in time by the presentation of a stimulus that regularly elicits some response, then the neutral stimulus will eventually acquire the capacity to elicit the response in question.[1] The essential form of this law is exhibited in the following schema: If A, then B. In this schema A and B represent observable conditions or events—A the paired presentation of two stimuli of specified types, B the elicitation of a new response by one of the stimuli. Because language is flexible, any given law can be stated in different ways. However, all qualitative laws (i.e., laws not stated in the form of a mathematical equation) can be written as an *if-then* statement. For example, the statement "All

---

[1] Actually, the above formulation of the Law of Classical Conditioning, while not uncommon in the literature, is an oversimplification of the facts. Although the response elicited by the originally neutral stimulus (the so-called *conditioned stimulus*) is often similar in form to the response elicited by the stimulus with which it is paired (the so-called *unconditioned stimulus*), there are a number of experiments in which the response elicited by the conditioned stimulus after conditioning has been found to be substantially different in form from that elicited by the unconditioned stimulus. As yet no simple formulation of the Law of Classical Conditioning has been advanced that adequately accounts for the different findings that are obtained depending upon the particular type of unconditioned stimulus employed and the particular response recorded. A brief summary of some of the literature bearing on this problem is given by Kimble (1961, pp. 52–59).

blondes are highly susceptible to sunburn," which is an example of a simple empirical law, may be rephrased as an *if-then* statement as follows: If an individual is blonde, then that individual is highly susceptible to sunburn.

In distinction to qualitative laws of the sort considered above, some empirical laws are expressed in the form of a mathematical equation. An example from the field of sensory processes is Emmert's Law, which is concerned with the apparent size of visual afterimages. For purposes of illustration, let us imagine that a subject gazes steadily with one eye at a white square against a black background and then shifts his gaze to a plain, flat surface such as a wall. Under these circumstances he will experience a temporary negative afterimage—a dark square against a lighter background—which seems to be located on or near the projection surface (i.e., the wall or whatever other surface the subject looks at after gazing at the original stimulus). The apparent size of the afterimage depends upon the distance of the projection surface from the subject and upon the size and distance from the subject of the original stimulus object. Representing the apparent height of the afterimage by h, the distance of the projection surface by d, the height of the original stimulus by H, and the distance of the stimulus by D, Emmert's Law may be stated mathematically as follows: $h = (H/D)d$. Thus, for a given set of viewing conditions (H and D fixed) the apparent height of the afterimage is directly proportional to the distance of the projection surface.

As noted earlier, an individual fact is predicted (or, if it has already occurred, explained) by logically deducing a statement describing that fact from certain other statements (premises). The premises on which the prediction of an individual fact is based always include statements of two kinds: (*a*) one or more empirical laws and (*b*) one or more statements of individual fact. The nature of prediction may be illustrated with an example based upon Emmert's Law. Let us suppose, for example, that a subject gazes steadily at a 1-in. square located 18 in. from his eye and then shifts his gaze to a projection surface 36 in. from his eye. On the basis of Emmert's Law we predict that under these circumstances the subject will experience an afterimage having an apparent height of 2 in. The premises and conclusion of this prediction may be written as follows:

$$h = \left(\frac{H}{D}\right) d$$

$$H = 1 \text{ in.}$$
$$D = 18 \text{ in.}$$
$$\underline{d = 36 \text{ in.}}$$
$$h = 2 \text{ in.}$$

The first equation is a statement of Emmert's Law; the next three equations are statements of individual fact, namely, descriptions of the size and distance of the original stimulus and the distance of the projection surface.

The last statement, the conclusion, is the fact predicted—that the apparent height of the afterimage is 2 in. (The derivation of this statement from the others is a matter of simple arithmetic: the appropriate values are simply substituted in the first equation.)

The circumstances that are taken into account in explaining or predicting a particular event—or that are manipulated to control the outcome of an event—are referred to as *antecedent events* (or *antecedent conditions*); the event explained, predicted, or controlled, is referred to as a *consequent event*. In the Law of Classical Conditioning, for example, the antecedent event is the pairing of two stimuli; the consequent event is the elicitation of the response in question by the originally neutral stimulus. When a law concerns attributes that are expressed in the form of measurements, we speak of these attributes as antecedent and consequent variables. For example, in the above illustration based upon Emmert's Law, the antecedent variables are H, D, and d; the consequent variable is h.

At this point in our discussion it will be useful to contrast the meanings of the terms "hypothesis" and "law." The term "hypothesis" is generally used to refer to a statement whose truth is uncertain, a statement that is adopted provisionally with the explicit understanding that further evidence may lead to its abandonment. The term "law" is commonly used in two somewhat different senses. In its stricter sense, "law" is used to refer to a general statement that is true. In this sense of the term no general statement can ever be known with certainty to be a law, for no general statement of a factual nature can be known with certainty to be true. (Speaking schematically, a general statement asserts that every instance of A is an instance of B. "Every instance of A" means every possible instance, not merely those instances that have actually been observed. Thus, in formulating a general statement we are hazarding a conjecture—making an inductive leap from "some" to "all," as it is sometimes put—whose truth cannot be certain.) It follows that, strictly speaking, every empirical generalization, including those commonly referred to as "laws," is properly regarded as a hypothesis in the sense that this term was defined above—a provisional statement, whose truth is uncertain. However, the term "law" is often used in a freer sense to refer to a hypothesis that is highly confirmed, one concerning whose truth there is little serious doubt. Although this use of the term is necessarily somewhat vague—it is not exactly clear at what point a generalization ceases to be a hypothesis and becomes a law—the vagueness in this case seems harmless and not likely to be a source of confusion. In view of the widespread use of the term "law" in the latter sense, this is the sense in which the term is used in this book.

It is often said that empirical laws are discovered. In a certain sense, this is true. It seems reasonable, for example, to say that Pavlov discovered the phenomenon of classical conditioning. However, recognition of the fact that statements customarily called laws are actually hypotheses serves to emphasize that empirical generalizations are in fact conjectures—that is, inventions or constructions of man. The establishment of useful empirical generalizations may be viewed as a trial-and-error process in which, on the basis of initial findings, a general statement is tentatively proposed, then tested further. In some cases the generalization stands, i.e., is confirmed by all succeeding tests; in others, it is found to be in error and is discarded or revised.

A CLASSIFICATION OF BEHAVIORAL LAWS

The aim of psychology is the prediction and explanation of behavior; accordingly, the laws of chief interest to psychologists are those in which the consequent variable is some characteristic of behavior. A classification of such laws based upon the antecedent variables to which behavior is related has been proposed by Spence (1956). In this subsection we shall briefly examine Spence's classification.

R-R (response-response) laws describe how certain characteristics of behavior are related to other aspects of behavior of the same individual. One subclass of *R-R* laws are those concerning correlations among symptoms of behavior disorders—for example, the finding that depressed behavior is usually accompanied by behavior that indicates feelings of guilt. The use of psychological tests is based upon another subclass of *R-R* laws, namely, those concerning the relationships between performance on specific tests and performance in various situations of practical interest. For example, a test is of value in selecting applicants for a job only if performance on that test is known to be related to performance on the job. While *R-R* laws are useful in enabling us to predict one characteristic of behavior on the basis of another, these laws do not provide information that can be utilized in the control of behavior; *R-R* laws indicate, for example, how to recognize an individual who will do well in a given job, but do not tell us how to produce such an individual through training or other means.

In contrast to laws of the *R-R* variety, *S-R* (stimulus-response) laws describe how behavior is influenced by environmental conditions and thus provide information that makes possible, to some extent at least, the control of behavior through the manipulation of environmental conditions. One subclass of *S-R* laws relate behavior to characteristics of the immediate stimulating environment—for example, the manner in which perception of size varies as a function of the size and distance of a physical object, or the manner in which latency of a reflex response (e.g., withdrawal from a painful stimulus) varies as a function of stimulus intensity. Spence also includes in the *S-R* category laws relating characteristics of behavior to environmental events occurring in the past experience of an organism. Most laws in the field of learning are of this type. Examples of such laws are those relating the speed with which an animal performs a response to the number of previous trials on which that response has been rewarded (e.g., by food) and to the amount and type of reward received.

O-R laws are those in which response characteristics are related to so-called *organic variables,* i.e., anatomical and physiological conditions of the organism, and thus belong to the area of physiological psychology. Laws within this category concern the effects upon behavior of such antecedents as the administration of drugs and hormones, the removal of endocrine glands or of portions of the nervous system, and electrical stimulation of various parts of the brain. A closely related class of laws, *S-O* laws, are concerned with physiological changes occurring in response to various types of environmental (stimulus) events. Although these laws are not strictly speaking behavioral laws—they do not refer directly to response variables—they are nonetheless an important link in understanding the physiological processes underlying behavior. One subclass of *S-O* laws that have received considerable attention in recent years are laws specifying the physiological reactions to emotion-provoking stimuli. Another subclass of *S-O* laws are the laws of sensory physiology that specify how characteristics of a sensory stimulus are translated into characteristics of neural firing, i.e., that describe the variations occurring in patterns of neural firing as a result of variations in characteristics of the physical stimulus.

It will be noted that not every behavioral law can be fitted into one of the categories described above. For example, forgetting curves, which describe how behavior changes as a function of time since learning, do not fall into any of the above categories. Moreover, these categories provide for the classification of only the simpler behavioral laws; more complex laws, in which behavior is related to antecedent variables of more than one type, are not accommodated. (An example of a complex law involving two types of antecedent variable would be one describing how an *S-R* relationship—e.g., a learning curve—varies among groups differing in some organic variable such as concentration in the blood of certain hormones.) Of course, categories including such complex laws could be defined. However, the value of the classification scheme described above is that it calls attention to the major classes of variables with which behavioral laws are concerned and provides a useful overview of empirical laws in the field of psychology. With this accomplished, it is doubtful whether a detailed enumeration of categories to accommodate every behavioral law would serve any useful purpose.

THEORIES

The function of scientific theories is to explain established empirical laws and to predict (i.e., lead to the discovery of) new laws.

Every scientific theory contains statements of two kinds: (1) postulates and (2) theorems. The postulates of a theory are assumptions; the theorems, which are statements of empirical laws, are logically deduced from the postulates. Thus, in terms of their logical relationship, the postulates and theorems of a theory are analogous to the premises and conclusion, respectively, of a syllogism. However, while a syllogism consists of but two premises and a single conclusion, a theory usually consists of several postulates and several theorems.

A theory with which everyone is familiar is the heliocentric (sun-centered) theory of the solar system, the essential ideas of which were propounded in the sixteenth century by the Polish astronomer Copernicus. The basic laws with which this theory is concerned (i.e., its theorems) are descriptions of the apparent motion of the heavenly bodies—the sun, moon, planets, and stars. The most familiar of these laws concern the motion of the sun—for example, that it periodically rises in the east, arcs slowly overhead, and sets in the west; and that during the summer it rises higher in the sky than during the winter. The postulates of this theory are so ingrained in the thinking of educated individuals, and so highly confirmed, that their status as assumptions is easily overlooked. Two of these postulates are the following: (1) The earth is a large spherical body that rotates about its axis like a top. (2) It is one of nine major planets that revolve around the sun. The complete set of postulates consists of a set of statements describing the assumed properties of the solar system, i.e., the distances of the various planets from the sun, the positions of their orbits, their rate of revolution around the sun, and so on. From such postulates it is possible to explain (logically deduce) all the known laws concerning the apparent motion of the heavenly bodies.

As previous discussion has already intimated, there is no set of general rules or procedures for formulating the postulates of a theory. Rather, the creation of the postulates of a theory, like the formulation of empirical laws, is perhaps best characterized as a trial-and-error process. The process is not, of course, a haphazard affair in which any and all possible postulates are tried in an indiscriminate manner; in framing a set of postulates, a theorist naturally brings to bear as much relevant information as he can marshal. But there are no hard-and-fast rules that enable him, starting with any fixed set of empirical facts, to derive a useful set of postulates. Here the theorist is on his own, and the success of his venture depends upon his individual creative ability—his capacity for invention—and, perhaps, a certain element of luck.

Typically, the postulates of a theory are of such a nature that their truth cannot be evaluated directly; rather, they are evaluated indirectly on the basis of the agreement (or disagreement) with observation of the theorems they imply. When the theorems are confirmed by experiment, this lends credence to the postulates from which those theorems are deduced; when the theorems are in disagreement with observation, belief in the postulates is lessened. As a general rule, acceptance of a scientific theory is usually not an all-or-nothing matter. It is often found that some of the theorems of a given theory are confirmed while others are not. Such a state of affairs need not—and usually does not—lead to abandonment of the theory as a whole; more typically, an attempt is made to correct the theory by making changes of a minor nature, i.e., by the modification of selected postulates or the inclusion of certain additional ones. Indeed, the development of many scientific theories has proceeded from a first rough draft through a series of gradual refinements. On the other hand, not all advances in theory result from a process of gradual refinement; occasionally a venerated theory is abruptly deposed by a radically different one that does a better job.

Hull (1943) has called attention to the fact that there is a certain parallel—and an important distinction—between scientific theories and everyday argumentation. In a rational argument (e.g., concerning a matter of politics) we proceed from certain premises and arrive deductively at certain conclusions. In this respect argumentation is similar to scientific theorizing. However, the considerations determining our acceptance of the two classes of propositions—premises and conclusions—are often very different in argumentation than in evaluating a scientific theory. On the one hand, in argumentation the conviction with which we regard a given conclusion is determined, as a rule, by the degree of our belief in the premises from which that conclusion is derived; if we are committed to our premises, then we are committed to the logical implications of those premises. In evaluating a scientific theory, on the other hand, this process is inverted, i.e., our acceptance of the postulates of a scientific theory depends, as we have noted above, upon the extent to which the theorems derived from those postulates are confirmed by observation. Whereas in an argument our primary commitment is to the premises from which we argue, in evaluating a theory our primary commitment is—or should be—to the facts of observation.

Let us now consider to what extent the method used in science for evaluating the postulates of a theory is justified by logical considerations. In examining the nature of logical deduction, we saw that valid deduction (i.e., proper use of the rules of logic) insures that if the premises of a logical argument are true, then the conclusions will also be true. It follows that if the conclusion is false, the premises must contain at least one error. Thus, if a theorem of a scientific theory is contrary to experimental findings, we know that the postulates of the theory contain an error. On the other hand, the fact that the conclusion of a logical argument is true does not necessarily mean that the premises on which that conclusion is based are also true. Consider, for example, the following syllogism.

(*A*) All reptiles chase cats.
(*B*) Some dogs are reptiles.

(*C*) Some dogs chase cats.

The reasoning is logically sound, and the conclusion (Statement *C*) is factually true. However, it does not follow that the premises are true; indeed, both premises are patently false. Extending this observation to the testing of theories, it is seen that the procedure used in science for evaluating the postulates of a theory is fallible and may lead to acceptance of postulates that are false. For this reason the postulates of a scientific theory can never be known with certainty to be true; their acceptance is always provisional.

In Chapter 1 we distinguished two types of inference that can be made on the basis of experimental findings—(1) empirical generalization and (2) interpretation. An empirical generalization of the results of an experiment is a statement of an empirical law. On the other hand, the interpretation of an experimental finding consists in constructing a set of premises from which that finding can be logically deduced; thus, interpretation is seen to be an instance of theory construction on a limited scale. (Although the term "theory" is usually reserved for more ambitious undertakings in which several laws are deduced from a single set of premises, the construction of a set of premises to explain a single law is nonetheless a limiting case of this more general procedure.) It should be noted that assembling a set of premises from which one particular experimental finding can be deduced is not in itself an especially impressive accomplishment. Indeed, if our only concern were the derivation of one particular law, the number of alternative sets of premises that would serve this function is practically unlimited. Consequently, the explanation (interpretation) of a given experimental finding becomes of more than routine interest only when it is found that the premises employed in that explanation are useful in the derivation of other empirical laws as well.[2]

---

[2] Having read this far, one reader asked, in effect, "If certain known facts (laws) suggest a theory, how can it be said that those facts are deduced from the theory? Isn't the situation, in fact, the other way around, i.e., isn't the theory in some sense derived from the facts?" This difficulty arises from a confusion between the *logical* relationships and the *psychological* (pragmatic) relationships between facts and theories. While certain facts encompassed by a theory may be experimentally demonstrated before the theory is formulated and others may be experimentally demonstrated only afterwards, once the theory exists, the logical relationship of both sets of facts to the theory is the same: the facts (or, more precisely, statements describing the facts) are logically deduced from the postulates of the theory, and the facts in question are said to be explained by the theory. The psychological or pragmatic fact that a given set of facts may have suggested a particular theory has no bearing on the logical relationship existing between those facts and the theory.

We have seen that the function of the postulates of a theory is to serve as premises from which empirical laws can be deduced. A set of postulates that do not permit the deduction of theorems that can be subjected to experimental test are said to be *untestable*. It should be obvious from everything that has been said up to this point that an untestable set of postulates can serve no useful scientific purpose. The possibility of constructing a set of seemingly meaningful postulates that are in fact untestable is shown by the following example from the field of physics. Inasmuch as all other known forms of wave activity (e.g., sound waves) require a medium for their propagation, it was assumed by some physicists that the transmission of light, which has many of the characteristics of a wave phenomenon, also required a medium. However, since light readily travels through a vacuum, it was clear that the hypothetical medium for light was a less tangible substance than air or water. These considerations led to the postulation of a hypothetical medium called *ether,* which was assumed to be stationary and to occupy all space. Since the earth presumably moves through the ether, it follows from the above hypothesis that it should be possible to detect differences in the speed of light relative to the earth depending upon whether the light is traveling in the same direction as the earth or in the opposite direction, much as the speed (relative to the shore) of someone swimming in a river depends on whether he is swimming with the current or against it. However, all experimental attempts to detect variations in the speed of light depending upon its direction of travel failed. Then, as Feigl (1943) puts it, "H. A. Lorentz, certainly one of the greatest physicists, pardoned the ether of its undiscoverability by postulating an ingenious set of assumptions, which jointly guaranteed that whatever effects might be produced by the ether, such effects would be exactly cancelled by other counter-effects" (p. 386). Einstein subsequently realized that in its modified form the ether hypothesis was completely untestable and therefore without any scientific value.

Another requirement that the postulates of a theory must satisfy is *consistency.* A set of postulates is said to be *inconsistent* if certain of their logical consequences are contradictory to others, *consistent* if there are no contradictions among the implications. The reason for this requirement is obvious; if two theorems are contradictory, then experimental evidence relevant to those theorems, whatever its nature, at the same time both confirms and disconfirms the theory. Folklore serves as an example of a body of general principles flawed by inconsistencies. Consider, for example, the adages "Absence makes the heart grow fonder" and "Out of sight, out of mind." Whatever the outcome of a separation might be, it could be "explained" by one or the other of these two principles. The price paid for this explanatory flexibility is, of course, a complete lack of predictive capacity.

From time to time scientists of an antitheoretical persuasion have questioned whether theories serve any useful function in science. To this question it may be answered that theories frequently lead to the discovery of new and unsuspected laws, thereby increasing our ability to predict and control observable phenomena. Of course there is no guarantee that any given theory will lead to new discoveries, but the frequency with which this has occurred in the past encourages the belief that further developments of a theoretical nature will meet with similar success. However, there is perhaps an even more fundamental observation to be made on behalf of theory. Examination of the history of science indicates that the construction, testing, and revision of theories is an intrinsic part of the development of scientific knowledge. It would therefore seem that the justification of theory must ultimately rest upon the same grounds as the justification of science as a whole and of knowledge in general. We shall not here undertake to justify the whole of science; however, it is suggested that the justification, if it may be called that, rests not only upon practical or utilitarian considerations, but upon cultural—i.e., intellectual and esthetic —grounds as well.

SPENCE'S THEORY OF DISCRIMINATION LEARNING— AN ILLUSTRATIVE BEHAVIOR THEORY

To illustrate the nature of theory in greater detail we will briefly examine a theory of discrimination training proposed by Spence (1937). This theory was designed to deal with learning situations in which an animal is trained to make a choice between two stimuli differing in a single characteristic, as, for example, when a chimpanzee is trained to choose between two similar boxes, one painted light gray, the other painted dark gray. An illustrative procedure to accomplish such training is the following: On each trial the chimp is presented with both boxes and permitted to choose one. One box ($S_{(+)}$) always contains food; the other ($S_{(-)}$) is always empty. If the chimp chooses $S_{(+)}$, he finds the food inside and is allowed to eat it; if he chooses $S_{(-)}$, he receives no food on that trial.

Spence's theory makes certain assumptions concerning the reaction tendencies to $S_{(+)}$ and $S_{(-)}$ considered separately and other assumptions concerning the manner in which these separate tendencies jointly affect performance. His six basic assumptions (postulates), numbered for convenience of later reference, are the following:

1. As a result of training trials on which approaching $S_{(+)}$ is rewarded by food, there develops a tendency to approach $S_{(+)}$ whenever it is presented. This hypothetical tendency to approach $S_{(+)}$ is referred to as *excitatory tendency*.

2. As a consequence of the learned tendency to approach $S_{(+)}$, there is also a tendency to approach other stimuli that are similar to $S_{(+)}$ but differ from it along the lightness dimension. That is, just as the animal

tends to approach $S_{(+)}$ when that stimulus is presented, it will also tend to approach other boxes that are painted lighter or darker than $S_{(+)}$, even though the animal has had no direct experience with such boxes. (When this occurs, we say that the tendency to respond to $S_{(+)}$ has *generalized* to neighboring stimuli.) The strength of the tendency to approach any given box is assumed to depend upon the similarity of that box to $S_{(+)}$; more specifically, the strength of the excitatory tendency to approach boxes of different lightness is assumed to vary in the manner shown in the top part of Figure 12-1. The strength of the excitatory tendency (i.e., tend-

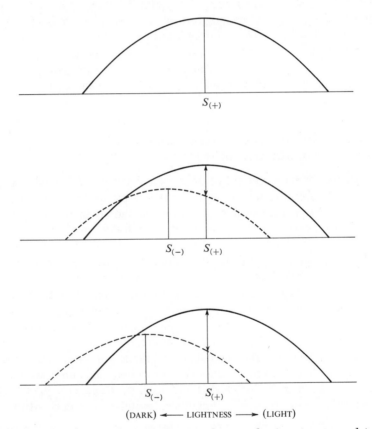

$S_{(+)}$

$S_{(-)}$ $S_{(+)}$

$S_{(-)}$ $S_{(+)}$

(DARK) ◄—— LIGHTNESS ——► (LIGHT)

FIGURE 12-1 *Curves showing theoretical strength of excitatory and inhibitory tendencies to stimuli at different points on a stimulus continuum (lightness). Top: Strength of excitatory tendency to $S_{(+)}$ and to neighboring stimuli. Middle: Strength of excitatory tendency to $S_{(+)}$ and neighboring stimuli (solid ness). Top: Strength of excitatory tendency to $S_{(+)}$ and to neighboring stimuli. (dashed curve). Bottom: Same as middle, except $S_{(+)}$ and $S_{(-)}$ are more widely separated on the stimulus continuum, i.e., less similar in lightness. Arrows above $S_{(+)}$ in middle and bottom diagrams represent amount of effective excitatory tendency to $S_{(+)}$. Adapted from Spence (1937).*

ency to approach) is seen to be strongest to $S_{(+)}$, slightly weaker to stimuli that are close to $S_{(+)}$ in lightness, and still weaker to stimuli that are far removed from $S_{(+)}$, either above it (lighter) or below it (darker).

3. Spence's third assumption concerns the effects of trials on which the subject approaches $S_{(-)}$ and finds no food. He assumes that as a consequence of such experiences there develops a tendency to inhibit the response of approaching $S_{(-)}$. Spence refers to this tendency as *inhibitory tendency*.

4. Just as the tendency to approach $S_{(+)}$ generalizes to other stimuli along the lightness dimension, so does the inhibitory tendency associated with $S_{(-)}$ generalize to other stimuli. The strength of the inhibitory tendency associated with $S_{(-)}$ and that generalized to neighboring stimuli is represented by the dashed curve in the middle section of Figure 12-1.

5. Spence's fifth assumption concerns the manner in which the excitatory tendency and inhibitory tendency associated with a given stimulus combine. He assumes simply that the inhibitory tendency subtracts from the excitatory tendency and that the *effective* excitatory tendency associated with any given stimulus is that in excess of the corresponding inhibitory tendency. Thus, the effective excitatory tendency associated with any given stimulus corresponds to the vertical distance between the solid curve and the dashed curve in the middle section of Figure 12-1. The arrow between the two curves at the point above $S_{(+)}$ indicates the magnitude of the effective excitatory tendency associated with $S_{(+)}$. Similarly, in Figure 12-2 the effective excitatory tendency corresponding to four

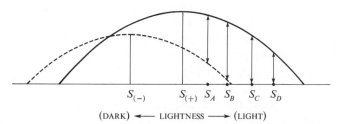

$S_{(-)}$ $S_{(+)}$ S_A S_B S_C S_D

(DARK) ◀── LIGHTNESS ──▶ (LIGHT)

FIGURE 12-2 *Curves showing theoretical strength of excitatory and inhibitory tendencies to stimuli at different points on a stimulus continuum. S_A and S_B are two test stimuli close (in lightness) to the training stimuli; S_C and S_D are two test stimuli remote from the training stimuli. Adapted from Spence (1937).*

stimuli (S_A, S_B, S_C, and S_D) differing in lightness is indicated by arrows above the corresponding points on the baseline. (Beyond the point where the curve representing inhibitory tendency meets the baseline—for example, at the points corresponding to S_C and S_D—the effective excitatory tendency is the distance between the solid curve and the baseline.)

6. In order to derive testable deductions from the above postulates it is necessary to specify the manner in which the theoretical construct "effective excitatory tendency" is related to behavioral measures. Spence has assumed that in situations in which the subject is given a choice between two stimuli the relative frequency with which each of the two stimuli is selected is determined by the relative strengths of the effective excitatory tendencies corresponding to the two stimuli. That is, he assumes that if the effective excitatory tendency for the two stimuli is equal, they will be chosen equally often; if unequal, the stimulus with the greater effective excitatory tendency will be chosen more frequently.

From the above postulates Spence has deduced the following two theorems concerning choice reactions:

THEOREM 1. If an organism is trained to choose the lighter of two stimuli ($S_{(+)}$ in Figure 12-2) and then given a choice between two test stimuli located close to the training stimuli (e.g., S_A and S_B in Figure 12-2), then the lighter of the two test stimuli (S_B in Figure 12-2) will be chosen more frequently than the darker.

The basis for this deduction is apparent from inspection of Figure 12-2, which shows the effective excitatory tendency for S_B to be greater than that for S_A.

THEOREM 2. If an organism is trained to choose the lighter of two stimuli and then given a choice between two test stimuli that are remote from the training stimuli (e.g., S_C and S_D in Figure 12-2), then the darker of the two test stimuli (S_C in Figure 12-2) will be chosen more frequently than the lighter.

The basis for this deduction is apparent from inspection of the effective excitatory tendencies shown in Figure 12-2 for S_C and S_D. Thus, according to Spence's theory, the preference exhibited by an organism when presented with two stimuli that are remote from the training stimuli (Theorem 2) will be in the direction opposite to the preference exhibited when presented with two stimuli that are near the training stimuli (Theorem 1). Using rats as subjects, Ehrenfreund (1952) has confirmed both of the above theorems.[3]

---

[3] At this point in the discussion a reader of an early draft of the manuscript expressed uneasiness because, although it was clear to her that the two theorems discussed above follow logically from Spence's assumptions, the theorems did not correspond to her intuitive expectations, i.e., she could not appreciate intuitively why in one case the lighter of two test stimuli should be preferred and in another case the darker of two stimuli should be preferred. In connection with this difficulty, it should be noted that the postulates presented above do not take into account complications arising from the use of verbal labels, and hence, theorems based upon these postulates are strictly applicable only to inarticulate organisms, i.e., those lacking speech. In particular, it appears that in tests of the kind referred to in Theorems 1 and 2, the behavioral outcome depends largely upon the capacity of the subjects to employ relevant verbal labels. In one study bearing on this question (Kuenne, 1946), children ranging from three years to six years of age were trained to choose between two stimuli

Although Spence has not extended his theory to situations other than those involving the simultaneous presentation of two stimuli, such extensions have been made by other investigators. Gynther (1957), for example, has employed an eyelid conditioning procedure and human subjects to test several predictions based upon this theory. In Gynther's study $S_{(+)}$ and $S_{(-)}$ were two small lights located directly in front of the subject and separated by approximately $2\frac{1}{2}$ in. On any given trial only one of the two lights was presented. Each presentation of $S_{(+)}$ (the light on the right) was followed by a puff of air to the subject's eye; presentation of $S_{(-)}$ (the light on the left) was never followed by the air puff. Because in Gynther's procedure subjects did not select one of two simultaneously presented stimuli, the response measure considered by Spence—relative frequency with which a given stimulus is selected—could not be used in Gynther's study as a measure of effective excitatory tendency. In order to extend the theory to his conditioning procedure Gynther assumed the proportion of test trials on which a given stimulus elicits the response of eyelid closure to be an indication of the strength of the effective excitatory tendency associated with that stimulus. In other words, he assumed that if two stimuli are presented separately for, say, ten test trials each, eyelid closure will be elicited more often by the stimulus having the greater effective excitatory tendency. (In this context "test trials" simply refers to those trials selected for purposes of obtaining observations relevant to the theory, i.e., trials sufficiently far along in training to afford the development of appreciable excitatory and inhibitory tendencies.)

One of the predictions investigated by Gynther was the following:

THEOREM 3. For any given number of conditioning trials with $S_{(+)}$ (i.e., trials on which $S_{(+)}$ is paired with a puff of air to the eye), the frequency with which $S_{(+)}$ elicits a conditioned eyelid response will be less if a number of negative trials with $S_{(-)}$ are interspersed with conditioning trials than if no negative trials with $S_{(-)}$ are employed.

In other words, subjects who on some trials are presented with $S_{(+)}$ followed by an air puff and on other trials are presented with $S_{(-)}$ not followed by an air puff will subsequently exhibit a conditioned response to $S_{(+)}$ less frequently than subjects who have had a comparable number of

---

differing in size. Whereas children who failed to verbalize the characteristic in which the training stimuli differed performed in accordance with the theory, those who verbalized the nature of the difference did not. The performance of the latter subjects was more consistent with our intuitive expectations, i.e., the direction of preference exhibited by these subjects was the same for a pair of test stimuli remote from the training stimuli as for a pair close to the training stimuli.

Although the above observations may serve to reconcile Spence's theory with intuition, it is important to recognize that in evaluating the scientific value of a theory the intuitive appeal of the postulates and/or theorems is wholly irrelevant. Indeed, many of the propositions advanced in science at first seem intuitively incredible, although with sufficient exposure to, and familiarity with, the principles in question, intuition usually accommodates itself in time. As we have already noted, the ultimate test of a theory is the extent to which its theorems are confirmed by observation.

training trials with $S_{(+)}$ and none with $S_{(-)}$. The basis for this prediction may be seen by comparing the middle and upper portions of Figure 12-1. For subjects who have received trials with $S_{(-)}$, the tendency to respond to $S_{(+)}$ is reduced by the inhibitory tendency generalized from $S_{(-)}$, as shown in the middle portion of the figure. For subjects who have been trained using $S_{(+)}$ only, there is no generalized inhibitory tendency to subtract from the excitatory tendency associated with $S_{(+)}$. The latter situation is represented by the upper portion of the figure.

A second prediction tested by Gynther was the following:

> THEOREM 4. If a subject receives both positive trials with $S_{(+)}$ and negative trials with $S_{(-)}$ (in any specified proportions), the frequency with which $S_{(+)}$ elicits a conditioned response will be less if $S_{(+)}$ and $S_{(-)}$ are highly similar than if they are distinctively different.

The basis of this prediction may be seen by comparing the middle and lower portions of Figure 12-1. The middle section of the figure represents a situation in which $S_{(+)}$ and $S_{(-)}$ are relatively similar, i.e., close to one another on the stimulus dimension; the bottom section represents a situation in which the two stimuli are less similar. It is apparent from these two drawings that the amount of inhibitory tendency generalized from $S_{(-)}$ to $S_{(+)}$ is greater when the two stimuli are similar than when they are distinct, resulting in less effective excitatory tendency to $S_{(+)}$ in the former case than in the latter. This theorem and the preceding one were both confirmed in Gynther's study, as were a number of additional theorems not considered here.

The extension of Spence's theory to the pecking behavior of pigeons (in a version of the Skinner box adapted for use with pigeons) has been considered by Hanson (1959). In Hanson's study pigeons were trained to peck at a sheet of translucent plastic through a small circular window in the wall of the apparatus. The plastic sheet was illuminated from behind by colored light, whose hue could be varied by the experimenter. $S_{(+)}$ was light having a dominant wavelength of 550 millimicrons (yellow-green); $S_{(-)}$ was light of a longer wavelength (more yellow than $S_{(+)}$). During discrimination training, $S_{(+)}$ and $S_{(-)}$ were presented alternately for periods ranging from 1 min. to 3 min. in duration. When $S_{(+)}$ was present (i.e., when the light was yellow-green), pecking was occasionally rewarded by the presentation of food; on the other hand, the pigeon was never rewarded for pecking in the presence of $S_{(-)}$. (Under these conditions, the subjects eventually stopped responding in the presence of $S_{(-)}$ but continued responding in the presence of $S_{(+)}$.) In order to relate Spence's theory to this specific experimental situation, Hanson made the assumption that rate of pecking (number of pecks per minute) is positively related to effective excitatory tendency. (On this assumption it was possible, by presenting a variety of different wavelengths and determining the rate of responding in the presence of each, to assess the effective excitatory tendency at several points on the stimulus continuum following discrimination training. One of the deductions that Hanson's findings confirmed was the following:

THEOREM 5. After discrimination training in which a response is rewarded in the presence of $S_{(+)}$ but not in the presence of $S_{(-)}$, the stimulus to which rate of responding is greatest will be located at a point on the stimulus continuum above (or below) $S_{(+)}$ in the direction opposite $S_{(-)}$.

The basis for this theorem may be seen by examining Figure 12-2. It will be noted that the stimulus having the greatest effective excitatory tendency is not $S_{(+)}$ but a stimulus located between S_B and S_C, where the dashed curve meets the baseline.

Thus far in discussing Spence's theory of discrimination training we have emphasized the theory's success; that is, we have considered only theorems that have received experimental confirmation. However, as is often true of scientific theories, the theory as it stands has certain implications that are contrary to fact. The theorem we consider next is one that has been disconfirmed by experimental evidence. This theorem refers to discrimination training of the type employed in Hanson's study described above. In the statement of this theorem "discrimination training" refers to training in which $S_{(+)}$ (responses occasionally rewarded) and $S_{(-)}$ (responses never rewarded) are both employed; "simple conditioning" refers to training similar to discrimination training so far as $S_{(+)}$ is concerned but in which the animal has no experience at all with $S_{(-)}$.

THEOREM 6. Following discrimination training, no stimulus on the stimulus continuum will evoke as high a rate of responding as that evoked by $S_{(+)}$ following simple conditioning.

This theorem follows from a comparison of the upper and middle portions of Figure 12-1, which represent the situation following simple conditioning and discrimination training, respectively. It will be seen that at no point on the stimulus continuum in the middle diagram is the effective excitatory tendency as great as the effective excitatory tendency associated with $S_{(+)}$ in the upper diagram. However, Hanson's findings were clearly contrary to this prediction. It will be recalled that in his study $S_{(+)}$ was a light having a dominant wavelength of 550 millimicrons (yellow-green). In agreement with Theorem 5, subjects given discrimination training subsequently showed the highest rate of responding in the presence of a light having a dominant wavelength of 540 millimicrons (slightly greener than $S_{(+)}$). However, contrary to Theorem 6, the mean rate of responding to the latter stimulus was approximately twice the mean rate of responding to $S_{(+)}$ by a group of subjects that had received simple conditioning using $S_{(+)}$ only.

How are we to regard the theory in the light of this negative evidence?

The fact that the theory has led to many successful predictions (only a few of which have been considered here) encourages the belief that the theory may be basically sound and that it may be possible to resolve the discrepancy described above by a modification of certain details of the theory. The overall pattern of evidence suggests the fault might lie in the special assumption made to relate the theory to the type of training procedure employed by Hanson—the assumption concerning the relationship between rate of responding and effective excitatory tendency. (This assumption, it will be recalled, was not a part of the theory as originally proposed by Spence.) It seems likely that in a revised version of the theory there would be some sort of relationship between rate of responding and effective excitatory tendency; however, instead of being a simple positive relationship as assumed by Hanson, this relationship may be complicated by factors not fully understood at present. Of course, modifying the theory so as to account for only one additional experimental finding would be an accomplishment of rather limited consequence. What is to be hoped for is that a modification that successfully incorporates Hanson's discrepant finding will also have the effect of bringing within the compass of the theory other findings obtained in similar experimental situations.

THEORETICAL CONSTRUCTS

It will be noted that the concepts referred to in Spence's theory are of two types. On the one hand, variables such as the position of a stimulus on a specified continuum (e.g., the wavelength of a given light) or the number of times a given response occurs in the presence of a given stimulus are empirical concepts of the type considered in the preceding chapter; the values of such variables can be determined by suitable observations. On the other hand, the terms "excitatory tendency," "inhibitory tendency," and "effective excitatory tendency" refer to hypothetical variables that cannot be directly observed or measured. Terms of the latter type are referred to as *theoretical concepts* or—to emphasize that such concepts are invented or constructed by man—as *theoretical constructs*. The relationships among the empirical variables and theoretical constructs of Spence's theory may be represented schematically as shown in Figure 12-3. The symbols enclosed by the dashed line represent theoretical constructs; those outside represent empirical variables.

(In the following discussion of the relationships pictured in Figure 12-3, S_A refers to any given stimulus other than $S_{(+)}$ or $S_{(-)}$. The remaining symbols, which are summarized in the key to Figure 12-3, will be explained as they are introduced.)

Each arrow in the diagram represents a mathematical relationship between the variables connected by the arrow. For example, $E_{(+)}$, the excitatory tendency evoked by $S_{(+)}$, is a mathematical function of N_R, the

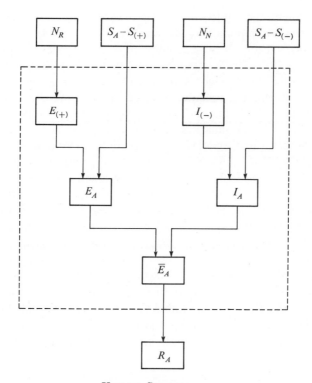

KEY TO SYMBOLS

N_R = Number of rewarded approaches to $S_{(+)}$

$S_A - S_{(+)}$ = Distance on the stimulus continuum between S_A (any given stimulus) and $S_{(+)}$

N_N = Number of nonrewarded approaches to $S_{(-)}$

$S_A - S_{(-)}$ = Distance on the stimulus continuum between S_A (any given stimulus) and $S_{(-)}$

$E_{(+)}$ = Excitatory tendency evoked by $S_{(+)}$

$I_{(-)}$ = Inhibitory tendency evoked by $S_{(-)}$

E_A = Excitatory tendency evoked by S_A

I_A = Inhibitory tendency evoked by S_A

$\overline{E}_A$ = Effective excitatory tendency evoked by S_A

R_A = Response of approaching S_A; more specifically, some measure of the performance of this response, e.g., frequency of occurrence

FIGURE 12-3 *Schematic representation of relationships among empirical variables and theoretical constructs in Spence's theory of discrimination learning.*

number of times the subject has been rewarded for approaching $S_{(+)}$. (Although this assumption was not stated explicitly in the above description of Spence's theory, it is an assumption of the broader theory of which the discrimination theory is a part, and is implicit in Postulate 1, given at the beginning of the previous subsection.)   Without going into the details of the mathematical function involved, the fact that $E_{(+)}$ is a mathematical function of N_R may be written symbolically as follows: $E_{(+)} = f(N_R)$.   (This notation indicates, without specifying the exact form of the relationship, that a mathematical equation could be written in which $E_{(+)}$ appears on the left of the equality sign and N_R, possibly with some constants, appears on the right.)   Similarly, the arrows leading to E_A, which represents the excitatory tendency evoked by S_A, indicate that the value of E_A is a function of $E_{(+)}$ and of the difference $S_A - S_{(+)}$, which represents the distance between S_A and $S_{(+)}$ on the stimulus continuum.   Stated symbolically, $E_A = f[E_{(+)}, (S_A - S_{(+)})]$.   This relationship is stated in the second postulate of Spence's theory and is represented graphically in Figure 12-2, which shows that the excitatory tendency associated with S_A depends upon $E_{(+)}$, i.e., the height of the curve at $S_{(+)}$, and upon the distance of S_A from $S_{(+)}$.   The symbol $I_{(-)}$ represents the inhibitory tendency evoked by $S_{(-)}$.   As indicated in Figure 12-3, the value of $I_{(-)}$ depends upon N_N, the number of trials on which the nonrewarded response of approaching $S_{(-)}$ has occurred (Postulate 3).   The arrows converging upon I_A (the inhibitory tendency evoked by S_A) indicate that the value of I_A depends upon the value of $I_{(-)}$ and upon the difference $S_A - S_{(-)}$, i.e., the distance of S_A from $S_{(-)}$ on the stimulus continuum (Postulate 4). The symbol $\bar{E}_A$ represents the effective excitatory tendency evoked by S_A. (The use of the bar in the symbol $\bar{E}$ does not imply that a mean value is involved; it merely serves to distinguish $\bar{E}$, the symbol for effective excitatory tendency, from E, the symbol for (gross) excitatory tendency.)   The arrows converging on $\bar{E}_A$ represent the mathematical relationship $\bar{E}_A = E_A - I_A$, which is the substance of the fifth postulate of Spence's theory.   Finally, R_A represents the observed frequency of occurrence of the response of approaching S_A.   The arrow connecting $\bar{E}_A$ with R_A represents the assumed relationship (Postulate 6) between effective excitatory tendency and response frequency.

It is a characteristic of the theory described above (but not of every theory) that the consequent empirical variable (R_A) is expressed as a mathematical function of certain theoretical constructs, and these theoretical constructs are in turn expressed as mathematical functions of antecedent empirical variables (or as a function of other theoretical constructs that are ultimately functions of empirical variables).   Consequently, it is mathematically possible to eliminate reference to the theoretical constructs altogether and to write a single complex equation relating R_A directly to the antecedent empirical variables of the theory, i.e., an equation of the general form $R_A = f[N_R, (S_A - S_{(+)}), N_N, (S_A - S_{(-)})]$. Theoretical constructs that, in the mathematical sense described above, intervene between the antecedent empirical variables of a theory on the one hand and the consequent empirical variables on the other hand, and that can be eliminated in the manner indicated above, are referred to as *intervening variables*. Because intervening variables are not logically essential to the theory of which they are a part (i.e., because the substance of the theory can be stated in the form of a complex equation without any reference to the intervening variables), some writers have questioned the usefulness of such constructs. However, although intervening variables are dispensable from a strictly logical point of view, it would appear that such constructs nonetheless serve an important function. We have seen that the intervening variables of the theory considered above are an outgrowth and elaboration of the basic idea that discrimination learning is the outcome of two separate processes, one (excitatory) involving the consequences of rewarded experiences with $S_{(+)}$, the other (inhibitory) involving the consequences of nonrewarded experiences with $S_{(-)}$. It seems highly improbable that any theorist would have arrived at the same end result—i.e., the complex equation, derivable from the theory, which relates R_A directly to the antecedents of the theory—without analyzing the total process into simpler components and without using the intervening variables that such an analysis suggests. Indeed, the resolution of complex processes into simpler component processes would seem to be a fundamental characteristic of scientific analysis and theory formation. As the above theory illustrates, the use of intervening variables may serve as an integral part of such analysis.

On the whole, behavioral events are more accessible to observation than the physiological processes underlying behavior. Although we do not as yet know a great deal about the connections between behavior and corresponding physiological processes, it is obvious that there must be lawful relationships between the two classes of events. Quite naturally, there have been numerous attempts to explain behavioral phenomena in terms of underlying physiological processes. One way this may be accomplished is to relate the theoretical constructs of a behaviorial theory to physiological variables. (For example, one hypothesis that has gained currency is that behavioral changes occurring during learning are the result of physiological changes at the junctures between neurons in the central nervous system. This hypothesis might be incorporated into Spence's theory of discrimination learning by assuming that increments in $E_{(+)}$ following rewarded approaches to $S_{(+)}$ are the result of physiological changes at the junctures of neurons in a specified region of the central nervous system. Such an assumption—or set of assumptions—would make possible the derivation of additional theorems concerning the role

of physiological variables in discrimination learning. The specific antecedent and consequent variables brought within the compass of the theory
would depend, of course, upon the details of the additional assumptions.
The additional antecedent variables might, for example, include such techniques as extirpation of portions of the brain, administration of drugs,
electrical stimulation of the brain, and so on; the consequent variables
might include changes in the brain detectable by chemical analysis or
microscopic examination of brain tissues. Following a terminological
convention suggested by MacCorquodale and Meehl (1948), it has become
customary to refer to theoretical constructs having a physiological interpretation, i.e., related to antecedent and/or consequent variables the observation of which involves physiological techniques, as *hypothetical constructs*.[4] The distinction between intervening variables and hypothetical
constructs corresponds to our intuitive feeling that there is something more
tangible—more "real"—about a theoretical construct related to specific
body structures (and thereby given a definite spatial location) than about
a mathematical abstraction (intervening variable). Aside from its intuitive
appeal, however, it is questionable whether the distinction between intervening variables and hypothetical constructs has any fundamental import.
Physiological observations, after all, are not inherently different from any
other type of observation, behavioral or otherwise; indeed, the classification of observations as behavioral, physiological, and so on, is a matter of
convention or convenience and not, so far as anyone has been able to demonstrate, basic or inherent in the nature of things. It would seem that the
function of all theoretical constructs, whether intervening variables or hypothetical constructs, is basically the same—they are building blocks in
constructing theories from which predictions concerning observable phenomena can be derived.[5]

It has sometimes been asserted that in order to insure that a theory
has testable implications every construct in a theory must be defined in
terms of empirical variables. This proposal is misleading in two respects.
First, in contrast to empirical concepts, the meaning of theoretical constructs is not established by defining the constructs individually. The
meaning of any given theoretical construct resides in its relationships to
other constructs of the theory and to the empirical concepts that the theory
encompasses. These relationships are not necessarily established by definition as this term is usually understood, but may be specified by the
postulates of the theory. Second, in order for a theory as a whole to have
implications that can be tested by observation, it is not necessary that

---

[4] This manner of formulating the distinction between intervening variables and
hypothetical constructs is a somewhat simplified version, suggested by Bergmann
(1953), of the distinction originally proposed by MacCorquodale and Meehl (1948).

[5] The point of view expressed here is by no means universally accepted. For a
summary of the literature bearing upon this issue and of the philosophical complexi-
ties that the issue entails, the reader should consult Meissner (1960).

every construct of the theory be directly related to empirical variables; in some theories the requirement of testability is satisfied by specifying relationships between empirical variables and certain selected constructs of the theory. Hempel (1952) cites the modern theory of chemistry as a case in point. In this theory two classes of constructs may be distinguished —(1) elementary particles (protons, electrons, and neutrons) and (2) atoms. The theory distinguishes a large number of different types of atoms, each corresponding to a different chemical element (copper, iron, nickel, etc.) and conceived to be a specific configuration of protons, electrons, and neutrons. (The chemical elements, which may be defined in terms of observable chemical and physical properties, are empirical concepts.) The elementary particles (protons, electrons, and neutrons) are not given a direct empirical interpretation; however, the theory as a whole is tied to observation by the correspondences established between the various theoretical atomic structures on the one hand and the various chemical elements on the other hand. Thus, the supposed requirement that every construct in a theory be directly related to (or defined in terms of) empirical variables is seen to be unnecessarily stringent; a more reasonable requirement is that a theory as a whole must be related in an unequivocal manner to observable phenomena and that every construct in it be related indirectly, if not directly, to empirical variables.

ANALOGY IN THEORY

The postulates of some theories may be viewed as a set of assumptions concerning unobservable processes underlying a set of observable phenomena. To illustrate, in the kinetic theory of gases certain observable characteristics of gases—for example, that the volume of a fixed quantity of gas varies in specified ways as a function of variations in the pressure and temperature of the gas—are derived from certain assumptions about the molecular structure of gases. According to the assumptions of this theory, a gas consists of a swarm of tiny particles that are in constant motion, bouncing back and forth off the walls of the enclosing container with undiminished energy. In a theory of this kind the properties ascribed to the unobserved (molecular) processes are often based upon an analogy to some set of observable phenomena. For example, in the kinetic theory of gases the hypothetical particles comprising a gas are assumed to have properties analogous to certain (but not all) of the properties of an idealized rubber ball—namely, mass, velocity, and perfect elasticity (bounce).

In a similar manner, a number of theoretical constructs employed in psychological theory are based upon analogy to observable responses. For example, thinking has frequently been interpreted to consist of unobservable behavior having many of the same properties as observable behavior. Similarly, emotional reactions have often been assumed to be internal processes having the properties of observable responses.

One of the most widely used constructs of this type is the theoretical construct "fear." According to one formulation of this construct (Mowrer, 1939, 1947), fear is assumed to have the properties of a classically conditionable response such as salivation. That is, it is assumed (1) that certain types of painful stimulation (e.g., electric shock) have the innate capacity to elicit the fear reaction, just as certain types of stimulation (e.g., food) innately elicit the response of salivation, and (2) that a neutral stimulus repeatedly paired with such a stimulus will itself acquire the capacity to elicit the fear reaction, just as a neutral stimulus paired with food will acquire the capacity to elicit salivation. It is further assumed that occurrence of the fear reaction produces internal stimulation ("feedback") that is aversive, so that any response that regularly results in diminution of the fear reaction (thereby reducing the aversive stimulation produced by that reaction) will be strengthened.

The above theoretical formulation has been found to be useful in interpreting a wide variety of experimental findings. One of the findings relating most directly to this formulation has been obtained by Brown and Jacobs (1949) using rats as subjects. In the first part of this experiment a neutral stimulus (an intermittent tone and a blinking light presented in combination) was repeatedly paired with electric shock, a stimulus that presumably has the innate capacity to elicit the hypothetical fear reaction. (According to the assumptions outlined above, the originally neutral tone-light combination should, as a result of such preliminary training, acquire the capacity to elicit the hypothetical fear reaction.) The animals then received training in a second situation designed to assess the effects on behavior of terminating the tone-light combination alone. The response used for test purposes was jumping a small hurdle. Each trial began with the presentation of the tone-light combination; this compound stimulus was terminated (and the trial ended) immediately following the occurrence of a hurdle-jumping response. As predicted by the theoretical formulation described above, it was found that termination of the tone-light combination resulted in learning of the jumping response, indicated by the fact that this response occurred more and more promptly as training progressed. (According to the theory, termination of the tone-light combination strengthens the hurdle-jumping response because removal of the tone-light combination causes fear to subside, and with it the aversive feedback that fear produces.) That the effectiveness of terminating the tone-light combination depended upon the prior pairing of this stimulus with electric shock was indicated by the fact that a control group trained in an identical manner in the hurdle-jumping situation, but not given prior pairing of the tone-light combination with shock, did not learn the hurdle-jumping response.

It will be noted that, whereas we can directly observe the response of salivation, after which the assumed properties of the fear reaction are patterned, we cannot directly observe fear. It might be argued that we could observe fear if we wished to—that we could, for example, measure the rat's heart rate or blood pressure. We could, indeed, observe a variety of such physiological functions, but none of these can be equated with the construct "fear." (Heart rate and blood pressure, for example, vary with exercise as well as with emotion.) It may well be that certain physiological changes could fruitfully be related to the construct "fear" as consequent empirical variables, but observing such changes would not be the same as observing the theoretical construct "fear."

REFERENCES

BERGMANN, G. Theoretical psychology. *Annu. Rev. Psychol.*, 1953, **4**, 435–458.

BROWN, J. S. and A. JACOBS. The role of fear in the motivation and acquisition of responses. *J. exp. Psychol.*, 1949, **39**, 747–759.

EHRENFREUND, D. A study of the transposition gradient. *J. exp. Psychol.*, 1952, **43**, 81–87.

FEIGL, H. Logical empiricism. In D. D. Runes (ed.), *Twentieth century philosophy*. New York: Philosophical Library, 1943. Pp. 371–416.

GYNTHER, M. D. Differential eyelid conditioning as a function of stimulus similarity and strength of response to the CS. *J. exp. Psychol.*, 1957, **53**, 408 416.

HANSON, H. M. Effects of discrimination training on stimulus generalization. *J. exp. Psychol.*, 1959, **58**, 321–334.

HEMPEL, C. G. *Fundamentals of concept formation in empirical science. Int. Encycl. Unified Sci.*, Vol. 2, No. 7. Chicago: Univ. of Chicago Press, 1952.

HULL, C. L. *Principles of behavior.* New York: Appleton-Century-Crofts, 1943.

KIMBLE, G. A. *Hilgard and Marquis' conditioning and learning.* New York: Appleton-Century-Crofts, 1961.

KUENNE, MARGARET R. Experimental investigation of the relation of language to transposition behavior in young children. *J. exp. Psychol.*, 1946, **36**, 471–490.

MAC CORQUODALE, K. and P. E. MEEHL. On a distinction between hypothetical constructs and intervening variables. *Psychol. Rev.*, 1948, **55**, 95–107.

MEISSNER, W. W. Intervening constructs—dimensions of controversy. *Psychol. Rev.*, 1960, **67**, 51–72.

MOWRER, O. H. A stimulus-response analysis of anxiety and its role as a reinforcing agent. *Psychol. Rev.*, 1939, **46**, 553–565.

———. On the dual nature of learning—a re-interpretation of "conditioning" and "problem-solving." *Harvard Educ. Rev.*, 1947, **17**, 102–148.

SPENCE, K. W. The differential response in animals to stimuli varying within a single dimension. *Psychol. Rev.*, 1937, **44**, 430–444.

———. *Behavior theory and conditioning.* New Haven: Yale Univ. Press, 1956.

ADDITIONAL READINGS

FEIGL, H.   Operationism and scientific method: rejoinders and second thoughts. *Psych. Rev.*, 1945, **52,** 284–288.

FEIGL, H. and MAY BRODBECK.   *Readings in the philosophy of science.*   New York: Appleton-Century-Crofts, 1953.

HEMPEL, C. G. and P. OPPENHEIM.   Studies in the logic of explanation.   *Phil. Sci.*, 1948, **15,** 135–175, especially Part I.

MANDLER, G. and W. KESSEN.   *The language of psychology.*   New York: Wiley, 1959.   Part II.

MC GUIGAN, F. J.   *Experimental psychology.*   Englewood Cliffs, N. J.: Prentice-Hall, 1960.   Chaps. 11–13.

PART **IV**

measurement and psychophysics

It is readily apparent that many of the most impressive accomplishments of modern science derive from laws and theories formulated in quantitative form. It is also apparent that the utility of quantitative laws and theories depends largely upon the availability of suitable measurement procedures, i.e., procedures that permit the recording of observations in numerical form. Accordingly, there has been considerable emphasis in the field of psychology on the development of measurement techniques for recording observations of behavioral phenomena. Many forms of measurement used in the study of behavior are commonplace and require no special comment; on the other hand, some of the attempts to extend measurement to behavioral problems have required the development of new and unfamiliar measurement procedures. In order to evaluate some of the newer techniques psychologists in many quarters have become increasingly concerned with the fundamental character of the measurement process.

Chapter 15, the major chapter of Part IV, examines the logic underlying several approaches to the scaling (measurement) of sensory reactions. Chapters 13 and 14 provide background for Chapter 15: Chapter 13 describes several classical methods that figure prominently in the study of sensory processes; Chapter 14 briefly examines the basic principles underlying several familiar measurement procedures, thus providing a frame of reference for examining the psychological scaling methods described in Chapter 15.

stimulus thresholds

and differential sensitivity

TWO GENERAL TYPES OF QUESTION ARE FUNDAMENTAL TO THE QUANTITA-
tive study of sensory processes:

1. What is the weakest stimulus an individual can detect?
2. What is the smallest difference between two stimuli that an individual can discern?

For any given type of stimulus (sound, light, touch, or other) the weakest stimulus that can be detected is called the *stimulus threshold* (or *detection threshold*);[1] the smallest difference that can be discriminated is called a *just noticeable difference,* commonly abbreviated jnd. In this chapter we shall consider three general procedures—so-called psychophysical methods —designed to answer questions of the types stated above. Although we shall concentrate chiefly on the application of these methods to the assessment of differential sensitivity, i.e., the ability to discern stimulus differences, we shall also note briefly how each of these methods can be adapted to the determination of stimulus thresholds.

The designation *stimulus threshold* suggests that there is some hard-and-fast cutting point (minimum intensity) below which stimuli of a given kind are never detected and above which such stimuli are always detected. However, experimental findings indicate that this is not the case. While

---

[1] Because the techniques in question originated in German laboratories, the German term "limen" is often used in place of "threshold," its English equivalent.

it is true for any given type of stimulus that below a certain intensity stimuli are never detected and above a certain intensity stimuli are almost always detected, the transition is never abrupt: there is always a range of intensities over which the probability that a stimulus will be detected gradually increases from a value near zero to a value near one.   Similarly, for any given type of stimulus, there is no one difference such that all smaller differences are never discriminated and all larger differences always are.   Rather, the probability that a difference will be discriminated approximates zero for very small differences and gradually approaches unity as the size of the difference increases.   Thus, in a certain sense the concepts of stimulus threshold and jnd may be said to be statistical fictions, although such a characterization should not be construed as diminishing the importance or usefulness of these concepts.   The stimulus threshold is commonly taken to be the stimulus intensity for which there is a 50-50 chance of detection, i.e., for which the probability of detection is .50.   It is not possible to characterize the nature of the jnd in an equally simple manner that is applicable to all of the methods to be considered; the specific interpretation of this concept differs somewhat among the various methods, and—although a jnd determined by one method is comparable to other jnd's obtained by the same method—jnd's obtained by different methods are not strictly comparable.

Before turning to a detailed description of the methods to be considered, one further comment of a general nature is in order.   The above remarks concerning the jnd may have suggested that for any given stimulus dimension and any given method of assessing differential sensitivity, there is one, and only one, value of the jnd.   However, such is not the case.   As we shall note in greater detail later in the chapter, for many stimulus dimensions the value of the jnd depends upon the magnitude of the stimuli under consideration.   In determining the jnd for soft sounds, for example, the jnd is relatively small, whereas for louder sounds the jnd is larger.   Thus, as a general rule, the value of the jnd must be regarded as specific to a particular stimulus magnitude.   In describing the three psychophysical methods considered below, we shall overlook this complication and shall simply consider the manner in which the jnd is determined for any specific stimulus magnitude; later in the chapter we shall return to the question of how the jnd varies as a function of changes in stimulus magnitude.

THE METHOD OF ADJUSTMENT

The application of this method to the measurement of differential sensitivity will be considered first.

The distinctive feature of the *method of adjustment,* also known as the *method of average error,* is that the subject is presented with a variable stimulus that he (or the experimenter) adjusts until it appears equal to some fixed standard stimulus. The method may be applied to any attribute that can be varied continuously—as, for example, the intensity of light, or the intensity or frequency of an auditory stimulus. For purposes of illustration, we shall consider the discrimination of differences in the lengths of straight lines.

In order to collect our observations we require some means of presenting one line of fixed length to serve as a standard and a second line that can be varied in length to match the standard. For this purpose a simple apparatus such as pictured in Figure 13-1 might be used. This device con-

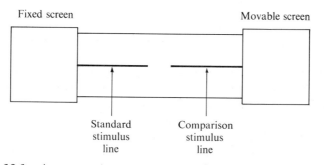

Fixed screen   Movable screen

Standard stimulus line   Comparison stimulus line

FIGURE 13-1 *Apparatus for presenting two lines, one of fixed length and the other of variable length.*

sists of three pieces of cardboard, on one of which are drawn two horizontal lines. The two remaining pieces of cardboard are used as screens to cover the ends of the two lines, thus determining the length of each line apparent to the subject. Let us suppose that the line on the left is taken as the standard and the one on the right as the variable or comparison stimulus. The position of the left-hand screen is fixed so that the left-hand line has some arbitrary length. The subject is then given a series of trials on each of which he is required to adjust the variable stimulus so that it appears to be equal in length to the standard. As a precaution against any systematic error that might be introduced by always starting with the variable line longer than the standard or always with the variable line shorter, at the beginning of some trials the experimenter sets the variable line obviously longer than the standard and at the beginning of other trials he sets the variable line obviously shorter than the standard. After each adjustment by the subject, the experimenter measures the length of the variable line and then sets it out of adjustment for the next trial.

Illustrative data—40 settings by one subject—are shown in Table 13-1. In this experiment the standard stimulus was a line 4 in. long, and settings of the variable stimulus were recorded to the nearest .02 in. It will be noted that the distribution is centered in the neighborhood of $4\frac{1}{3}$ in.—somewhat greater than the length of the standard—and that in its general features it resembles a normal curve, being more or less symmetrical, with a

TABLE 13-1 *Distribution of settings of variable line using method of adjustment*

ADJUSTED LENGTH (INCHES)	FREQUENCY
4.76–4.84	1
4.66–4.74	3
4.56–4.64	3
4.46–4.54	5
4.36–4.44	6
4.26–4.34	7
4.16–4.24	4
4.06–4.14	6
3.96–4.04	2
3.86–3.94	3

concentration of cases in the middle of the distribution and a gradual falling off of frequency on either side.   In the light of these data, what do we conclude is the least difference the subject can detect?   The distribution of settings suggests there is no simple answer to this question; rather, it seems that the subject's capacity to detect differences varies from trial to trial.   We might say that on some trials the subject detects (and corrects by adjusting) very small discrepancies between the standard and the variable stimulus, whereas on other trials he tolerates (fails to detect) rather large discrepancies.   In other words, the subject's performance is characterized on each trial by a certain error, the magnitude and direction of which varies from trial to trial.   If we wished, we could express the information presented in Table 13-1 in terms of the subject's errors simply by subtracting 4 in.—the correct length—from each setting.   The error scores thus obtained would have the same shape distribution as the original scores, the difference being that the errors would be centered close to zero, some being negative and others being positive.

If we cannot specify a fixed difference that the subject can always detect, can we at least find some manner of characterizing in a general way his sensitivity to differences?   Suppose a second subject had keener discrimination, i.e., was able to detect smaller differences than the first subject.   How would we expect the distributions of the two subjects to differ? The answer is fairly apparent: we would expect the settings of both subjects to be centered at approximately the same value, with the subject who has greater sensitivity to differences exhibiting less variability in his settings —i.e., tolerating relatively large errors less often—than the subject less sensitive to differences.   Thus, in the method of adjustment the general concept of jnd—which, as we have already noted, is a convenient statistical fiction—may be equated with some measure of the variability of a subject's settings, most commonly the semi-interquartile range, or *s*, the sample standard deviation. For the data presented in Table 13-1 the semi-inter-quartile range is .18 in., which is slightly less than 5 per cent of the standard.

The mean of the subject's settings is called the *point of subjective equality,* abbreviated PSE. This mean may be conceived as an estimate of μ, the mean of all possible settings by a given subject under a given set of conditions. The mean of the distribution presented in Table 13-1 is 4.32 in., which is in rough agreement with the true length of the standard.

Sometimes systematic factors operate to bias the subject's settings away from the value of the standard, as occurs, for example, in so-called optical illusions. One such illusion is the well known Müller-Lyer illusion pictured in Figure 13-2. Here, although the two segments of the horizon-

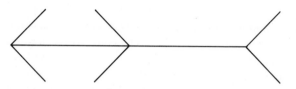

FIGURE 13-2 *Müller-Lyer illusion. The two horizontal line segments are actually equal in length, although they appear unequal.*

tal line are actually equal, the segment on the left appears shorter than that on the right. To assess the extent of the illusion using the method of adjustment we can make the right-hand segment of the line adjustable and instruct a subject to adjust it so that it appears equal to the fixed left-hand segment. Following such a procedure, the discrepancy between the PSE and the setting that is actually equal to the standard is an indication of the extent of the illusion. This discrepancy is called the *constant error,* abbreviated CE, and is given by the formula

$$CE = PSE - \text{Standard}$$

For one subject, with the left-hand segment of the Müller-Lyer illusion fixed at 5.5 in., the mean of ten settings of the right-hand segment was 4.2 in. In this instance the constant error was $4.2 - 5.5 = -1.3$ in., an error amounting to almost 25 per cent of the standard. This example serves to illustrate how the PSE and the derivative concept of CE may be of value in assessing the effect of factors that operate to bias a subject's judgments.

As noted earlier, each of the psychophysical methods may be adapted to the problem of determining stimulus thresholds, the least intense stimuli that a subject can detect. For example, using the method of adjustment to determine the stimulus threshold of auditory intensity (i.e., the least in-tense tone that a subject can hear), the following procedure may be employed: On some trials the tone is first set above the threshold and then adjusted by the subject until it is just imperceptible; on other trials the tone is set below the threshold and adjusted until it is just perceptible. The stimulus threshold is taken as the average of the subject's settings on the two types of trials.

THE METHOD OF CONSTANT STIMULI

It is not always convenient to provide a stimulus that can be varied continuously, as required by the method of adjustment. One method that can be used with stimuli that are varied in discrete steps is the *method of constant stimuli*. Used to assess differential sensitivity, this method employs one standard stimulus and a series of fixed comparison stimuli—the constant stimuli of the method's name. The comparison stimuli are presented several times each, one at a time in an irregular order, and on each presentation judged in relation to the standard. Two variations of the method of constant stimuli may be distinguished according to the variety of responses the subject is permitted. One procedure is to allow the subject to report the comparison stimulus as being equal to, greater than, or less than the standard. A difficulty with this procedure is that the range of comparisons to be included under the designation "equal" is a matter of individual interpretation, with some subjects using this response much more freely than others. This complication is avoided if the subjects are not permitted to characterize any pair of stimuli as equal but in each case must report the comparison stimulus as being greater than or less than the standard. The subject is thus forced to make discriminations to the limit of his capacity and is not permitted the "out"—of which subjects may avail themselves to different degrees—of reporting two stimuli as equal.

A representative set of data has been provided by Brown (1910), using a procedure in which a subject judged the weights of a series of containers all having the same external size and appearance. The object serving as a standard stimulus weighed 100 gm.; the comparison objects ranged in weight from 82 gm. to 110 gm. On each trial the subject first lifted the standard and then one of the comparison weights and indicated whether the comparison weight seemed heavier or lighter than the standard. The subject made 200 sets of judgments; in each set of judgments each of the comparison stimuli was presented once, the sequence of the stimuli being determined by chance. Thus, each comparison stimulus was judged in relation to the standard stimulus 200 times.

Brown's results are summarized in Figure 13-3, which shows the proportion of times each comparison stimulus was judged greater than the standard. It will be noted that the 82-gm. weight was almost never judged heavier than the standard. As the weight of the comparison stimulus increased, the frequency of "greater" judgments increased in a more or less regular fashion, reaching 100 per cent at the 110-gm. weight.

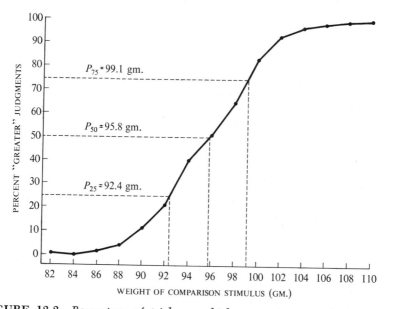

FIGURE 13-3 *Percentage of trials on which comparison stimuli (weights) were judged greater than a standard stimulus of 100 gm. The dashed lines indicate the values of weights judged greater than the standard 25 per cent, 50 per cent, and 75 per cent of the time. Although these values are not percentiles in the usual sense, they are determined in a manner analogous to that used in the determination of percentiles. Based upon data reported by Brown* (1910).

It is apparent from Figure 13-3 that the increase in frequency of "greater" judgments is gradual, with no abrupt changes at any point in the series. Thus, as in the case of the method of adjustment, we cannot identify any unique difference such that all greater differences can be detected and all lesser differences cannot; the frequency with which a difference is detected varies continuously with variations in the magnitude of the difference.

Even though there is no hard-and-fast cutting point separating differences that are perceptible from those that are not, it would nevertheless be useful to have some manner of characterizing and comparing the keenness of discrimination of different subjects under the same condition or of the same subject under different conditions. When data are plotted as shown in Figure 13-3, the discriminative capacity of the subject is indicated by the steepness with which the curve rises. For subjects having keen discrimination of differences, or under conditions favoring fine discrimination, it is necessary to present comparison stimuli only slightly greater than the standard to obtain close to 100 per cent "greater" judgments and to present comparison stimuli only slightly less than the standard to obtain zero per cent "greater" judgments.   In other words, for such subjects, or under such conditions, the curve will rise steeply from zero to 100 per cent.   On the other hand, for subjects having poor discrimination, or under conditions not favoring fine discrimination, zero per cent and 100 per cent "greater" judgments will be attained only with comparison stimuli far removed from the standard.

A variety of methods may be used to describe the steepness of a graph such as shown in Figure 13-3.   The simplest of these is analogous to determining the semi-interquartile range graphically from a cumulative distribution polygon.   Although the graph shown in Figure 13-3 was not obtained in the same manner as a cumulative polygon, certain similarities to a cumulative polygon are readily apparent.   Using the notation introduced in connection with percentiles (Chapter 2), the stimuli for which the proportions of "greater" judgments are 25 per cent and 75 per cent may be designated as P_{25} and P_{75}, respectively.   For the data presented in Figure 13-3, P_{25} is approximately 92.4 gm., and P_{75} is approximately 99.1 gm. To describe the steepness of the curve we compute $(P_{75} - P_{25})/2 = (99.1 - 92.4)/2 = 3.35$ gm.   This measure may be construed as the jnd, which, as we have previously noted, is merely a convenient statistical fiction.   For a subject whose discriminative capacity is keener, or under conditions where discrimination is better, the graph corresponding to that in Figure 13-3 would be steeper, and the jnd would be smaller.   Conversely, for a subject whose discriminative capacity is coarser, or under conditions where discrimination is poorer, the graph would rise more gradually, and the jnd would be larger.

Using data obtained by the method of constant stimuli, the PSE is taken as the stimulus judged greater than the standard 50 per cent of the time.   For Brown's subject the PSE, designated as P_{50} in Figure 13-3, is seen to be approximately 95.8 gm.—somewhat less than the standard.

When used to determine stimulus thresholds, the method of constant stimuli makes no use of a standard stimulus but employs a series of stimuli of varying intensity ranging from below the threshold to above it.   As the subject is presented with each stimulus he must report whether or not he detected it.   For example, if the stimuli are tones of varying intensity, the subject must report whether or not he can hear each of the stimuli; if the stimuli are sugar solutions of varying concentrations, the subject must report whether or not each solution tastes sweet; and so on.   A graph similar to that presented in Figure 13-3 is plotted showing the increase in the relative frequency of positive responses with increases in stimulus intensity.   The threshold is usually taken to be the stimulus that the subject detects 50 per cent of the time.

THE METHOD OF LIMITS

While the method of constant stimuli can always be used to assess differential sensitivity using stimuli that vary in discrete steps, a disadvantage of this method is that it requires a very large number of stimulus presentations if stable results are to be obtained.   A somewhat less time-consuming procedure that also makes use of stimuli varying in discrete steps is the *method of limits*.   In this method the comparison stimuli are presented to the subject one at a time in the order of increasing or decreasing magnitude, and the subject is required to indicate whether each comparison stimulus appears less than, equal to, or greater than the standard.   Usually the entire series of comparison stimuli is presented several times, alternately in ascending and descending order.   The method of limits may be illustrated by its application to the visual discrimination of angles.

> The standard stimulus in our illustrative experiment consisted of two straight lines drawn on a 5-by-8-in. card in the form of a V.   The lines were each 3 in. long and were separated by an angle of 50°. The comparison stimuli, each drawn on a separate 5-by-8-in. card, were similar V's varying in angular separation from 39° to 61° in steps of 1°.   The card with the standard stimulus remained in the subject's view throughout the experiment, and the comparison stimuli were presented one at a time beside the standard stimulus.   Each ascending series was begun with an angle obviously smaller than the standard and continued until the subject first reported one of the angles as greater than the standard.   Similarly, each descending series was begun with an angle obviously greater than the standard and continued until the subject reported one of the angles as less than the standard.

The results are shown in Table 13-2, in which each column lists the responses given in an ascending or descending series of comparison stimuli. It will be noted that the first series was an ascending series starting with the 39° comparison stimulus.   In this series all the comparison stimuli from 39° to 44° were reported by the subject as less than the standard, and the stimuli from 45° to 49° were reported as equal to the standard; the first comparison stimulus reported greater than the standard had a separation of 50°.   A comparison of the various columns indicates that the points of transition between "equal" and "greater" and between "equal" and "less" varied from series to series.

The first step in analyzing data obtained by the method of limits is to compute the so-called interval of uncertainty (IU), i.e., the range of values of the comparison stimulus that are reported as appearing equal to the standard.   The upper limit (UL) for a given series is taken as the point midway between the first (or last) "greater" report and the adjacent report of "equal."   Similarly, the lower limit (LL) is taken as the point

TABLE 13-2 *Judgments of angular separation using method of limits*

Comparison Stimulus: Angular Separation in Degrees	Type of Series (Ascending or Descending)							
	A	D	A	D	A	D	A	D
61		G						
60		G				G		
59		G				G		
58		G		G		G		G
57		G		G		G		G
56		G		G		G		G
55		G		G		G		G
54		G		G		G		G
53		G		G		G	G	G
52		E		G	G	G	E	G
51		E	G	G	E	G	E	E
50	G	E	E	E	E	E	E	E
49	E	E	E	E	E	E	E	E
48	E	E	E	E	E	E	E	L
47	E	E	E	E	E	E	E	
46	E	E	E	E	L	E	L	
45	E	E	L	E	L	L	L	
44	L	L	L	L	L		L	
43	L		L		L		L	
42	L		L		L		L	
41	L				L			
40	L				L			
39	L							
UL	49.5°	52.5°	50.5°	50.5°	51.5°	50.5°	52.5°	51.5°
LL	44.5°	44.5°	45.5°	44.5°	46.5°	45.5°	46.5°	48.5°

Mean UL $\approx 51.1°$
Mean LL $\approx 45.8°$

$IU = UL - LL \approx 5.3°$

$jnd = \dfrac{IU}{2} \approx 2.7°$

$PSE = \dfrac{UL + LL}{2} \approx 48.5°$

$CE = PSE - 50° \approx -1.5°$

midway between the first (or last) stimulus reported less and the adjacent stimulus reported equal.[2]   In Table 13-2 upper and lower limits for each

[2] Sometimes the data are not so orderly as those in Table 13-2. That is, the "equal" responses may not be grouped all together but may be intermixed with judgments of "greater" or "less." The criteria customarily used in determining the UL and LL of such irregular series are as follows: In an ascending series the first change of report (whether to "equal" or "greater") is taken as the LL; the point of transition to the first report of "greater" is taken as the UL.   In a descending series the first change of report (whether to "equal" or "less") is taken as the UL and the point of transition to the first report of "less" is taken as the LL.

series are recorded at the bottom of the respective column.   To determine the interval of uncertainty averaged over all series the mean of the several upper limits and the mean of the several lower limits are computed; the difference between these two means is taken as the overall interval of uncertainty.   For the data reported in Table 13-2 the IU is seen to be 5.3°.

The point of subjective equality is taken to be the point midway between LL and UL, i.e., the mean of LL and UL.   For the data of Table 13-2 the PSE is 48.5°, somewhat below the actual point of equality.   It is not unusual for the PSE to differ somewhat from the value of the standard. As in the other psychophysical methods, the discrepancy (CE) is due in part to sampling error and, in some instances, to certain systematic factors operating to bias the subject's judgments.   Such systematic factors may be thought of as being comparable to, though not so striking as, the factors that bias the subject's judgments in illusions (e.g., the Müller-Lyer illusion considered earlier in this chapter).

Using the method of limits, the jnd is defined as the distance from the PSE to either boundary of the IU—in other words, half the interval of uncertainty.   For the data presented in Table 13-2 the jnd, to the nearest tenth of a degree, is $(IU)/2 \approx 2.7°$.

As applied to the discrimination of differences, the method of limits differs in a rather fundamental respect from the two methods considered earlier.   On the one hand, the methods considered earlier force the subject to discriminate to the limit of his capacity: the method of adjustment requires him to set the comparison stimulus so that it appears to be *exactly* equal to the standard, and when judgments of "equal" are precluded, the method of constant stimuli forces the subject, however small the difference, to characterize the comparison stimulus as greater or less than the standard. On the other hand, the use of an "equal" category is inherent in the method of limits, with the result that the subject may characterize a range of stimuli as being so close to the standard that he cannot detect any difference from it.   As noted earlier, the use of an "equal" category leaves it to the subject's discretion what sort of a difference shall be called equal.   While some subjects may reserve this designation for extremely small differences, others may apply it to any difference that is at all doubtful.   Thus, differences among subjects in the size of the jnd for a given type of stimulus may reflect differences in the way the subjects interpret the judgment of "equal," rather than differences in differential sensitivity.   That the use of the "equal" category is a matter of individual interpretation is substantiated in a study by Fernberger (1931), in which it was shown that, using three categories in the method of constant stimuli, the range of stimuli included in the "equal" category was modified by variations in the instructions given subjects.   Presumably, even among subjects instructed alike, similar differences arise as a result of differences in the way a given set of instructions is interpreted.

The use of the method of limits to determine stimulus thresholds is free of the above difficulty, for in this application the method does not employ an "equal" category. Here the subject merely indicates whether or not he detects the stimulus in question. The subject is given several ascending and descending series, and the average point of transition is taken as the stimulus threshold.

A variation of the method of limits devised by Békésy (1947) for the determination of stimulus thresholds of auditory stimuli makes use of stimuli that vary continuously rather than in discrete steps. In Békésy's method the subject depresses a telegraph key for as long as he hears the tone. While the key is depressed, the tone is gradually diminished in intensity, constituting a descending series. When the subject can no longer hear the tone he releases the key, and the intensity of the tone gradually increases, constituting an ascending series. In this way the tone is made to oscillate closely about the subject's stimulus threshold.

APPLICATIONS OF THE PSYCHOPHYSICAL METHODS

Once methods for measuring differential sensitivity and stimulus thresholds are available, it is possible to investigate the manner in which these quantities vary in relation to other variables—in other words, to formulate empirical laws concerning differential sensitivity and stimulus thresholds. Indeed, studies of this kind make up a large part of the literature concerning sensory processes. To attempt an extensive survey of this body of research is beyond the scope of the present book, but a small number of representative findings will be cited briefly for purposes of illustration.

A basic problem in the field of sensory psychology concerns the manner in which differential sensitivity varies as a function of stimulus magnitude. Research indicates that for a great many stimulus dimensions— the loudness of sounds, the brightness of lights, the heaviness of lifted weights, and the length of lines, to mention but a few—as stimulus magnitude increases, the size of the jnd increases also. For many stimulus dimensions the size of the jnd is roughly proportional to stimulus magnitude, a fact that may be expressed in the form of the following equation:

$$\mathrm{jnd} = kS \qquad (13\text{-}1)$$

in which k is a constant (which varies from one sense modality to another), and S is the magnitude of the standard stimulus.[3] For example,

---

[3] Because the value of the jnd for a given value of S differs somewhat depending upon which of the psychophysical methods is used to assess differential sensitivity, there are corresponding variations in the value of k depending on the method employed.

suppose that in judging lifted weights the value of k for a given individual using a given psychophysical method is .02. Using a standard stimulus of 100 gm. (approximately $3\frac{1}{2}$ oz.), the jnd would be $.02(100) = 2$ gm. On the other hand, using a standard stimulus of 500 gm., the jnd would be $.02(500) = 10$ gm. The relationship described in Equation (13-1) was first suggested by E. H. Weber in 1834 and has come to be known as *Weber's Law*. An alternative formulation of Weber's Law may be obtained by dividing both sides of Equation (13-1) by S, yielding the following equation:

$$\frac{\text{jnd}}{S} = k \tag{13-2}$$

According to this equation, if the size of the jnd is expressed as a proportion of the magnitude of the standard stimulus, the resulting fraction is a constant, i.e., the same for all values of the standard.

For many stimulus dimensions Weber's Law provides a good approximation of the size of the jnd over the middle range of stimulus values, but for values of the standard near the stimulus threshold the size of the jnd is considerably larger than predicted on the basis of Equation (13-1). An equation that fits the experimental findings somewhat better than Equation (13-1) is the following:

$$\text{jnd} = kS + c$$

in which k and c are both constants (Luce and Galanter, 1963). In this equation the value of c, relative to the product kS, is negligible for large values of S, but constitutes an appreciable proportion of the value of the jnd for small values of S. Other proposed modifications of Weber's Law are discussed by Guilford (1954, pp. 39–42).

The phenomenon of dark adaptation (Hecht, 1934) provides a classic example of a law involving changes in the stimulus threshold. As most of us have observed informally, when we first go into the dark (e.g., in a movie theater) vision is poor, but gradually our eyes become accustomed to the dark, and vision improves. This phenomenon may be studied systematically by determining the stimulus threshold for light after varying intervals in the dark. As a rule, some variation of the method of limits is used for this purpose. Typical results are shown in Figure 13-4, which indicates that with increasing time in the dark there is a gradual lowering of the threshold. An interesting feature of these results is that the curve consists of two distinct segments. The first portion of the curve reflects adaptation of the cones, the receptors active at normal daylight levels of illumination; the second segment reflects the slower but more extensive adaptation of the rods, the receptors that are effective at low, nighttime levels of illumination.

An ingenious application of psychophysical methods to animal subjects has been devised by Blough (1956), using a modification of Békésy's

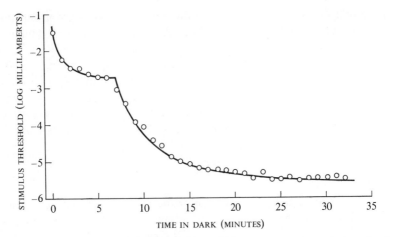

FIGURE 13-4 *Changes in threshold for light as a function of time in dark. Adapted from Hecht (1934).*

version of the method of limits. In Blough's procedure pigeons were placed in a darkened test chamber provided with a visual stimulus—a circular aperture illuminated from behind by a dim light of adjustable intensity—and two response keys, *A* and *B*, situated one above the other just below the stimulus. First, the pigeons were trained to peck at Key *A* when the light was on, and at Key *B* when the light was off. This was accomplished by arranging conditions so that (*1*) when the light was off, and only then, pecking Key *B* was rewarded by presenting the pigeon with food and (*2*) pecking Key *A* turned off the light. (Even in the dark, not every response to Key *B* was rewarded: it was necessary to peck at Key *B* several times in order to receive food. Similarly, when the light was on, it was necessary to peck Key *A* several times in order to turn the light off.) Following this preliminary training, the procedure was made into a psychophysical experiment as follows: conditions were arranged so that each peck of Key *A* that failed to extinguish the light nevertheless caused the light to dim slightly, much as in Békésy's technique depressing a telegraph key causes a tone to grow gradually dimmer; conversely, each peck of Key *B*, unless it resulted in presentation of food, caused the light to grow slightly brighter. Thus, as the pigeon pecked Key *A*, the intensity of the light gradually diminished to the point where the pigeon could no longer see it, whereupon the pigeon switched to Key *B*. However, pecking Key *B* caused the light to grow brighter, so that it soon became visible again, causing the pigeon to switch back to Key *A*. Under these conditions the pigeon's behavior controls the intensity of the light, causing it to oscillate above and below the threshold of vision in much the same manner as an auditory stimulus is made to "track" the auditory threshold in Békésy's technique. Hence, the average setting of the light may be taken as the stimulus threshold. Now, if a pigeon is first exposed to bright light and then placed in a darkened test chamber, we would expect that during the period in the dark the pigeon would undergo dark adaptation, and this change should be reflected in a gradual lowering of the threshold. Indeed, that is exactly what happens, and the dark-adaptation curve traced by the pigeon closely resembles that obtained using human subjects, clearly showing cone and rod segments similar to those seen in Figure 13-4. The fact that as a result of suitable training procedures pigeons can be made to "tell" us when they see a light and when they do not is consonant with the position stated in Chapter 11, that verbal reports concerning private events are responses learned as a consequence of appropriate discrimination training.

Finally, it may be noted that the measurement of differential sensitivity occupies a prominent role in the field of sensory scaling. This application of the concept of jnd will be considered in detail in Chapter 15.

PROBLEMS

1. In a psychophysical experiment the subject's task was to adjust a light of variable intensity so that it appeared equal in brightness to a standard stimulus having an intensity of 50 units. Twelve settings of the variable stimulus by Subject *A*, arranged in order of magnitude, were as follows: 45, 46, 47, 47, 48, 48, 48, 49, 49, 50, 50, 51. Twelve settings of the variable stimulus by Subject *B*, also arranged in order of magnitude, were as follows: 39, 41, 44, 46, 47, 48, 49, 50, 51, 52, 55, 57. (*a*) Determine the PSE for each of the above subjects. (*b*) Determine the constant error of each subject. (*c*) Determine the semi-interquartile range of each of the above distributions. (*d*) Which of the two subjects exhibits finer discriminative capacity?

2. In a psychophysical experiment using the method of constant stimuli, each of a series of comparison stimuli (lights of different intensity) was judged 100 times in relation to a standard stimulus having an intensity of 50 units. The values of the comparison stimuli and the frequency with which each was judged greater than the standard by one subject were as follows:

Intensity of Comparison Stimulus (Arbitrary Units)	46	47	48	49	50	51
Frequency of "Greater" Judgments	8	15	35	65	85	95

Plot a graph showing variations in percentage of "greater" judgments as a function of intensity of the comparison stimulus. Determine the numerical values of (*a*) the jnd (i.e., half the distance between the two points on the stimulus continuum for which the proportions of "greater" responses are .25 and .75), (*b*) the PSE, and (*c*) the CE.

3. For a second subject tested in the manner described in Problem 2, the results were as follows:

Intensity of Comparison Stimulus (Arbitrary Units)	46	47	48	49	50	51
Frequency of "Greater" Judgments	2	5	25	75	95	98

Plot these results on the same axes as the results presented in Problem 2. Which of the two subjects has finer discrimination?

4. In a psychophysical experiment employing the method of limits and designed to assess differential sensitivity, the standard stimulus was a light having an intensity of 50 units. A series of comparison stimuli ranging from 43 to 53 intensity units in steps of one unit were employed. The results obtained in four series—two ascending and two descending—with one subject are given below. (The symbols L, E, and G indicate that the comparison stimulus in question was judged, respectively, less than, equal to, or greater than the standard.)

INTENSITY OF COMPARISON STIMULUS

TYPE OF SERIES	43	44	45	46	47	48	49	50	51	52	53
Ascending	L	L	L	L	E	E	E	E	G		
Descending			L	E	E	E	E	G	G	G	G
Ascending	L	L	L	L	E	E	E	E	G		
Descending			L	E	E	E	E	G	G		

Following the computational procedures illustrated in Table 13-2, determine the LL and UL for each series and compute the values of (a) the mean LL and mean UL averaged over all series, (b) the IU, (c) the jnd, (d) the PSE, and (e) the CE.

5. Using a standard stimulus having an intensity of 50 units, the mean jnd for a sample of subjects was found to be 2 intensity units. According to the simple version of Weber's Law described in Equations (13-1) and (13-2), what would be the value of the jnd (a) using a standard stimulus having an intensity of 200 units and (b) using a standard stimulus having an intensity of 1,000 units?

REFERENCES

BÉKÉSY, G. VON   A new audiometer. *Acta. Oto-Laryng. Stockh.*, 1947, **35,** 411–422.   Cited by S. S. Stevens, Problems and methods of psychophysics. *Psychol. Bull.,* 1958, **55,** 177–196. Pp. 183–184.

BLOUGH, D. S.   Dark adaptation in the pigeon. *J. comp. physiol. Psychol.,* 1956, **49,** 425–430.

BROWN, W.   The judgment of difference, with special reference to the doctrine of the threshold in the case of lifted weights. *Univ. Calif. Publ. Psychol.,* 1910, **1,** 1–71.

FERNBERGER, S. W.   Instructions and the psychophysical limen. *Amer. J. Psychol.,* 1931, **43,** 361–376.

GUILFORD, J. P.   *Psychometric methods* (2d ed.).   New York: McGraw-Hill, 1954.

HECHT, S. Vision: II. The nature of the photoreceptor process. In C. Murchison (ed.), *A handbook of general experimental psychology*. Worcester, Mass.: Clark Univ. Press, 1934.

LUCE, R. D. and E. GALANTER. Discrimination. In R. D. Luce, R. R. Bush, and E. Galanter (eds.), *Handbook of mathematical psychology*. New York: Wiley, 1963. Pp. 191–243.

ADDITIONAL READINGS

ANDREAS, B. G. *Experimental psychology*. New York: Wiley, 1960. Chap. 5.

GALANTER, E. Contemporary psychophysics. In T. M. Newcomb (ed.), *New directions in psychology*. New York: Holt, Rinehart and Winston, 1962. Pp. 87–156. A discussion of recent developments in the field of psychophysics, including studies of the effects of rewards and penalties for correct and incorrect responses.

WOODWORTH, R. S. and H. SCHLOSBERG. *Experimental psychology* (rev. ed.). New York: Holt, 1954. Chap. 8. A detailed discussion of methods used in determining stimulus thresholds and differential sensitivity. Summarizes several studies bearing upon Weber's Law.

CHAPTER **14**

measurement (*1*): *basic concepts*

MEASUREMENT—THE USE OF NUMBERS IN DESCRIBING EMPIRICAL PHE-
nomena—plays a basic role in many branches of modern science. Its
prominent position results from the advantages, for describing certain types
of characteristics, that it affords over qualitative description. One of the
chief advantages of measurement is increased precision of description. For
example, lacking a procedure for measuring height, we might describe an
individual's height as short, average, or tall. The use of such crude descriptive categories has two chief limitations: first, individuals differing appreciably in height are lumped indiscriminately in the same category, and second,
because the precise limits of the various categories are not clearly specified,
uniform usage of these categories by different observers cannot reasonably
be expected. On the other hand, by means of measurement much finer
differentiations of height can be made uniformly by different observers. A
second advantage of measurement derives from its role in the formulation
of quantitative laws. Although the fact that a given attribute can be
measured does not guarantee it will be found to enter into lawful relationships with other variables, only measurable variables can enter into the
formulation of quantitative laws. Compared with laws formulated in qualitative terms, quantitative laws have the advantage that deductions may be
derived from them using the powerful procedures of mathematics (e.g.,
algebra and calculus), with the result that predictions based upon quantitative laws are frequently more detailed and precise than those based upon
laws formulated in qualitative terms. To be sure, there are a number of
important scientific areas that do not lend themselves to measurement and
the formulation of quantitative laws, and in such areas qualitative description and qualitative laws play an indispensable role; nonetheless, the fact

remains that some of the most useful scientific laws are those expressed in quantitative form, and the value of such laws almost invariably rests upon the availability of associated measurement procedures.

ELEMENTARY NUMBER THEORY—
AN ORIENTATION TO THE CONCEPT OF NUMBER

In view of the central role played by numbers in the measurement process, an understanding of the concept of number will be useful as background for our examination of measurement. In modern mathematics numbers are viewed as a system of abstract mathematical concepts having a variety of empirical interpretations, i.e., practical applications. Familiar uses of numbers include counting (i.e., describing how many objects or individuals are contained in a group) and the measurement of such variables as distance, time, and temperature; applications within the field of psychology include the use of numbers to describe various aptitudes (e.g., verbal fluency) and the intensity of various sensory experiences (e.g., the loudness of tones). In each case, employing numbers to describe an empirical phenomenon is useful because the formal relationships among numbers are in some way analogous to observable relationships among the objects or events being described. However, numerical relationships that have a meaningful interpretation in connection with one type of measurement may have no comparable interpretation in connection with another. For example, we may say in connection with measures of length that the difference between 90 in. and 100 in. is the same as the difference between 140 in. and 150 in., but it is problematic whether we are justified in saying that the difference between an IQ of 90 and an IQ of 100 is the same as the difference between an IQ of 140 and an IQ of 150. In this chapter we shall briefly examine the nature of numbers and the various ways that numbers are used in the description of empirical phenomena. The purpose of this discussion will be to provide a frame of reference for examining and evaluating some of the measurement procedures developed comparatively recently in the field of psychology, examples of which are considered in the following chapter.

COUNTING—THE PROTOTYPE OF MEASUREMENT

The basic properties of numbers may be illustrated with reference to the process of counting. (Indeed, as we shall see later in the chapter, many of the most familiar forms of measurement may be construed as special applications of counting.) In examining the properties of numbers that are essential to the process of counting, it is instructive to consider how the functions served by counting might be performed—in a primitive society, say—without the use of numbers as we know them.   One of the basic items of information afforded by counting is the relative size of groups, i.e., information concerning which of two groups contains more members.   The fundamental empirical procedure for comparing two groups with respect to size is to place the members of the groups in one-to-one correspondence. A colorful example of this basic procedure is given by Kershner and Wilcox (1950): A tribal chieftain, wishing to determine which of two tribes—his or a neighboring tribe—has more warriors, might call a "peace conference," in which at some stage of the proceedings each member of Tribe A is paired with a corresponding member of Tribe B, perhaps in some ritualistic dance. If, when every member of Tribe A is so occupied, there are some members of Tribe B left over, the chieftain can conclude that Tribe B has more warriors than Tribe A (and therefore would have an advantage in battle). On the other hand, if neither group had any members left over after placing the members of the two groups in one-to-one correspondence, he would conclude that the two tribes had the same number of warriors.   This procedure, placing the members of two groups in one-to-one correspondence, is the basic operation for comparing groups with respect to size.   Whenever we say that two groups are the same size or that one has more members than the other, we are making reference, implicitly if not explicitly, to the outcome of such a procedure.

A second basic operation underlying the interpretation of numbers as used in counting is the procedure of combining groups.   Described in general terms, this procedure consists in treating the members of two or more groups interchangeably as members of a single combined group.   For example, the chieftain of Tribe A, contemplating an attack on Tribe B and finding that Tribe B has more warriors than Tribe A, might form an alliance with Tribe C, making arrangements for the members of Tribes A and C to join forces and serve interchangeably in battle against members of Tribe B. In the same way that we might inquire which of two groups, A or B, has more members, we may also inquire whether the combination of two groups (e.g., A and C) has more or less members than a third group, B.   The procedure for making such a comparison consists, of course, in establishing a one-to-one correspondence between the members of Group B on the one hand and the combined members of Groups A and C on the other hand, treating the members of the latter two groups as interchangeable for purposes of making the comparison.

In comparing two groups, it is not always feasible or convenient to bring the members of one group into physical proximity with members of the other so that the members of the two groups can be set in direct one-to-one correspondence.   To circumvent this difficulty some intermediate group may be used for purposes of making a comparison.   For example, the chieftain of Tribe A might assemble a collection of as many pebbles as there are warriors in his tribe, i.e., a group of pebbles that can be set in exact one-to-one correspondence with his warriors. He might then visit Tribe *B*, taking with him this collection of pebbles and comparing the number of pebbles with the number of warriors in Tribe *B*. Such a procedure is useful because of the empirical fact (law) that two groups that match the same intermediate group also match one another.

The same chieftain might find it convenient to assemble several different sets of pebbles for ready reference, one corresponding in number to the number of warriors in his tribe; another, to the number of cattle on his farm; a third, to the number of huts in his village; and so on. It is but a small step to the development of a series of "all-purpose," "standard" groups for use in the indirect comparison of various groups of practical interest (warriors, cattle, etc.). It would be a simple matter—and highly convenient—to arrange such a collection of standard groups in a series according to size so that each group contains one more pebble than the one before it in the series, i.e., so that the combination of any given group in the series (n) with the first group in the series (1) would match the succeeding group in the series ($n + 1$). A further improvement would be the identification, for ease of reference, of each of the standard groups by a distinctive symbol. Although any of several arbitrary systems of symbols would serve this purpose, let us for reasons of simplicity assume that the symbols with which we are familiar—1, 2, 3, and so forth—are employed.

The system of hypothetical standard groups described above may be viewed as a concrete representation of the number system—or, more precisely, as a representation of that portion of the number system known as the *natural numbers*. This system serves as a frame of reference for describing the size of any collection of objects. To describe the size of any given collection we simply specify to which of the standard groups it corresponds in size. In effect, this is what we accomplish when we count the number of objects in a collection; the last number reached in the counting process identifies the standard group to which the collection being counted corresponds in size. Extending an observation made earlier, if we wish to compare two groups with respect to size, it is not necessary to set the members of the two groups in direct correspondence with one another; instead, the comparison can be made indirectly using the set of standard groups (numbers) as an intermediate device. If two groups both match the same standard group, they are of the same size; if they do not match the same standard group, we may determine which is larger by noting which one matches a standard group higher in the series.

The rules of arithmetic describe a set of relationships of great importance. For example, the statement $2 + 3 = 5$ asserts that if any collection matching Standard Group 2 is combined with a collection matching Standard Group 3, the combination will match Standard Group 5 (and, hence, will match any other collection that matches Standard Group 5) Such rules are enormously useful in that they enable us to predict the outcome of various sorts of combinations before such combinations are actually performed.

Given any two numbers, we may distinguish between them three basic relationships—their order, the difference between them, and the ratio of one to the other. For example, consider the numbers 4 and 12. Of these two numbers, 12 is greater, i.e., comes after 4 in the number series; the difference between them, $12 - 4$, is 8; and their ratio, $12/4$, is 3. In using certain types of measurement procedures, all three of these relationships among numbers have an empirical interpretation; in the case of other measurement procedures only certain of these relationships have a meaningful empirical interpretation. As further background for our discussion of different types of measurement, we shall briefly examine the empirical meaning of these three relationships in connection with counting.

The empirical interpretation of the order among numbers has already been explained and need not be repeated in detail here. Briefly, if, as a result of counting, two groups are assigned different numbers, that group assigned the number higher in the number series is the larger of the two groups.

The empirical interpretation of the difference between two numbers rests upon the physical operation of combining groups. When we say the difference between 12 and 4 is 8, we mean that if a group of 8 members is combined with a group of 4 members, the combination will be equal in size to a group having 12 members. (Alternatively, the difference between two numbers may be interpreted in terms of a physical operation that is essentially the inverse of the operation of combination. This operation, which may be called *physical subtraction,* consists in setting the objects of two groups in one-to-one correspondence and taking as a third group those members of the larger group that are left over after all members of the smaller group have been paired. Thus, if we set the members of a group of 4 in one-to-one correspondence with members of a group of 12, there will be 8 members of the latter group left over after all members of the former group have been used.)

The ratio of two numbers, like the difference, may be interpreted in terms of the operation of combination. The ratio between the number 12 and the number 4 is the number 3. This abstract mathematical relationship corresponds to the physical fact that the combination of three groups of 4 is equal in size to a group of 12. (Alternatively, the ratio of two numbers may be interpreted in terms of successive applications of the operation of physical subtraction. If the members of a group of 4 are set in one-to-one correspondence with members of a group of 12, some members of the larger group will be left over after all members of the smaller group are used. We may then repeat the process, pairing the members of the group of 4 with the members left over from the group of 12, until the members of the group of 4 are again used up. If this procedure is repeated enough times, all the members of the original group of 12 will eventually be exhausted. The mathematical statement that $12/4 = 3$ corresponds to the empirical fact that, using a group of 4 and a group of 12, three repetitions of the above procedure will use up all the members in the larger group.)

MEASUREMENT SCALES—A CLASSIFICATION

Measurement may be defined as the use of numbers to describe attributes of objects or events. The procedures (rules) for measuring any given attribute are said to establish a *scale* of the attribute in question—the procedures for measuring length establish a scale of length, those for measuring time establish a scale of time, and so on. On the basis of the types of measurement procedures used and of the types of empirical interpretations that can be made of the numbers employed, it is possible to distinguish several broad classes of measurement scales. The three types of scales that we shall consider are (1) *ordinal,* (2) *interval,* and (3) *ratio* scales of measurement. We shall consider first the most primitive of the three, ordinal scales.

ORDINAL SCALES

Ordinal scales are so named because only one characteristic of the numbers assigned using such a scale—namely, their order—has an empirical interpretation. In order to establish an ordinal scale for measuring some attribute it is necessary to have an empirical criterion for ordering objects (or events) with respect to the attribute in question—that is, a procedure such that, given any two objects possessing that attribute, it is possible to determine whether the two objects are physically equal with respect to that attribute or, if the objects are not physically equal, which is greater. One of the simplest examples of an ordinal scale of measurement is the scale of hardness devised by Friedrich Mohs in the early part of the nineteenth century. In this scale the physical procedure for ordering minerals with respect to hardness is the scratch test: if a sharp point of mineral *A* scratches a flat surface of mineral *B,* mineral *A* is said to be harder than mineral *B;* if neither scratches the other, the two minerals are said to be of equal hardness. To anchor his scale to the number series Mohs selected a set of ten minerals ranging in hardness from the softest known mineral (talc) to the hardest (diamond) and assigned these minerals the numbers from 1 to 10, 1 indicating the softest mineral in the series, 10 the hardest. Minerals not included in the series of standards are assigned intermediate numbers on the basis of the scratch test. For example, steel, which scratches feldspar (No. 6) and is scratched by quartz (No. 7), is assigned the value 6½ (Spencer, 1961).

It is fairly obvious that in order for a scale constructed in this way to serve a useful purpose the empirical procedure for ordering objects must satisfy certain criteria. One such requirement is that the relationship "physically greater" must be *transitive*. This means that the relationship must be such that if object *A* is physically greater (e.g., harder) than object *B,* and object *B* is physically greater than object *C,* then object *A* is physically greater than object *C.* (In terms of the scratch test, if *A* scratches *B,* and *B* scratches *C,* then *A* scratches *C.*) Similarly, the relationship "physically equal" must be transitive; in other words, if *A* is physically equal to *B,* and *B* is physically equal to *C,* then *A* must also be physically equal to *C.* Whether a given physical relationship satisfies the above requirements is an empirical question, i.e., one that can be settled by observation. Certain procedures that upon superficial examination might seem reasonable as a basis for establishing an ordinal scale of measurement do not, as a matter of fact, meet these criteria. Suppose, for example, that we wish to establish an ordinal scale for describing the skill of professional boxers. It might occur to us to take as our basis for ordering any two boxers the outcome of a match between them. However, we would find this criterion unsatisfactory as a basis for establishing an ordinal scale of boxing skill because the relationship of winning is not, as a matter of fact, transitive—it is not always the case, when boxer *A* has defeated boxer *B,* and *B* has defeated *C,* that *A* defeats *C.*

Let us now consider the interpretations that can be made of numbers assigned using an ordinal scale of measurement. Here we might rephrase an old adage as follows: "You get no more out of a scale than you put into it." The only information taken into account in assigning numbers to objects using an ordinal scale is the order (or equality) of the objects in question. Accordingly, the only characteristics of the numbers having empirical significance (meaning) is their order. The numbers assigned to two objects using an ordinal scale of measurement indicate whether the two objects are physically equal with respect to the attribute in question or, if not, which is greater—and nothing more. The difference between two numbers has no empirical meaning, nor does their ratio. The fact that the numbers 1 and 3 (the values assigned to talc and calcite, respectively, on the Mohs scale of hardness) differ by the same amount as the numbers 4 and 6 (the numbers assigned to fluorite and feldspar) does not mean that the difference in physical hardness between the first pair of minerals is the same as the difference in hardness between the second pair. Indeed, the procedures used in establishing the scale provide no basis whatsoever for interpreting the magnitude of differences. Similarly, the fact that the value assigned to feldspar is twice as great as the value assigned to calcite has no physical interpretation.

Thus, aside from considerations of convenience, the use of the numbers 1 through 10 in the Mohs scale of hardness is seen to be purely arbitrary, and any other set of ten numbers could have been employed, provided only that the numbers were assigned in such a way that the order relationships among the numbers corresponded to the ordering of the minerals by the scratch test.

INTERVAL AND RATIO SCALES

Arranged in terms of how many characteristics of numbers have empirical significance, ordinal scales of measurement would be ranked lowest and ratio scales highest, with interval scales occupying an intermediate position. Thus, if we were to consider the three types of scales in an order corresponding to the empirical significance of the numbers provided by each type of scale, we would consider interval scales of measurement next. However, the concepts necessary for understanding the properties of interval scales of measurement can be developed most effectively by first considering ratio scales. Accordingly, these two types of scale, interval and ratio, will be considered together in the present subsection.

Perhaps the most familiar measurement procedures providing ratio scales of measurement are those employed in the measurement of length, mass, and temporal duration. The development of a ratio scale, like that of an ordinal scale, presupposes a procedure for ordering objects with respect to the attribute being measured. In this regard, the requirements are the same as in establishing an ordinal scale of measurement: criteria must be specified for determining whether two objects are physically equal, or which is greater, and these physical relationships must satisfy the requirements (e.g., transitivity) considered in connection with ordinal scales of measurement. To illustrate, the procedure for ordering any two rigid rods with respect to length consists in placing the rods side by side, so that they coincide at one end, and noting whether they also coincide at the other end, or if one is longer. The analogous operation for comparing two objects with respect to mass involves placing the objects in opposite pans of a balance. (See Figure 14-1.) If the two objects balance, they are said to be equal with respect to mass; if the balance tips in the direction of one of the objects, that object is said to have the greater mass.

The characteristics distinguishing ratio scales from ordinal scales derive from the use of a procedure for physically combining two or more objects with respect to the attribute being measured. In measuring length, for example, the lengths of two rigid rods are combined by placing the rods

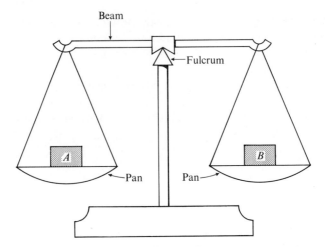

FIGURE 14-1 *Schematic representation of balance used for measuring mass. The essential components of the balance are (1) a beam, (2) a pair of pans suspended from opposite ends of the beam, and (3) a fulcrum, a wedge-shaped object with a narrow edge, upon which the beam and pans are balanced.*

end-to-end in a straight line; in measuring mass, the masses of two objects are combined by placing those objects in the same pan of a balance. Given (*a*) a procedure for ordering objects with respect to a particular attribute and (*b*) a method of combining them with respect to the same attribute, a ratio scale may be established by the following three rules or conventions (Hempel, 1952):

1. A unit of measurement is established by adopting an arbitrary object as a standard and assigning that object the value 1. For example, the *meter*, a unit of length, is defined as the distance between two lines engraved on a particular metal bar (kept in a vault in Sèvres, France), replicas of which have been distributed to nations throughout the world. Similarly, the *gram*, a unit of mass, is defined as the mass of a particular cylinder of metal.

2. Objects, or combinations of objects, that are physically equal are assigned the same numerical value.

3. The combination of two or more objects is assigned a numerical value equal to the sum of the values assigned to the separate objects.

Thus, if two rods, each equal in length to the standard meter, are placed end to end, the combination is said to be 2 meters long; a single rod equal in length to the combination is also 2 meters long; the combination, say, of a rod 2 meters long and a rod 3 meters long is 5 meters long; and so on.

A system of measurement based upon the procedures described above has a number of implications (strictly speaking, an infinite number) of the following sort: since the combination, say, of a rod 6 meters long with a rod 4 meters long is assigned the same numerical value (10 meters) as the combination of a rod 8 meters long with a rod 2 meters long, the two combinations should be physically equal in length. While such implications follow logically from the system of measurement described, there is no necessary reason why natural phenomena must conform to the implications of man-made systems. That lengths as measured by the above system do, as a matter of fact, conform to implications such as described above is an empirical finding of great importance, a finding upon which the value of the system rests.

It will be noted that there is a close parallel between measurement procedures of the kind described above and counting: although any given application of these measurement procedures need not actually involve counting, the results obtained are equivalent to a count of the number of units of measurement that must be combined to equal the object being measured. Because of the close parallel between counting and measurement of the type here under consideration, each of the three relationships among numbers (order, differences, and ratios) considered earlier in connection with counting has a similar interpretation in connection with this type of measurement. The interpretation of order is essentially the same as in the case of ordinal scales of measurement and need not be considered in detail here. The interpretation of differences and ratios will be illustrated with reference to measures of length. The differences between two lengths, x meters and y meters, is the amount that would, if combined with the smaller, yield a combination physically equal to the larger. That is, the empirical meaning of the statement, "The difference between 6 meters and 10 meters is 4 meters," is that the combination of an object 4 meters in length with one 6 meters in length is physically equal to an object 10 meters in length. The ratio between two lengths specifies how many objects of the shorter length must be combined in order for the combination to equal the longer length. Thus, when we say that a distance of 10 meters is five times as great as a distance of 2 meters, we mean that a combination of five objects each 2 meters long is physically equal to an object 10 meters long. We see that, as in the case of counting, the interpretation of intervals and ratios among measurements of this kind rests upon a procedure of combination.

Having examined the characteristics of ratio scales, we turn now to a consideration of interval scales. The essential features of an interval scale may be illustrated by a ratio scale with a "misplaced zero"—for example, a ruler from which 2 in. have been removed, as shown in Figure 14-2.

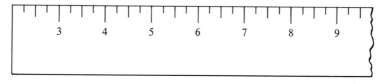

FIGURE 14-2 *Model of an interval scale—a ruler with a "misplaced zero."*

Using such a ruler, the order of the numbers assigned to different physical objects and the differences among the numbers would have meaningful empirical interpretations, but the ratios among the numbers assigned to objects would not.   Suppose, for example, that using the ruler shown in Figure 14-2 the numbers assigned to three objects, A, B, and C, were 4, 6, and 8 units, respectively.   The order of these numbers indicates that if the three objects were compared in length by placing them side by side, A would be found to be the shortest, and C the longest, of the three.   If we examine the differences among the values assigned to the three objects, we note that the difference between the values assigned to A and B is the same as the difference between the values assigned to B and C.   The equality of the two differences indicates that the length that must be combined with A to make the combination physically equal to B is the same as the length that must be combined with B to make the latter combination physically equal to C.   However, the ratios among the values assigned to the three objects have no meaningful empirical interpretation: for example, although the value assigned to C is twice the value assigned to A, it would not be the case that a combination of two objects equal in length to object A (each of which would be assigned a value of 2 in. using an ordinary ruler) would be equal in length to object C (which would be assigned a value of 6 in. using an ordinary ruler).

Although it serves to illustrate the properties of interval scales, the example of a sawed-off ruler is trivial because there would never be any good reason to use such an instrument for serious measurement.   Certain other examples sometimes cited—e.g., calendar time (which is based upon an arbitrary zero)—seem equally trivial.   On the other hand, the Fahrenheit and Centigrade scales of temperature, frequently cited as examples of interval scales of measurement, deserve more serious consideration.   (To simplify the present discussion we shall consider only the Centigrade scale, which assigns the value 0° C. to the temperature of ice water and the value 100° C. to the temperature of water boiling at sea level.)   It is readily apparent that the Centigrade scale of temperature is not a ratio scale, for the zero point is clearly arbitrary.   It makes no sense to assert, for example, that a temperature of 20° C. is twice as great as a temperature of 10° C.—that is to say, no useful empirical interpretation of such an assertion is known.   On the other hand, we are inclined to regard differences (intervals) on this scale as being meaningful in ways that differences on an ordinal scale are not.   For example, our intuition suggests that the difference between 40° C. and 50° C. is less than the difference between 50° C. and 100° C., equal to the difference between 50° C. and 60° C., and greater than the difference between 50° C. and 55° C.   However, establishing specific criteria to support our intuition is somewhat problematic.   In considering scales such as used in the measurement of length and of mass, we saw that the interpretation of differences among measures rested upon a method of combining objects with respect to the attribute in question. However, there is no way of combining two objects with respect to temperature so that the combination has a temperature equal to the sum of the temperatures of the separate objects; consequently, differences in temperature cannot be interpreted in a manner analogous to differences in length or in mass.   At bottom, the justification for regarding temperature as an interval scale appears to rest upon the fact that temperature is related to a number of other variables by numerical laws.   Consider, for example, the following experiment.   A specific quantity of water is heated by burning a quantity of some fuel, say gasoline.   If we represent the temperature of the water before heating by t_1, the temperature after heating by t_2, and the amount of fuel by m, the increase in the temperature of the water as a result of heating, $t_2 - t_1$, is related to the amount of fuel as follows: $t_2 - t_1 = km$, in which k is a constant whose value depends upon the particular fuel employed.   In other words, the increase in temperature is directly proportional to m, the amount of fuel burned.   One implication of the relationship between increase in temperature and amount of fuel burned is that if a given quantity of fuel is sufficient to raise the temperature of a given body of water from, say, 40° C. to 50° C., the same amount of fuel will raise the temperature of the same body of water from 60° C. to 70° C. (More generally, within the range of temperatures between 0° C. and 100° C. a given amount of fuel will raise the temperature of a given amount of water the same number of degrees, regardless of the initial temperature of the water.)   In contrast to measures of temperature, measures obtained using purely ordinal scales such as the Mohs scale of hardness do not bear lawful relationships, expressible in the form of algebraic functions, to other empirical variables.   The distinction between measures of temperature and measures obtained with scales such as the Mohs scale would seem to warrant the classification of the temperature scale in a different category than ordinal scales of measurement, i.e., in a category in which differences (intervals), but not ratios, have a meaningful empirical interpretation.   It is well to keep in mind, however, that the interpretation of differences in temperature is of a different sort than the interpretation of differences in such measures as length or mass.   As we have already noted, differences in length are interpreted in terms of an operation for combining objects with respect to length, differences in mass are interpreted in terms of an operation for combining objects with respect to mass; on the other hand, differences in temperature are not interpreted in terms of a method of combination, but in terms of lawful numerical relationships to other empirical variables.   The basis for regarding the Centigrade scale of temperature as an interval scale is of special interest because, as we shall see in the next chapter, the claim of many psychological scales to a status higher than ordinal measurement, like that of the temperature scale, is based upon indirect criteria rather than upon the availability of a mode of combination.

REFERENCES

HEMPEL, C. G.   *Fundamentals of concept formation in empirical science.   Int. Encycl. Unified Sci.,* Vol. 2, No. 7.   Chicago: Univ. of Chicago Press, 1952.

KERSHNER, R. B. and L. R. WILCOX   *The anatomy of mathematics.*   New York: Ronald, 1950.   A work marked by a singularly lively style without sacrificing rigor.

SPENCER, L. J.   Abrasives.   *Encyclopaedia Britannica,* Vol. 1.   Chicago: Benton, 1961.   Pp. 54–55.

ADDITIONAL READINGS

BERGMANN, G. and K. W. SPENCE.   The logic of psychophysical measurement. *Psychol. Rev.,* 1944, **51**, 1–24.   A somewhat technical discussion of the basic principles of measurement.

REESE, T. W.   The application of the theory of physical measurement to the measurement of psychological magnitudes, with three experimental examples.   *Psychol. Monogr.,* 1943, **55**, No. 3, 1–89.   Includes a detailed discussion of the basic principles of measurement.

STEVENS, S. S.   Mathematics, measurement, and psychophysics.   In S. S. Stevens (ed.), *Handbook of experimental psychology.*   New York: Wiley, 1951.   Pp. 1–49.

TORGERSON, W. S.   *Theory and methods of scaling.*   New York: Wiley, 1958. Chaps. 1 and 2.   A discussion, at an intermediate level of difficulty, of the basic principles of measurement.

CHAPTER 15

measurement (2): sensory scaling

THE BASIC IDEAS UNDERLYING SENSORY SCALING MAY BE ILLUSTRATED with reference to a series of taste stimuli—for example, a series of salt solutions varying in concentration of salt.   As the concentration of salt in a solution varies, there is a corresponding variation in taste experience: very dilute solutions have a weak salt taste, highly concentrated solutions have a strong taste.   In the terminology of Chapter 11, each of a series of stimuli (S_A, S_B, · · ·) varying in concentration gives rise to a corresponding sensory-perceptual event (P_A, P_B, · · · , respectively).   Thus, we may distinguish between two basic kinds of continua, represented schematically in Figure 15-1: (1) a *stimulus continuum,* on which each stimulus

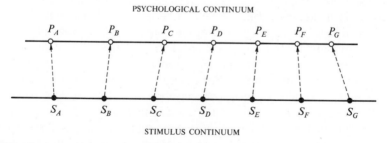

FIGURE 15-1 *Schematic representation of a stimulus continuum and the psychological continuum to which it gives rise. Spacing of P values on the psychological continuum differs from spacing of S values on the stimulus continuum.*

has a specific location, and (2) a corresponding *psychological continuum,* on which each sensory-perceptual event has a location.

It is common to refer to certain psychological continua as *sensory continua* and to others as *perceptual continua*. For example, the loudness of sounds, the pitch of musical tones, the color of visual stimuli, and the intensity of tastes are customarily referred to as sensory continua; on the other hand, the subjective lengths of lines, the apparent size of geometric figures, the apparent numerosity of collections of dots, and the apparent velocity of moving objects are referred to as perceptual continua. In referring to continua of the former group, the particular reaction evoked by a particular stimulus is called a *sensation;* when referring to continua of the latter group, the reaction evoked by a particular stimulus is called a *percept* or *perception*. Many writers have attempted to clarify the nature of the distinction between sensation and perception, but as yet there is no simple manner of formulating the distinction that has gained wide acceptance. (This does not necessarily mean that there is no difference, only that we cannot at present say exactly what the difference, if any, is.) In any event, whether the distinction is of a fundamental character or purely verbal, the general principles and procedures discussed in this chapter are applicable to both sensory and perceptual continua; accordingly, comments of a general nature should be understood to apply to both. In order to avoid excessive repetition of the somewhat awkward label *sensory-perceptual event,* the simpler term *sensation* will frequently be employed instead. The term is used merely for convenience of exposition and is not intended to denote something distinct from perception.

The position of any given stimulus along the stimulus continuum is determined by the physical characteristics of the stimulus and, in the case of many stimulus continua, may be described in numerical terms—e.g., percentage of maximum possible salt concentration. The basic idea underlying sensory scaling is that the location of sensory-perceptual events (or, as we shall say, *sensations*) along the psychological continuum may also be described in numerical terms. It should be noted that, although the location of sensations along the psychological continuum is presumably related in a systematic manner to the location of the corresponding stimuli along the stimulus continuum, the spacing of sensations is not necessarily the same as the spacing of stimuli. For example, let us suppose that three salt solutions, S_A, S_B, and S_C, have concentrations of 2 per cent, 4 per cent, and 6 per cent, respectively, of the maximum possible concentration of salt. It is to be expected that of these three stimuli S_A will give rise to the weakest sensation; S_C, to the strongest. However, the fact that the three stimuli are equally spaced along the stimulus continuum (each exceeds the preceding one by two percentage units), does not necessarily imply that the corresponding sensations will be equally spaced along the psychological continuum. The noncorrespondence of distances on the two types of continua is indicated in Figure 15-1, where equal steps on the stimulus continuum are shown as giving rise to steps of decreasing size on the psychological continuum.

According to the point of view presented in Chapter 11, "stimulus continuum" is an empirical concept; "psychological continuum," a theoretical construct. A given stimulus is publicly observable, and its location on the stimulus continuum can be determined by direct measurement procedures; on the other hand, a given sensation is not publicly observable, and its location on the psychological continuum cannot be determined by direct measurement in the usual sense. The location on the psychological continuum of the sensation produced by any given stimulus is inferred on the basis of the observable behavior of a responding organism, usually a human subject. Thus, sensation may be viewed as an intervening variable—i.e., a theoretical construct, capable of description in numerical terms, intervening between an observable physical stimulus on the one hand and observable behavior on the other hand.

The general notion that sensations vary along psychological continua and that the location of a particular sensation on a particular continuum can be specified in numerical terms has obvious intuitive appeal. However, the specific manner in which a given psychological continuum should be scaled—i.e., the set of procedures to be used in assigning numbers to specific sensations—is not immediately clear. Indeed, we shall find that a variety of disparate procedures, some of which lead to very different results, have been proposed to accomplish this aim. In this chapter we shall examine a number of representative scaling procedures. The classification, for purposes of exposition, of the procedures to be considered presents something of a problem, for there appear in the literature almost as many classification schemes as there are writers in the field. Some classification schemes are based upon the theory underlying the procedure in question, some upon the type of scale obtained, and others upon the specific experimental procedures employed. For our purposes it will be useful to classify scaling methods according to the type of judgment required of the subject. On this basis we shall distinguish four major classes of scaling procedures, which, for expository convenience, we shall identify by the following brief names: (1) *discrimination methods,* (2) *equisection methods,* (3) *category methods,* and (4) *direct-estimate methods.*

Although certain of the procedures to be described could be adapted for use with animal subjects (as, indeed, some of them have been), the great majority of work in the area of sensory scaling has employed human subjects. To simplify the following discussion we shall confine our attention to procedures used with human subjects. In many cases (possibly all) these procedures may be viewed as special cases of more general procedures applicable to human and infrahuman subjects alike.

DISCRIMINATION SCALES

In all the procedures employed for scaling sensations the subject is presented with two or more stimuli and required to act in accordance with a specific set of instructions.   (The stimuli may be presented all at once, two or more at a time, or one at a time in succession.)   Of the tasks posed for the subject by the various scaling procedures, the simplest is that in which he is presented with two stimuli at a time (or in close succession) and merely required to judge which of the two is higher on the stimulus continuum—which of two weights is heavier, which of two lights is brighter, which of two sounds is louder, and so on.   (Alternatively, the task required of the subject is sometimes construed as providing a verbal report concerning his own sensations.   In other words, it is said that the subject reports not whether S_A or S_B is higher on the stimulus continuum but which of two sensations—that produced by S_A or that produced by S_B—is higher on the psychological continuum.   However we choose to describe the subject's task, if we are to make use of his responses for purposes of scaling his sensations, we must accept the basic assumption that a sensory-perceptual event intervenes between the external stimulus and his overt response; whether the subject construes the task as describing stimuli or describing sensations would seem to be of little consequence.)

It is apparent from considerations presented in Chapter 13 that if two stimuli are widely enough separated on the stimulus continuum, the subject's judgments will be perfectly consistent, i.e., the stimulus that is in fact higher on the stimulus continuum will be judged higher 100 per cent of the time.   However, as is evident from data presented in connection with the method of constant stimuli, if the two stimuli are sufficiently close together on the stimulus continuum, the subject's judgments will not be entirely consistent, i.e., the stimulus that is in fact lower on the stimulus continuum will occasionally be judged as higher.   Moreover, the frequency of such errors is systematically related to the separation of the two stimuli on the stimulus continuum: the closer together two stimuli are located on the stimulus continuum, the greater is the frequency of such errors.   One approach to the scaling of sensations is based upon the ease with which the corresponding stimuli are discriminated, i.e., the basic datum from which the separation of two sensations on the psychological continuum is derived is the consistency of judgments concerning the relative positions of the corresponding stimuli.   In its simplest form, this approach assumes that if S_B is judged greater than S_A with the same frequency as S_D is judged greater than S_C, then the sensations produced by S_A and S_B are separated by the same distance on the psychological continuum as the sensations produced by S_C and S_D.   In the two subsections that follow we shall consider two scaling methods based upon discrimination data—(a) the *method of summated jnd's* and (b) the *method of paired comparisons*.

SUMMATED JND'S

Gustav Fechner, in 1860, proposed that the intensity of a sensation could be quantified by specifying the distance—measured in jnd units—of the corresponding stimulus from the stimulus threshold. This approach to sensory scaling may be illustrated with reference to the hypothetical data presented in Table 15-1.

TABLE 15-1 *Stimulus values corresponding to successive jnd's above the stimulus threshold (hypothetical data)*

STIMULUS	VALUE ON PSYCHOLOGICAL CONTINUUM (JND'S ABOVE THRESHOLD)	VALUE ON STIMULUS CONTINUUM (PHYSICAL UNITS)
S_A	0	2.00
S_B	1	3.00
S_C	2	4.50
S_D	3	6.75
S_E	4	10.12
S_F	5	15.19
S_G	6	22.78

The first step in this scaling procedure is to determine the stimulus threshold using one of the psychophysical methods described in Chapter 13. In Table 15-1 it has been arbitrarily assumed, for purposes of illustration, that the stimulus threshold (identified as S_A) has a value of 2.00 physical units on the stimulus continuum; as a matter of definition, the corresponding sensation is assigned a value of zero on the psychological continuum. The next step is to determine the value on the stimulus continuum of the stimulus (identified as S_B in Table 15-1) that is one jnd higher than the stimulus threshold (S_A). (It has been assumed that, using one of the methods described in Chapter 13 for assessing differential sensitivity, S_B has been found to have a value of 3.00 physical units on the stimulus continuum.) Because this stimulus is one jnd above the stimulus threshold, the sensation corresponding to this stimulus is assigned the value 1 on the psychological continuum. Next, we determine the location on the stimulus continuum of the stimulus (S_C) that is one jnd higher than S_B; inasmuch as S_C is two jnd's above the stimulus threshold, the corresponding sensation is assigned a value of 2 on the psychological continuum. The (hypothetical) values of seven stimuli ($S_A, \cdots, S_G$) on the stimulus continuum and the values of the corresponding sensations on the psychological continuum are shown in the table. The values on the stimulus continuum have been computed on the assumption that the value of each stimulus is 50 per cent greater than that of the preceding one, i.e., that a jnd is produced by an increase of 50 per cent of the physical value of any stimulus. (It should be noted that in actual practice no assumption need be made concerning the size of the jnd; the values of successive stimuli on the stimulus continuum would be determined experimentally using one of the psychophysical methods described in Chapter 13.)

The relationship between values on the psychological continuum and values on the stimulus continuum is represented graphically in Figure 15-2.

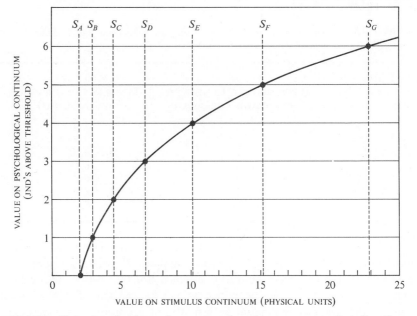

FIGURE 15-2 *Psychophysical function based on summated jnd's (hypothetical data).*

This type of relationship—between psychological values on the one hand and physical values on the other hand—is called a *psychophysical function.* Such a function enables us to determine the value on the psychological continuum of the sensation produced by any given stimulus: the value of the stimulus in question is located on the horizontal axis, and the corresponding value on the psychological continuum, indicated by the height of the curve, is read on the vertical axis.   As is typical of psychophysical functions based upon summated jnd's, the curve is negatively accelerated, i.e., rises steeply at first, more gradually further on.   The shape of the function is a consequence of the fact that as we progress upward along the stimulus continuum there is an increase in the size of the stimulus increment necessary to produce a just noticeable difference.   (It will be recalled that according to Weber's Law, which holds at least approximately for many stimulus dimensions, the stimulus increment necessary to produce a just noticeable difference is a constant proportion of the magnitude of the stimulus in question and, hence, is larger for stimuli high on the continuum than for stimuli low on the continuum.)[1]

[1] If Weber's Law is assumed to hold strictly throughout the stimulus continuum, it follows mathematically that intensity of sensation (*P*) is related to stimulus in-

Let us now inquire into the significance of the scale values assigned to sensations using the method of summated jnd's. For purposes of illustration, we shall consider the significance of the scale values 2, 4, and 6 assigned to S_C, S_E, and S_G, respectively, in our hypothetical example. Purely as a matter of definition, we may say that the sensation produced by S_E is two jnd's higher than that produced by S_C, and that produced by S_G is two jnd's higher than that produced by S_E. But if measurements are to be of more than academic interest, they must have significance beyond the meaning inherent in the measurement process itself. That is to say, measures of such variables as length, mass, and temperature are of scientific value because each of these concepts is useful in the formulation of empirical laws. Do scale values obtained using the method of summated jnd's enter into lawful relationships with other variables in a similar manner? As yet only a limited amount of research has been devoted to this question; consequently, a definitive answer cannot be given at the present time. However, for purposes of illustration, it is of interest to consider some of the kinds of variables to which we might expect values on a psychological continuum to be related. The following list is adapted from Shepard (1960).

1. *Generalization of a conditioned response.* If a pigeon is trained as described in Chapter 12 to peck at a plastic key illuminated by light of one wavelength and is then tested with light of other wavelengths, rate of responding falls off as the difference between the test stimulus and the original training stimulus increases. It seems reasonable to expect that the law relating decrement in rate of responding to amount of stimulus change will be simpler when stimulus change is measured in psychological units than when measured in physical units.

2. *Overt errors in paired-associates learning.* Let us suppose that in a paired-associates learning task subjects are required to learn a different verbal response (e.g., nonsense syllable) to each of the stimuli described in Table 15-1. In such a task we would expect the number of confusions between two stimuli to be greater, the closer the stimuli are to one another on the stimulus continuum. For example, we would expect the response appropriate to S_D to occur more frequently in response to stimuli close to S_D than to stimuli far from it on the stimulus continuum. Here, again, we would expect that the relationship between the frequency of such errors and the difference between stimuli could be more simply described when differences between stimuli are expressed in psychological units than when they are expressed in physical units.

---

tensity (S) as follows: $P = c \log S + a$, in which c and a are constants. This relationship, known as *Fechner's Law,* asserts that the intensity of sensation is directly proportional to the logarithm of stimulus intensity. The relationship is not a law in the sense used in Chapter 12 (P is a theoretical construct, not an empirical construct), and it might be better named *Fechner's Theorem,* being a logical consequence of certain postulates, one of which is Weber's Law.

3. *Disjunctive reaction time.* In a disjunctive reaction time experiment a subject is required to make one response to one stimulus and a different response to a second stimulus; whichever stimulus is presented, the subject is supposed to make the appropriate response as quickly as he can. For example, a subject seated with his left hand on one response key (e.g., an ordinary telegraph key) and his right hand on another key might be required to lift his left hand as quickly as possible to a light of one color, his right hand as quickly as possible to a light of another color. A general finding in experiments of this type is that the greater the difference between the two stimuli, i.e., the easier the discrimination, the shorter is the disjunctive reaction time. Here we might expect disjunctive reaction time to be related in a relatively simple manner to psychological distance. We might expect to find, for example, that the mean disjunctive reaction time is the same using S_B and S_D of Table 15-1 as using S_D and S_F.

4. *Judged similarity.* Finally, we might expect pairs of stimuli that are separated by equal psychological distances to seem equally different when direct judgments are made of the similarity of pairs of stimuli. Suppose, for example, that one pair of stimuli consists of S_B and S_D; a second pair, of S_E and S_G. Since in each pair the two stimuli are separated by two jnd's, it might be expected that S_D would seem to differ from S_B as much as S_G differs from S_E. As we shall note in greater detail in the section dealing with equisection methods of scaling, this expectation has been confirmed for two continua, the pitch of musical tones and the value (lightness) of visual stimuli.

PAIRED COMPARISONS: THURSTONE'S SCALING MODEL

In the method of paired comparisons a fixed set of stimuli (e.g., ten salt solutions differing in concentration) are employed, and a scale value is determined for the sensation produced by each stimulus. The experimental procedure consists in presenting the stimuli to a subject two at a time and having the subject indicate which member of each pair seems greater. Each pair of stimuli to be judged by the subject is presented a large number of times, intermixed with presentations of other pairs. The resulting data are a series of relative frequencies indicating, for each pair, the proportion of trials on which one stimulus was judged greater than the other. The procedure most commonly followed in practice is to have the subject (or subjects) judge every possible pair of stimuli that can be formed by selecting two stimuli at a time from the total number of stimuli employed. (If the total number of stimuli employed is represented by k, there are $k(k - 1)$ such pairs to be judged.) To simplify the present exposition, however, we shall consider a modified procedure in which one stimulus from the series is selected as a standard and every other stimulus is judged in relation to this one. Following this modified procedure, the subject is presented on each trial with the standard stimulus and one other stimulus from the set to be judged, and the subject indicates which of the two seems greater.

Thurstone (1927) has proposed a set of assumptions—commonly referred to as a theoretical model—from which a variety of closely related scaling procedures may be derived. Of particular interest for present purposes is the determination of scale values, in accordance with this theory, from data obtained by the experimental procedure of paired comparisons.

Thurstone's model may be said to start with the observation that there is a certain amount of variability connected with sensory processes. For example, if a given comparison stimulus is judged in relation to a given standard stimulus on a large number of trials, on some trials the comparison stimulus may be judged greater than the standard and on other trials as less. In line with this general observation, Thurstone assumes that the sensory reaction produced by any given stimulus varies somewhat from trial to trial, having a higher value on the psychological continuum on some trials than on others. For example, it is assumed that if a subject tastes the same salt solution several times, his sensory reaction will vary slightly from trial to trial, with the result that the solution seems saltier on some trials than on others. In terms of the notation used in Figure 15-1, it is assumed that a given stimulus (e.g., S_D) usually produces one sensory reaction (P_D) but occasionally produces instead the sensory reaction appropriate to one or another of its neighboring stimuli, i.e., P_B, P_C, P_E, or P_F. The relative frequency with which various sensory reactions occur in response to a given stimulus is assumed to vary with their position on the psychological continuum, near values of P occurring more often than remote values. For example, sensory reactions P_C and P_E would occur more frequently in response to S_D than would P_B and P_F.

Thus, within the context of Thurstone's model we must distinguish between the sensory reaction "characteristically" evoked by a given stimulus and the reaction evoked by that stimulus on a particular trial. We shall use the symbol A to represent the value of the sensory reaction elicited on a particular trial by S_A, the symbol B to represent the value of the sensory reaction elicited on a particular trial by S_B, and so on. In terms of this notation, the ideas set forth above may be stated as follows: The numerical value of A is not a fixed quantity but varies from one presentation of S_A to the next; similarly, the numerical value of B varies from one presentation of S_B to the next; and so on. In this context, A, B, C, etc., are random variables, each having a different probability distribution.

One of the basic assumptions of Thurstone's model is that the probability distribution of each of the random variables referred to above is a normal distribution. Figure 15-3 shows the hypothetical probability distributions of U and V, the sensory reactions elicited by S_U and S_V, respectively. Let us consider first the distribution of sensory reactions to S_U.

It is seen that the modal (most frequent) sensory reaction to this stimulus has a value of 5 on the psychological continuum; sensory reactions having values between 4 and 5, and between 5 and 6, occur with considerable frequency; those with values between 3 and 4, and between 6 and 7, occur somewhat less frequently; and those with values between 2 and 3, and between 7 and 8, occur still less frequently.   The mean and variance of the distribution of reactions to S_U are represented by μ_U and σ_U^2, respectively. The second distribution shown in Figure 15-3, that describing the relative frequencies of sensory reactions to S_V, is similar to the first except in central tendency.   The higher central tendency of the second distribution ($\mu_V = 8$) is a consequence of the fact that S_V has a higher position on the stimulus continuum than S_U.

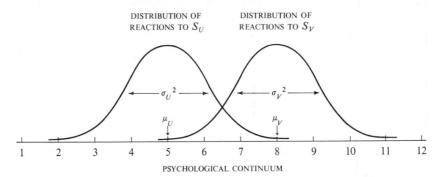

DISTRIBUTION OF REACTIONS TO S_U DISTRIBUTION OF REACTIONS TO S_V

PSYCHOLOGICAL CONTINUUM

FIGURE 15-3 *Hypothetical distributions of sensory reactions to two stimuli, S_U and S_V. The curve on the left represents the distribution of sensory reactions over a series of repeated presentations of S_U; that on the right, the distribution of reactions over a series of presentations of S_V. Adapted from Thurstone (1927).*

Let us suppose that S_U and S_V are salt solutions of different concentrations and that these stimuli are employed in a psychophysical procedure as follows: On each trial the subject tastes both solutions and reports whether S_V seems more or less salty than S_U.   (This procedure is seen to be a special case of the method of constant stimuli, in which S_U serves the role of the standard stimulus and S_V is the comparison stimulus.)   According to Thurstone's model, the subject's judgment concerning which solution tastes saltier depends upon the sensory reactions elicited by the two stimuli on the trial in question.   Suppose that on a particular trial S_U elicits a sensory reaction somewhat lower than usual (e.g., $U = 3$) and S_V elicits a reaction somewhat higher than usual (e.g., $V = 9$).   In this case, since the sensory reaction elicited by S_V has a higher value on the psychological continuum than that elicited by S_U, the subject reports on this trial that S_V tastes more salty than S_U.   On the other hand, suppose that on another trial S_U evokes a sensory reaction higher than usual (e.g.,

$U = 7$) and S_V evokes a reaction lower than usual (e.g., $V = 6$). In this case, since the value of V is less than the value of U, the subject reports that S_V tastes less salty than S_U. In general, the subject's judgment on a given trial is assumed to depend upon the difference $V - U$. When this difference is positive (i.e., when V is greater than U), S_V is judged as more salty than S_U; when the difference is negative (i.e., when V is less than U), S_V is judged as less salty than S_U. (In the first instance considered above $V - U = 9 - 3 = 6$, and S_V was judged more salty than S_U; in the second instance, $V - U = 6 - 7 = -1$, and S_V was judged less salty.)

It will be recalled that, in general, scaling a psychological continuum consists in determining the numerical value on the psychological continuum of the sensory reaction elicited by each stimulus on the stimulus continuum. Within the context of Thurstone's model, scaling a psychological continuum consists in determining, for each stimulus on the stimulus continuum, the numerical value of μ, the mean of the distribution of sensory reactions elicited by the stimulus in question.[2] The basic logic of Thurstone's approach is to infer the distance separating two values of μ on the psychological continuum (e.g., the distance between μ_U and μ_V) from observations concerning the relative frequency with which one stimulus is judged greater than the other. Thus, if S_V were judged greater than S_U 55 per cent of the time and less than S_U 45 per cent of the time, it would be concluded that μ_U and μ_V (the mean reactions to S_U and S_V, respectively) were rather close on the psychological continuum; on the other hand, if S_V were judged greater than S_U 95 per cent of the time and less than S_U only 5 per cent of the time, it would be concluded that μ_U and μ_V were more widely separated than in the first case. In other words, when the mean sensory reactions evoked by two stimuli are widely separated on the psychological continuum, the relative positions of the two stimuli in question will be judged correctly most of the time; when the mean sensory reactions are not widely separated, the relative positions of the two stimuli will be judged correctly less often.

In order to determine more exactly the manner in which the proportion of correct judgments concerning S_U and S_V varies as a function of the separation of μ_U and μ_V on the psychological continuum, it is necessary to consider the probability distribution of the difference $V - U$. This theoretical distribution is represented schematically in Figure 15-4. Note that in this figure a vertical line has been drawn at the value zero. The unshaded area to the right of this line represents the probability that on any given trial $V - U$ will be positive (and, hence, S_V judged to be greater

[2] Using the notation of Figure 15-1, the sensory reaction "characteristically" elicited by S_U would be represented by the symbol P_U; that "characteristically" elicited by S_V, by the symbol P_V. In Thurstone's model P_U and P_V are given a statistical interpretation—i.e., they are construed as the means of separate probability distributions—and therefore, in the context of Thurstone's model, are equivalent to μ_U and μ_V, respectively.

than S_U); the shaded area to the left represents the probability that $V - U$ will be negative (and, hence, S_V judged to be less than S_U).

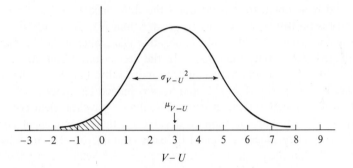

FIGURE 15-4 *Probability distribution of V − U. The difference V − U represents the difference on any given trial between the sensory reaction to S_V and the reaction to S_U. The value of V − U fluctuates randomly from trial to trial: when the difference is greater than zero, S_V is judged to be greater than S_U; when less than zero, S_V is judged to be less. Adapted from Thurstone (1927).*

In order to determine the mean and variance of the probability distribution of the difference $V - U$ it is necessary to make certain additional assumptions concerning the distribution of V and of U, i.e., the distribution of sensory reactions to S_V and to S_U. Several alternative sets of assumptions are possible, each leading to somewhat different results. (There are available a number of experimental checks that enable an investigator to decide which of the various possible sets of assumptions are applicable in a given situation.) To keep the present discussion as simple as possible we will consider only one of the possible sets of assumptions that can be made concerning V and U, that set of assumptions for which subsequent developments are least complicated. Two assumptions are involved: First, it is assumed that the random variables U and V are independent, i.e., that over a series of trials on which S_U and S_V are presented to a subject there is no systematic tendency for higher than average values of U to be associated with higher than average values of V or vice versa. Second, it is assumed that the variance of sensory reactions to S_U and the variance of sensory reactions to S_V are the same—in other words, that $\sigma_U^2 = \sigma_V^2 = \sigma^2$. (It will be noted that in the present discussion we are considering only two representative stimuli, S_U and S_V. To state the theory more fully it should be added that similar assumptions are made concerning every pair of stimuli used in an experiment.)

Under the assumptions stated above, μ_{V-U} and σ_{V-U}^2, the mean and variance of the probability distribution of $V - U$, may be determined using Formulae (8-1) and (8-2), respectively. Substituting in Formula (8-1), we obtain $\mu_{V-U} = \mu_V - \mu_U = 8 - 5 = 3$. Recalling that we are considering the special case in which $\sigma_U{}^2 = \sigma_V{}^2 = \sigma^2$, and substituting in Formula (8-2), we obtain $\sigma_{V-U}{}^2 = \sigma^2 + \sigma^2 = 2\sigma^2$. Taking the square root of $\sigma_{V-U}{}^2$, we obtain the following formula for σ_{V-U}, the standard deviation of the distribution of $V - U$:

$$\sigma_{V-U} = \sqrt{2\sigma^2} \tag{15-1}$$

In order to determine the specific numerical value of σ_{V-U} we must know the numerical value of σ^2. Fortunately, this is a question that can be settled by an arbitrary decision. We noted earlier (Chapter 14) that in developing an interval or ratio scale of measurement it is necessary to make an arbitrary decision concerning the unit of measurement to be employed. In the present case it is convenient to select our unit of measurement in such a way that σ has a value of 1—in other words, to adopt σ as the unit of measurement. Substituting in Formula (15-1), we obtain the value of σ_{V-U} as follows: $\sigma_{V-U} = \sqrt{2(1)^2} = \sqrt{2} \approx 1.41$.

We are now in possession of sufficient information, given the separation of μ_U and μ_V, to determine the relative frequency with which S_V will be judged greater than S_U. This determination, it will be recalled, is equivalent to determining the area of the unshaded portion of the distribution shown in Figure 15-4. The area in question may be obtained by referring to a table of areas of the normal distribution. To enter the table of the normal curve we must first determine the value of z corresponding to the point at which the vertical line is erected—that is, we must determine the distance, in σ_{V-U} units, between zero and μ_{V-U}, the mean of the distribution. The necessary computation is summarized in the following formula:[3]

$$z = \frac{0 - \mu_{V-U}}{\sigma_{V-U}} = \frac{0 - \mu_{V-U}}{\sqrt{2}} \tag{15-2}$$

The use of Formula (15-2) may be illustrated by applying it to the situation pictured in Figure 15-3 (which shows the probability distributions of U and V) and in Figure 15-4 (which shows the probability distribution of the difference $V - U$). In this illustrative case $\mu_U = 5$, $\mu_V = 8$, and $\mu_{V-U} = 3$. Substituting the last of these values in Formula (15-2), we obtain $z \approx (0 - 3)/1.41 \approx -2.1$. Referring to Table A-2, the shaded and unshaded portions of the distribution in Figure 15-4 are found to be approximately .02 and .98, respectively. Thus, in the situation pictured in Figure

[3] Formula (15-2) may be viewed as an adaptation of Formula (5-1), with the difference that the variable under consideration is the difference $V - U$ rather than X. The counterparts in Formula (15-2) of the terms X, μ, and σ appearing in Formula (5-1) are $V - U$, μ_{V-U}, and σ_{V-U}, respectively. The value zero appearing in Formula (15-2) is the particular value of $V - U$ with which we are concerned in the problem under consideration.

15-3 S_V would be judged greater than S_U approximately 98 per cent of the time and less than S_U approximately 2 per cent of the time.

In the foregoing presentation of Thurstone's scaling model we have assumed, for illustrative purposes, that the scale values of μ_U and μ_V were known, and from this information we determined the proportion of the time that S_V would be judged greater than S_U. In actual practice, however, the situation is exactly the reverse. That is, in practice the proportion of times that S_V is judged greater than S_U is determined experimentally, and the problem is to work backwards to determine the separation of μ_V and μ_U on the psychological continuum. The value of z in Formula (15-2) is derived, using a table of the normal curve, from the proportion of times S_V is judged greater than S_U; the unknown quantity is μ_{V-U}. It is convenient, for computational purposes, to solve Formula (15-2) for the unknown quantity, μ_{V-U}, as follows: $\mu_{V-U} = -z\sqrt{2}$. Finally, the fact that we are interested in the separation of μ_V and μ_U on the psychological continuum may be made explicit by substituting the difference $\mu_V - \mu_U$ for the mean μ_{V-U} (to which the difference is numerically equal) as follows:

$$\mu_V - \mu_U = -z\sqrt{2} \tag{15-3}$$

According to Equation (15-3), the separation on the psychological continuum of μ_V and μ_U—the average sensory reactions elicited by S_V and S_U, respectively—is directly related to the value of z based upon the relative frequency with which S_V is judged greater than S_U.

To illustrate the use of Equation (15-3) to compute values on the psychological continuum let us imagine that a psychophysical experiment concerned with judgments of weight is conducted as follows: Four objects that are indistinguishable except for differences in weight are employed as stimuli. The object employed as a standard stimulus will be designated S_U; the objects employed as comparison stimuli, S_X, S_Y, and S_Z. On each trial the subject lifts the standard stimulus and one of the three comparison stimuli and reports whether the latter seems lighter or heavier than the former. For purposes of illustration, we will assume that the results are as shown in the second and third columns of Table 15-2.

TABLE 15-2 *Computation of values on psychological continuum from proportions of "greater" and "less" judgments (hypothetical data)*

STIMU-LUS	PROPORTION OF TIMES JUDGED LESS THAN STANDARD	PROPORTION OF TIMES JUDGED GREATER THAN STANDARD	z	DISTANCE OF MEAN FROM μ_U	VALUE ON PSYCHOLOGICAL CONTINUUM ASSUMING $\mu_U = 2$
S_X	.60	.40	.253	−.36	1.64
S_Y	.30	.70	−.524	.74	2.74
S_Z	.20	.80	−.842	1.19	3.19

According to these hypothetical data, on 60 per cent of trials where S_X was compared with the standard stimulus, S_X was judged less than the standard; on 40 per cent of such trials, S_X was judged greater. Comparable proportions for trials involving comparison of S_Y with the standard and those involving comparison of S_Z with the standard are also given in the table. These results have been represented schematically in Figure 15-5.

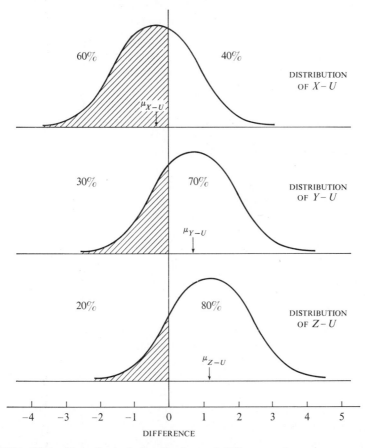

FIGURE 15-5 *Hypothetical distributions of differences in sensory reactions. Each of three comparison stimuli (S_X, S_Y, and S_Z) is judged in relation to the same standard stimulus (S_U). The unshaded area in each distribution represents the proportion of trials on which the comparison stimulus in question is judged greater than the standard. Top: comparisons of S_X and S_U. Middle: comparisons of S_Y and S_U. Bottom: comparisons of S_Z and S_U.*

The top curve represents the probability distribution of the hypothetical difference $X - U$; the middle curve, the distribution of the difference $Y - U$; and the bottom curve, the distribution of the difference $Z - U$.

From the fact that S_X was judged less than S_U more often that it was judged greater, we may infer that μ_X is lower than μ_U and—what amounts to the same thing—that μ_{X-U} is less than zero. More specifically, the distance separating μ_X from μ_U on the psychological continuum may be estimated by substituting the appropriate values in an equation having the general form of Equation (15-3), the difference being that we substitute μ_X in place of μ_V. From Table A-3 we find that the value of z corresponding to an area of .60 (the shaded portion of the top distribution in Figure 15-5) is .253; substituting in Equation (15-3), we have $\mu_X - \mu_U = -.253\sqrt{2} \approx -.253(1.41) \approx -.36$. Similar computations based upon the distribution of responses to S_Y and S_Z are summarized in Table 15-2. From the values given in the fifth column of the table we see that μ_X, μ_Y, and μ_Z are located on the psychological continuum .36 units below μ_U, .74 units above μ_U, and 1.19 units above μ_U, respectively; it remains only to determine the value of μ_U, and the values of μ_X, μ_Y, and μ_Z follow automatically. The value assigned to μ_U depends upon how the zero point on the psychological continuum is determined. If we were to follow the practice discussed earlier in connection with scales based upon summated jnd's, we would assign the value zero to the mean of the distribution of sensory reactions elicited by the threshold stimulus, i.e., the stimulus that is perceptible on 50 per cent of its presentations. A more common practice, however, is to assign the value zero in an arbitrary manner—as is done in the centigrade and Fahrenheit scales of temperature, for example —thereby obtaining an interval, as opposed to ratio, scale. Following the latter practice, we may assign μ_U any arbitrary value that is convenient. If, for example, we assign μ_U the value 2, the resulting values of μ_X, μ_Y, and μ_Z are 1.64, 2.74, and 3.19, respectively.

To simplify the above discussion we assumed that all of the stimuli to be scaled were judged against a single common standard (S_U). As we noted earlier, however, in actual practice it is more common to have each stimulus judged in relation to every other stimulus in the series. Analysis of the results of this more elaborate procedure, although somewhat more complicated, is similar in concept to that described above, in which only one stimulus is employed as a standard. In effect, the scaling procedure employed when the more elaborate experimental procedure is used is this: each stimulus in turn is regarded as a standard stimulus, and the entire series of stimuli is scaled in the manner described in our illustrative example. The result is several different scalings of the series, in each of which a different stimulus serves as standard. The overall scale value assigned to any given stimulus (or, more precisely, to the mean of the distribution of sensory reactions elicited by that stimulus) is the average of the scale values obtained in the several different scalings. For a detailed description of the computational methods employed, the reader is referred to Guilford (1954, Chap. 7) and Torgerson (1958, Chap. 9).

In assessing psychological scales afforded by the scaling procedure described above, three general types of question are of interest: (1) the consistency of the results obtained in scaling a given psychological dimension when different stimuli are employed as a standard, (2) the extent to which scale values provided by this method facilitate the formulation of behavioral laws, and (3) the relationships between scale values provided by this method and those provided by other methods of scaling psychological continua—for example, the method of summated jnd's. (The third criterion is seen to be a special case of the second, but one which appears to be of sufficient interest to warrant separate attention.) Although some rather sophisticated—and complex—methods are available for evaluating the consistency of Thurstone's scaling procedure, essentially these methods amount to a determination of whether the spacing on the psychological continuum of the sensations produced by a given set of stimuli is the same when different stimuli are employed as standards. At present, the number of investigations concerned with the consistency of Thurstone's scaling procedure is too limited to permit any conclusions of a sweeping nature; however, the results of at least one investigation (Guilford, 1954, Chap. 7) are promising in this regard. In this study each of seven weights was judged in comparison with every other weight in the series; seven different analyses were then performed, in each of which scale values were computed for all seven stimuli using a different stimulus as the standard. Making due allowance for sampling fluctuations in the data, the scale values assigned in the seven separate scalings were in reasonably good agreement. (It should be pointed out that the allowance made for sampling fluctuation in arriving at this assessment is impressionistic and not based upon formal statistical analysis.) As we shall have occasion to note in greater detail at a later point, scale values obtained by the method of paired comparisons have been found (Edwards and Thurstone, 1952) to agree very closely with scale values obtained by the method of successive categories, another scaling procedure derived from Thurstone's theory and described later in the chapter. Aside from this one study, however, there have been few, if any, systematic comparisons of the method of paired comparisons with other scaling procedures considered in this chapter. Consequently, the nature of the relationships of this scaling method to others is unknown at the present time. There appears to be a similar paucity of findings concerning relationships between scale values obtained by the method of paired comparisons and other behavioral variables. However, because of the close relationship between scale values obtained by the method of paired comparisons and those obtained by the method of successive categories, certain experimental findings that will be discussed in connection with the latter method may be presumed to apply to the method of paired comparisons as well.

In concluding our discussion of the method of paired comparisons, the reader is reminded that we have considered the simplest special case, that in which (1) the magnitude of the sensory reaction to one of the two stimuli presented on a given trial is independent of the magnitude of the reaction to the other stimulus presented on that trial and (2) the variance of the distribution of sensory reactions is the same for all stimuli in the series. Procedures that are applicable under less restrictive conditions are described by Guilford (1954, Chap. 7) and Torgerson (1958, Chap. 9).

EQUISECTION SCALES

In the scaling procedures considered thus far, the subject considers stimuli presented two at a time and judges which of the two is greater with respect to the attribute under consideration (e.g., weight, saltiness, loudness, brightness). In the procedures to be considered next, the subject is required to make judgments concerning the psychological distances—or, as they are also called, the *sense distances*—separating different pairs of stimuli.[4] For example, a subject might be presented with the four stimuli shown in Figure 15-6 and required to judge whether the difference between

FIGURE 15-6 *Arrangement of stimuli for comparing sense distances. The subject's task is to judge whether the sense distance between S_A and S_B is less than, equal to, or greater than the sense distance between S_C and S_D.*

S_A and S_B seems less than, equal to, or greater than the difference between S_C and S_D. Alternatively, it may be arranged so that one of the stimuli, say S_D, can be varied by the subject; the subject may then be required to adjust the variable stimulus until the difference between S_C and S_D seems equal to the difference between S_A and S_B. Another variation of this general approach to scaling is illustrated by the procedure used to develop the Munsell scale of value, a scale for measuring the lightness of grays in psychological units (Munsell, Sloan, and Godlove, 1933). In the pro-

---

[4] Strictly speaking, it is inaccurate to speak of the sense distance, or psychological distance, separating two stimuli, S_A and S_B. What is meant, of course, is the distance on the psychological continuum between the corresponding sensations, P_A and P_B. However, it has become common practice to refer to the latter distance elliptically as the sense distance between stimuli.

cedure used by these investigators, subjects were presented with a white surface and a black surface and asked to select, from a wide assortment made available to them, a series of gray papers that divided the range between black and white into eight steps that were psychologically equal. Because this method involves the subdivision of an interval between two extreme stimuli into a number of equal intervals or sections, this method is commonly referred to as the *method of equisection*. For expository convenience, this designation will here be used to refer to all scaling procedures involving the direct comparison of sense distances.

THE MEL SCALE OF PITCH

For a more detailed examination of the equisection method of scaling we shall consider a scale developed by Stevens and Volkmann (1940) for describing the pitch of musical tones.[5] In this investigation subjects were seated individually at an apparatus resembling the keyboard of an electric organ. Five keys were employed, each of which, when depressed, produced a pure tone through a set of earphones worn by the subject. The situation may be represented schematically as shown in the following diagram, in which the symbols S_A, S_B, $\cdots$, S_E represent the physical stimuli

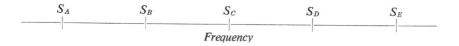

(tones) produced by the five keys. The frequencies of the two end tones (S_A and S_E) were fixed by the experimenter; the frequencies of the intermediate tones (S_B, S_C, and S_D) were controlled by the subject by adjusting three knobs situated near the corresponding keys. The subject's task was

---

[5] For some readers a brief summary of the physical characteristics of auditory stimuli may be helpful at this point. Under normal circumstances the immediate stimulus for hearing is the vibration of air molecules. In the case of so-called pure tones (which are rarely heard except in the laboratory), each air molecule oscillates back and forth in a simple rhythmic pattern described by mathematicians as sinusoidal motion. The pitch of a tone—whether it is a high note or a low note—depends chiefly upon the frequency (rapidity) of oscillation, high frequencies resulting in sensations of high pitch, low frequencies, in sensations of low pitch. On the other hand, the loudness of a tone depends chiefly upon the amplitude of oscillation, more vigorous oscillation being associated with greater loudness. Tones encountered outside the laboratory (e.g., tones produced by musical instruments or by the human voice) may be conceived as mixtures of pure tones. The pattern of vibration of air molecules underlying such tones is more complex than that associated with pure tones, but it may be thought of as being basically the same as the motion corresponding to a pure tone, with minor perturbations superimposed upon the basic vibration pattern. The distinctive quality (timbre) of different musical instruments and of different voices is determined by the proportions in which various pure tones are mixed in producing complex tones.

to adjust the frequencies of the three middle tones until the sense distances separating adjacent pairs of stimuli were all equal.   Subjects were given all the time they needed and were instructed to compare each interval with every other interval before reaching a final decision concerning the adjustment of the frequencies.   The procedure was repeated three times using partially overlapping segments of the stimulus continuum: in one portion of the experiment the frequencies of the end stimuli (S_A and S_E) were 40 and 1,000 cycles per second, respectively; in a second portion, 200 and 6,500 cycles per second; and in a third, 3,000 and 12,000 cycles per second. The results for the middle range of stimuli are reproduced in Table 15-3.

TABLE 15-3   *Frequencies of five tones separated by equal sense distances. From Stevens and Volkmann (1940)*

TONE	S_A	S_B	S_C	S_D	S_E
FREQUENCY (CYCLES PER SECOND)	200	867	2,022	3,393	6,500

The frequencies listed for S_A and S_E are those fixed by the experimenter; the remaining frequencies are mean settings by ten subjects.   The relationship between pitch (psychological continuum) and frequency (stimulus continuum) is shown graphically in Figure 15-7.

As a matter of convenience, stimulus frequencies have been spaced logarithmically on the horizontal axis, i.e., the spacing of frequencies on the horizontal scale is proportional to the logarithms of those frequencies. In effect, this method of plotting expands the lower part of the frequency scale and compresses the upper part, giving rise to a more conveniently shaped curve.   The location of the various points with respect to the vertical (pitch) scale requires explanation.   Although we do not at the outset know the actual numbers to be assigned to the various pitches, we do know that the five pitches should be evenly spaced, for the subjects have adjusted them so that intervals between pitches of adjacent stimuli are all psychologically equal.   Accordingly, the five data points in Figure 15-7 are separated by equal vertical distances (pitch differences).   (The dashed portions of the curve above and below the middle range are based upon additional data presented by Stevens and Volkmann (1940) but not reproduced here.)   All that remains to complete the scaling procedure is to fix the numerical values of the pitch scale by arbitrarily assigning values to any two points; when this is done, all other values on the pitch scale follow automatically.   (This procedure is analogous to the arbitrary assignment, in the Centigrade scale of temperature, of the values 0° and 100° to the freezing and boiling points of water, respectively.)   Since frequencies lower than 20 cycles per second are inaudible to most individuals, Stevens and Volkmann assigned a pitch value of zero to the tone produced by an auditory stimulus of 20 cycles per second; they named their unit the *mel* and arbitrarily assigned a value of 1,000 mels to the tone produced by a frequency of 1,000 cycles per second. This assignment of values leads to the pitch scale represented on the vertical axis at the right in Figure 15-7. The curve plotted in Figure 15-7 is the psychophysical

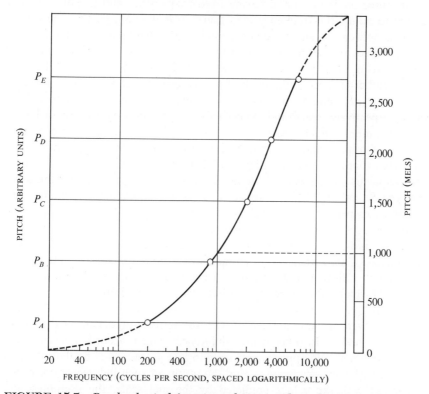

FIGURE 15-7 *Psychophysical function relating pitch to the frequency of an auditory stimulus. The scale on the left represents arbitrary units selected so that the five data points are separated by equal vertical distances, i.e., equal distances on the pitch continuum. The scale on the right is the mel scale, constructed by arbitrarily assigning a value of zero mels to a tone of 20 cycles per second and a value of 1,000 mels to a tone of 1,000 cycles per second. Adapted from Stevens and Volkmann (1940).*

function relating pitch, as scaled by Stevens and Volkmann, to frequency of the stimulus. Given the frequency of any auditory stimulus, this psychophysical function permits us to determine the value of the corresponding sensation on the psychological continuum of pitch. Similarly, given the frequencies of any two auditory stimuli, the curve enables us to determine the psychological distance between the corresponding sensations, i.e., the distance separating those sensations on the psychological continuum.

EVALUATING THE CONSISTENCY OF THE MEL SCALE

The psychophysical function shown in Figure 15-7 has certain implications that can be tested by experiment. Suppose, for example, that S_A, S_B, and S_C are three auditory stimuli having fixed frequencies, and a subject is required to adjust the frequency of a fourth stimulus, S_D, so that the sense distance between S_C and S_D appears equal to that between S_A and S_B. We would expect the sense distance between S_C and S_D to appear equal to that between S_A and S_B when the pitch of S_D exceeds that of S_C by the same number of mels as the pitch of S_B exceeds that of S_A. Thus, for example, if S_A, S_B, and S_C are tones having pitches of 500, 1,000, and 2,000 mels, respectively, we would expect subjects to adjust S_D to have a pitch of 2,500 mels—which according to Figure 15-7 is a tone having a frequency of approximately 5,000 cycles per second. Similarly, given any two fixed tones, S_A and S_C, Figure 15-7 leads to a prediction concerning the frequency of the variable tone, S_B, which will appear to be midway between S_A and S_C. For example, if S_A is a tone having a frequency of 1,000 cycles per second (1,000 mels) and S_C is a tone having a frequency of 10,000 cycles per second (approximately 3,000 mels), the tone appearing to be midway between S_A and S_C should be one having a pitch of approximately 2,000 mels, i.e., a frequency of approximately 3,000 cycles per second. Stevens and Volkmann examined the data of several investigations in which subjects performed judgments of the kinds described above and found that on the whole the settings made by the subjects in these experiments were in good agreement with the settings predicted on the basis of the mel scale. In other words, differences which, according to the mel scale of pitch, should appear equal were in fact judged equal by the subjects of the experiments examined. Had the results of such judgments not been congruent with the values predicted by the mel scale, the usefulness of this scale—and its status as an interval scale of pitch—would have been open to serious question. That the experimental findings were in fact congruent with predictions based upon the mel scale indicates, in a preliminary way at least, that this scale is useful in describing and predicting the nature of judgments concerning sense distances.

THE COMBINATION OF SENSE DISTANCES

In Chapter 14 we saw that the development of certain types of scales (e.g., those for measuring length, temporal duration, and mass) depends upon the availability of an appropriate mode of combining objects (or events) with respect to the attribute under consideration—i.e., a physical counterpart of the arithmetic operation of addition. The experimental procedure under consideration in the present section—the direct comparison of sense distances—would seem to afford a mode of combination analogous to the mode of combination underlying the measurement of length. Indeed, it appears that such a mode of combination is implicit in the construction of the mel scale and of any other scale developed in a similar manner.

The analogy between combination of psychological distances and combination of lengths may be illustrated by means of the following example. In discussing the combination of lengths (Chapter 14), we noted that according to the rules for measuring length, the combination of a 6-meter length with a 4-meter length is assigned the same value (10 meters) as the combination of an 8-meter length with a 2-meter length, and, hence, the two combinations should match one another—an implication that is confirmed experimentally. An analogous procedure involving the combination of psychological distances is represented in Figure 15-8.

STANDARD DISTANCES

$$P_A \qquad P_B \qquad P_C \qquad P_D \qquad P_E$$

50 52 54 56 58

Pitch (mels)

COMBINATION 1

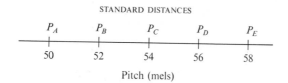

COMBINATION 2

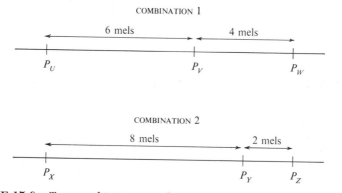

FIGURE 15-8 *Two combinations totaling 10 mels. If the combination of sense distances has properties analogous to the combination of lengths, the sense distance between P_U and P_W should appear equal to that between P_X and P_Z.*

Let us suppose that five auditory stimuli, S_A, S_B, $\cdots$, S_E, are selected so that the corresponding pitch sensations, P_A, P_B, $\cdots$, P_E, are spaced on the psychological continuum as shown in the top portion of the figure. Three additional stimuli, S_U, S_V, and S_W, are then adjusted so that the distance between P_U and P_V is equal to that between P_A and P_D (6 mels), and the distance between P_V and P_W is equal to that between P_A and P_C (4 mels). This arrangement is represented in the middle portion of the figure. The psychological distance between P_U and P_W is seen to be a combination of the distance between P_A and P_D with that between P_A and P_C. In a similar manner, three other stimuli, S_X, S_Y, and S_Z, are adjusted so that the distance between P_X and P_Y is equal to that between P_A and P_E (8 mels), and the distance between P_Y and P_Z is equal to that between P_A and P_B (2 mels). The latter combination is represented in the bottom portion of the figure. Following the rules described in Chapter 14 for assigning numbers, the psychological distance between P_U and P_W (Combination 1) and that between P_X and P_Z (Combination 2) would both be assigned a value of 10 mels. Accordingly, we would expect the two distances to be psychologically equal, i.e., to seem equal when directly compared.

Whether the mode of combination described above for combining psychological distances has properties analogous to that for combining lengths —and, hence, leads to results such as described above—is an empirical question, i.e., one that can be answered by suitable experimentation. As yet there has not been sufficient experimental work along these lines to warrant a definite answer to this question. However, the experimental findings surveyed by Stevens and Volkmann (1940), cited in the previous subsection, tend to support the view that the mode of combination of psychological distances described above has properties analogous to the combination of physical lengths. Although the tests afforded are somewhat less direct than the tests described here, the results of these studies demonstrate that the mel scale of pitch has the kinds of properties that would be expected if the suggested analogy exists between the two types of combination.

Finally, it should be noted that the method of combining sense distances considered in the present subsection is applicable not only to pitch, but to a variety of other sensory dimensions as well. There is no guarantee that if the mode of combination described above is found to have certain properties when used in connection with one sensory dimension, it will have similar properties when used in connection with other dimensions; the characteristics of the method must be evaluated separately for each continuum of interest.

THE PSYCHOLOGICAL BASIS FOR THE COMPARISON OF SENSE DISTANCES

Up to this point in our discussion it has been taken for granted that subjects can somehow make direct comparisons of sense distances. However, upon reflection, it is difficult to identify any specific learning experiences in the lives of most individuals that would enable them to apply the terms "equal" and "unequal" in a meaningful way to the sense distances between different pairs of stimuli. It would not be too surprising if, when we presented a subject with four stimuli and asked him whether the sense distance between the first two stimuli was less than, equal to, or greater than that between the second two, he should reply that he has never learned to compare so-called "sense distances" and the request therefore has no clear meaning for him. However, most subjects do not, in fact, regard such a request as unreasonable, and, indeed, there appears to be fair agreement among different subjects in the judgments rendered. What is the basis for such judgments and for the apparent agreement among subjects?

One possibility is that subjects somehow translate the concept of sense distance into some other characteristic for which they already have a verbal label. For example, in evaluating sense distances, subjects may actually be responding on the basis of the discriminability of the stimuli in question. That is, given any two stimuli, a subject may characterize the stimuli as "easy to discriminate," "difficult to discriminate," "very difficult to discriminate," or some other similar designation. Then, if two pairs of stimuli are characterized in the same way—i.e., both easy or both difficult—the subject may describe them as involving equal sense distances; if the two pairs are not judged to be equally discriminable, then according to the present hypothesis the pair involving the more difficult discrimination would be judged as representing the smaller sense distance.

The above hypothesis appears to have several testable implications. First, it suggests that subjects would show greater consistency with themselves and better agreement with other subjects when the comparisons to be made involve relatively small sense distances. (This prediction is based upon the additional assumption that beyond a certain point all differences are very easy to discriminate and that, when presented with differences of this magnitude, differences in discriminability are difficult to judge.) Unfortunately, no data bearing directly upon this prediction appear to be available at present. A second implication of the above hypothesis is that differences judged to be subjectively equal should prove to be equally discriminable. For example, suppose that S_A, S_B, S_C, and S_D are included among the stimuli employed in a paired-associates learning task and that the sense distance between S_A and S_B has been found to appear equal to that between S_C and S_D. It would be predicted that intrusion errors in which the response appropriate to S_A is evoked by S_B would occur with approximately the same frequency as intrusion errors in which the response appropriate to S_C is evoked by S_D. A third prediction, closely related to the second, is that the psychophysical function relating values on the psychological continuum to corresponding values on the stimulus continuum should have the same shape for psychological scales based upon summated jnd's as for equisection scales—or, what amounts to the same thing, two pairs of stimuli separated by equal sense distances should also be separated by the same number of jnd's.   This prediction has been confirmed for the pitch of musical tones (Stevens, Volkmann, and Newman, 1937) using an early version of the mel scale, and for the Munsell scale of value (Munsell, Sloan, and Godlove, 1933), described earlier.   Thus, existing findings tend to support the conjecture that judgments of so-called sense distances are essentially judgments of the discriminability of the stimuli in question.

CATEGORY SCALES

In the procedures to be considered next, the subject is presented with a series of stimuli that he is required to classify into a specified number of categories on the basis of his sensory reaction to each.   The entire series of stimuli may be made available to the subject at the beginning of the procedure and the subject required to sort them into a number of groups corresponding to the categories specified by the experimenter.   For example, the subject may be presented with several objects differing in weight and required to sort them into categories identified by the verbal labels *light, medium,* and *heavy.*   Alternatively, the stimuli may be presented to the subject one at a time and the subject required to indicate by an appropriate verbal response the category to which he assigns each stimulus.

The nature of the subject's task may be represented schematically as shown below.   The horizontal line represents the psychological continuum,

```
————————|————————————|————————————|————————
        Category 1      Category 2      Category 3
```

and the vertical marks represent boundaries that divide the continuum into a series of adjacent segments (categories).   (It should be noted that the method is not restricted to the use of three categories—any number may be employed.   In actual practice, however, the number of categories used rarely exceeds 11.)   The lower boundary of the lowest category does not necessarily represent zero on the psychological continuum, nor does the upper boundary of the highest category necessarily represent the upper limit of the continuum.   Rather, these two points are conceived merely as marking off a range of values sufficient to accommodate the sensations produced by the stimuli of a particular experiment, and in many experiments these values are such that the psychological continuum is best thought of as extending below (to the left of) the lower boundary of the lowest category and above (to the right of) the upper boundary of the highest category.

There are two major variations of the general procedure under consideration, distinguished by the instructions given the subject and by the assumptions underlying the analysis of the subject's responses. In one variation, the *method of equal-appearing intervals,* the subject is instructed to sort (or rate) the stimuli so that the category boundaries are equally spaced along the psychological continuum—i.e., so that the apparent width of all categories is the same—and his ability to comply with these instructions is taken for granted. In the second variation, commonly called the *method of successive categories,* it is not assumed that the subject can employ categories of equal width, and no such requirement is implied in the instructions given the subject. These two methods will be considered separately below.

THE METHOD OF EQUAL-APPEARING INTERVALS

In the scaling procedures considered thus far, the task posed for the subject has been a relatively simple one: he has been required merely to judge which of two stimuli is greater, or to judge whether two pairs of stimuli are separated by equal sense distances. The task imposed by the method of equal-appearing intervals—the use of categories of equal width on the psychological continuum—is more demanding. In effect, this method would seem to require that the subject somehow be able to determine the position of each sensation on the psychological continuum and communicate this evaluation in the form of a rating. As Torgerson has put the matter, "It is difficult to conceive how a subject could make these responses unless he had directly available to him, with all of its properties, a 'ruler' of the attribute to be scaled" (1958, p. 117). The tenability of such an assumption has been questioned by many psychologists, for it is not at all clear how such a "subjective ruler" might be acquired: although there is little problem in accounting for performance in which an individual renders judgments that are in agreement with an objective ruler (e.g., in accounting for the agreement between an individual's estimates of lengths of lines and actual measurements of those lengths), it is difficult to understand how an individual acquires a "subjective ruler" for assessing values on psychological continua. (In this connection it will be recalled that values on a psychological continuum are regarded as distinct from the values of corresponding stimuli on a physical continuum. Thus, even though a subject might be familiar with the system of physical measurement employed in measuring the values of stimuli on a physical continuum, such knowledge would not provide him with a "subjective ruler" for measuring the corresponding sensations on a psychological continuum.) In the last analysis, acceptance or rejection of the assumption that subjects can somehow directly evaluate the position of sensations on a psychological continuum must probably rest, like that of most scientific assumptions, upon the consistency of that assumption with the network of theory and empirical laws developed within the field of psychophysical judgment. If, in the light of accumulated evidence, such an assumption appears warranted, it would seem that the ability of subjects to assess the value of sensations on psychological continua must somehow rest upon an analogy to familiar forms of measurement such as the measurement of length. At the present time the status of this assumption must remain open to question.

To illustrate the treatment of data obtained by the method of equal-appearing intervals let us consider an experiment in which the subject receives a series of electric shocks of various intensities and rates the painfulness of each on an eleven-point scale. Typically in an experiment of this kind there is some variability in the ratings assigned to a given stimulus, and it is therefore customary to obtain several ratings of each of the stimuli employed. In order to obtain repeated ratings of each of a series of stimuli, a single subject may rate each stimulus several times, or a large number of subjects may each rate every stimulus once. The former procedure leads to the development of a scale for one particular individual, a scale that may or may not be applicable to other individuals; the latter procedure leads to the development of a scale reflecting the average sensory reaction of a population of individuals. Whether one subject is presented with the same series of stimuli several times, or several subjects are each presented with the series of stimuli once, it is customary to vary the sequence in which the stimuli are presented from one presentation of the series to the next (or from one subject to the next) so as to minimize any artifacts that might arise from a particular sequence. (For example, as a result of contrast effects, a stimulus of moderate intensity might seem especially intense if it follows a very weak stimulus and especially weak if it follows a very intense stimulus. By varying the order of presentation of the stimuli, such contrast effects presumably tend to average out.) For purposes of illustration, we will assume that one subject has rated the painfulness of each of several intensities of electric shock 100 times, giving the distribution of ratings in Table 15-4 for one intensity.

TABLE 15-4 *Frequency distribution of 100 ratings of one stimulus intensity (hypothetical data)*

CATEGORY	1	2	3	4	5	6	7	8	9	10	11
FREQUENCY	23	36	19	11	6	3	2	—	—	—	—

(A complete set of data would include a similar frequency distribution for each stimulus intensity employed.) The data shown in the table illustrate the so-called *end effect,* a truncation of the distribution at one end of the scale, with a consequent piling up of cases in categories near that end. The scale value assigned a given stimulus (in the present example, a given stimulus intensity) is some measure of the central tendency of the distribution of ratings assigned that stimulus. Because the distributions for stimuli near the ends of the scale are typically skewed as a result of the end effect, it is customary to employ the median as a measure of central tendency. Using Formula (3-3), the median of the distribution shown in Table 15-4 is computed as follows: $P_{50} = 1.5 + (27/36)1 = 2.25$. In a similar manner scale values would be computed for each of the stimulus intensities employed, although the necessary data are not presented here.

When values on the psychological continuum are determined for each of several stimuli, as is usually the case in practice, it is possible to plot a psychophysical function showing the relationship between values on the psychological continuum and corresponding values on the physical continuum. In determining the shape of this function for some particular range of stimulus values, we would expect it to make little difference how the particular stimuli rated were distributed over the stimulus continuum. For example, consider two series of stimuli distributed along the stimulus continuum as illustrated below. These two series of stimuli span the same

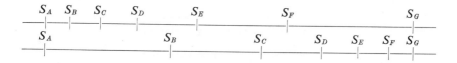

segment of the stimulus continuum, i.e., the limiting stimuli, S_A and S_G, have the same values in both series. However, the intermediate stimuli in the two series are distributed quite differently: in the first series the stimuli are separated by small steps in the lower portion of the range and by large steps in the upper portion; in the second series the pattern is reversed. If subjects' ratings accurately reflect the position on the psychological continuum of the sensations produced by various stimuli, we would expect the psychophysical function for the portion of the stimulus continuum between S_A and S_G to be the same whether ratings were based upon the first series of stimuli pictured above or the second. (This expectation is based upon the implicit assumption that the location of any particular sensation on the psychological continuum is determined solely by the physical value of the corresponding stimulus and is independent of the context of other stimuli within which the stimulus in question is presented.) However, Stevens and Galanter (1957) have shown that variations in the spacing of the stimuli rated can result in substantial changes in the shape of the psychophysical function. The effects observed by these investigators suggest that subjects attempt to distribute the stimuli to be rated as evenly as possible over the categories available, i.e., subjects seem to adjust the widths of the categories so that all categories are used with approximately the same frequency. The manner in which such a tendency affects the shape of the psychophysical function is shown by the hypothetical data pictured in Figure 15-9.

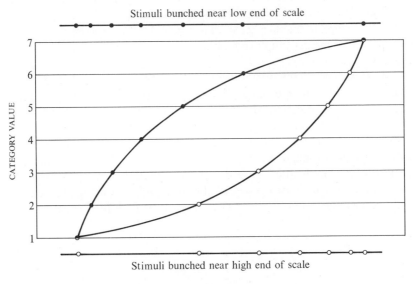

FIGURE 15-9 *Psychophysical functions based upon the method of equal-appearing intervals: the effects of changes in the spacing of stimuli. The upper curve is the psychophysical function for stimuli spaced as shown at the top of the figure; the lower curve, for stimuli spaced as shown at the bottom of the figure (hypothetical data).*

The two curves in this figure show, for two different distributions of stimuli, the psychophysical function that would be obtained if seven stimuli were rated on a seven-point scale and each stimulus was assigned by the subject to a separate category, i.e., the stimuli were distributed as evenly as possible among the categories available. The upper curve shows the psychophysical function that would be obtained using the distribution of stimuli represented at the top of the figure; the lower curve, the function that would be obtained using the distribution represented at the bottom of the figure. It is seen that the curves rise steeply where stimuli are bunched close together, slowly where stimuli are spread farther apart. By using spacings intermediate between those shown at the top and bottom of Figure 15-9, psychophysical functions intermediate in shape between those shown in the figure would be obtained.   The curves shown in Figure 15-9 are idealized in that they somewhat exaggerate the effects of spacing upon the psychophysical function; nevertheless, they serve to illustrate the general nature of the effects observed by Stevens and Galanter.

To the extent that a psychophysical function is influenced by the spacing of the stimuli rated, it does not accurately portray the relationship between values on the psychological continuum and corresponding values on the stimulus continuum.   Putting the matter somewhat differently, to the extent that scale values obtained by the method of equal-appearing intervals are influenced by the spacing of stimuli, those values do not accurately reflect what they are supposed to—the position on the psychological continuum of the sensations in question.   Stevens and Galanter suggest that a "pure" scale—i.e., one free of distortions resulting from stimulus spacing—may be achieved through a series of successive approximations using a procedure that they describe as follows:

> We will assume that *O* [the subject] expects the series of stimuli to be so arranged that all categories appear equally often.   Since at the outset we know nothing about the form of *O*'s category scale, we present to the first group of *O*s a series of stimuli spaced in some arbitrary manner along the continuum.   The results of this test give us a first approximation to the category scale.   For the second group of *O*s we space the stimuli so that they reflect equal intervals on the scale obtained from the first group of *O*s.   This gives a new curve—a second approximation to the "pure" scale.   Using this better approximation we respace the stimuli and repeat the procedure with a third group of *O*s.   We repeat this process until stability is reached, i.e., until the results of a test are such that no further change in spacing is called for.

> With enough homogeneous groups of *O*s, this iterative procedure could in principle reveal the unadulterated form of the category scale—the form in which the effects of expectation have been neutralized . . . (Stevens and Galanter, 1957, pp. 381–382).

The results of such iterative procedures suggest that the values obtained by the method of equal-appearing intervals are influenced by the discriminability of stimuli.   In general, the psychophysical function rises steeply in regions of the stimulus continuum where stimuli are readily discriminated, slowly in regions where discrimination is more difficult.   For stimulus dimensions on which the discriminability of stimuli decreases with increasing stimulus magnitude (more or less in accordance with Weber's Law), the resulting psychophysical function is concave downward, i.e., has the general shape of the upper curve in Figure 15-9.   The relationship between discriminability and scale values obtained by the method of equal-appearing intervals suggests that, to the extent permitted by the number of categories available, subjects tend to avoid placing in the same category two stimuli that are discriminably different.

The fact that scale values obtained by the method of equal-appearing intervals bear a close relationship to the discriminability of stimuli suggests that scale values obtained in this manner are similar in significance to scale values obtained by the method of summated jnd's, considered earlier.   Indeed, a study by Thurstone (1929) of judgments of the density of dots scattered irregularly in a square area tends to support this interpretation. However, at the present time the relevant experimental evidence is too meager to warrant a definite conclusion concerning whether or not, for a wide range of continua, scale values obtained by the method of equal-appearing intervals are essentially equivalent to those obtained by the method of summated jnd's.

THE METHOD OF SUCCESSIVE CATEGORIES

In the method of equal-appearing intervals the subject is instructed to rate (or sort) the stimuli in such a way that the categories represent equal segments of the psychological continuum, and in analyzing the data it is assumed that the subject is able to comply with these instructions.   In the method of successive categories, on the other hand, it is assumed merely that the categories employed by the subject represent adjacent segments of the psychological continuum but not necessarily segments of equal width.

A number of methods, alike in basic conception but differing in detail, for determining scale values of sensations corresponding to various stimuli may be derived from Thurstone's scaling model, described earlier.   To illustrate the general method let us assume that several intensities of electric shock, S_A, S_B, $\cdots$ have been rated for painfulness using three categories—"slightly painful," "moderately painful," and "very painful." We will assume that each intensity was rated 100 times and the ratings of two of the intensities, S_A and S_B, were distributed as shown in Table 15-5.

TABLE 15-5 *Frequency distributions of repeated ratings of two stimuli (hypothetical data)*

STIMULUS	CATEGORY		
	"Slightly Painful"	"Moderately Painful"	"Very Painful"
S_A	30	50	20
S_B	10	55	35

Thurstone's model, it will be recalled, assumes that any given stimulus (or stimulus intensity) gives rise over a series of repeated presentations to a normal distribution of sensory reactions—that is, the value on the psychological continuum of the sensory reaction evoked by a given stimulus fluctuates from trial to trial in a manner conforming to the normal distribution.   The hypothetical distributions of sensory reactions to S_A and S_B

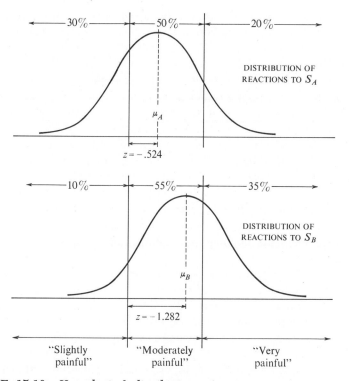

FIGURE 15-10 *Hypothetical distributions of sensory reactions to two intensities of electric shock. The solid vertical lines represent category boundaries separating judgments of "slightly painful," "moderately painful," and "very painful."*

are represented in the upper and lower parts, respectively, of Figure 15-10. The solid vertical lines in these diagrams represent the boundaries dividing the psychological continuum into three segments (categories), and the distributions have been positioned so that the area falling in each category represents the corresponding proportion given in Table 15-5; the vertical dashed lines represent μ_A and μ_B, the means of the two distributions. The determination of scale values corresponding to S_A and S_B consists in determining the location on the psychological continuum of μ_A and μ_B.

The category boundaries provide fixed points of reference for determining the positions of μ_A and μ_B. Turning our attention to the lower of the two category boundaries, that separating the "slightly painful" and "moderately painful" categories, we note that 30 per cent of the upper distribution lies below this boundary and 70 per cent lies above it. From Table A-3 we find that the corresponding value of z is $-.524$; in other words, the boundary in question is located $.524$ σ units below μ_A, or, what amounts to the same thing, μ_A is located $.524$ σ units above the boundary.

Similarly, we note that 10 per cent of the lower distribution lies below, and 90 per cent above, the same boundary. Again consulting Table A-3, we find that μ_B lies 1.282 σ units above the boundary in question. As in our previous discussion of Thurstone's scaling model, we shall make the simplifying assumption that the value of σ is the same for both distributions and shall arbitrarily adopt σ as our unit of measurement, i.e., let σ equal 1. (It should be noted that the model does not require this assumption and that the assumption can be checked by examination of the data. Even when this assumption does not hold, it is possible to compute scale values for each of the stimuli employed, but the computations are somewhat more complex than shown here. Guilford (1954) and Torgerson (1958) describe more complex procedures that can be employed when the dispersions of sensory reactions are not the same for all stimuli.) Since μ_A lies .524 units above the boundary taken as a reference point, and μ_B lies 1.282 units above the same boundary, it follows that μ_B lies $1.282 - .524 = .758$ units above μ_A.

In the above computations we took the lower of the two category boundaries as our point of reference in determining the separation of μ_A and μ_B. Alternatively, the upper boundary, that separating "moderately painful" from "very painful," may be taken as a point of reference. We see that in the upper distribution pictured in Figure 15-10, 80 per cent of the area lies below this boundary and 20 per cent of the area above it; consulting Table A-3, we find that μ_A is .842 σ units below this boundary. In the lower distribution the area is divided 65 per cent below and 35 per cent above this boundary, and Table A-3 indicates that μ_B is .385 σ units below it. On the basis of these calculations, μ_B is found to be $.842 - .385 = .457$ units above μ_A. It will be noted that the separation between μ_A and μ_B when the higher of the two category boundaries is taken as a point of reference is not the same as the separation when the lower of the two boundaries is taken as a point of reference. A discrepancy of this kind between the two estimates may arise as a consequence of sampling errors: the distributions of judgments shown in Table 15-5 are merely estimates of the corresponding distributions of all possible judgments and, like any estimates based upon the data provided by a sample, are subject to a certain degree of error as a result of sampling fluctuations. In the light of this consideration it would seem reasonable to take as our estimate of the separation between μ_A and μ_B the average of the separation computed taking the lower boundary as a point of reference and that computed taking the upper boundary as a point of reference, i.e., $(.758 + .457)/2 \approx .61$. Of course, if more than three categories are employed in rating a set of stimuli, there will be more than two boundaries available for computing the separation between the scale values for any pair of stimuli: in general, if there are k categories, there will be $k - 1$ boundaries available. Various methods may be employed to extend the procedure described above to situations in which more than three categories are employed. One of the simplest methods is to compute the separation of a given pair of stimuli $k - 1$ times, once for each of the $k - 1$ boundaries available, and then take the mean of the $k - 1$ determinations.

When several stimuli have been rated, as is usually the case in practice, it is customary to determine the scale separation of each successive pair of adjacent stimuli. For example, if S_A, S_B, S_C, S_D, $\cdots$ represent a series of stimuli arranged according to their position on the stimulus continuum, the separation would be computed between μ_A and μ_B, between μ_B and μ_C, between μ_C and μ_D, and so on for each successive pair of stimuli. Once the separations of successive means have been determined, it is necessary only to make an arbitrary decision concerning the point on the scale of measurement to be assigned the value zero, and the scale values of all means follow automatically. For example, we have determined above that μ_B lies .61 units above μ_A; if we assume, for purposes of illustration, that μ_C is found to lie .40 units above μ_B, and μ_D is found to lie .50 units above μ_C, and if we arbitrarily assign μ_A the value 2 (which is equivalent to assigning the value zero to some unspecified point on the continuum), the resulting scale values are as follows: $\mu_A = 2.00$, $\mu_B = 2.61$, $\mu_C = 3.01$, $\mu_D = 3.51$. Inasmuch as the zero point of the scale is purely arbitrary, the resulting scale is clearly an interval scale at best. This means that differences between scale values presumably have a meaningful interpretation but that ratios among scale values do not.

As in our discussions of other scaling methods, it is of interest to consider the relationship between scale values obtained by the method of successive categories and those obtained by alternative scaling methods. Despite the similarity of the experimental procedures employed, it appears that scale values obtained using the method of successive categories differ appreciably from those obtained using the method of equal-appearing intervals. For example, in one study (Jones and Thurstone, 1955) 51 descriptive adjectives were rated on a nine-point scale on the basis of meaning: adjectives implying great dislike were placed in the first category, those implying great liking were placed in the last category, and those implying intermediate degrees of liking or dislike were placed in intermediate categories. Scale values were determined by the method of equal-appearing intervals and by the method of successive categories. It was found that the two sets of values were approximately linearly related (i.e., related by a straight-line function) in the middle range of the scale, but that at both ends of the scale, values obtained by the method of equal-appearing intervals were less widely separated than values obtained by the method of successive categories. In other words, relative to the successive-category scale, the equal-appearing-interval scale was compressed at both ends. It seems likely that this result is a consequence of the end effect described earlier, i.e., the curtailing of the distributions of ratings of stimuli located near the ends of the scale: while the method of successive categories assumes that the underlying (theoretical) distributions are normal and adjusts the widths of the end categories to correct for the skewed shape of distributions near the ends of the scale, the method of equal-appearing intervals makes no such assumption and no adjustment.

On the other hand, scale values obtained by the method of successive categories have been found to be in extremely close agreement with scale values obtained by the method of paired comparisons. Edwards and Thurstone (1952) scaled ten foods on a continuum of preference two ways, once using the method of successive categories and once using the method of paired comparisons. The two sets of scale values were found to be related by a straight-line function, i.e., one set of scale values was directly proportional to the other. That the two sets of scale values were in very close agreement is indicated by the fact that the coefficient of correlation between values on the two scales was .988. Because the number of such comparisons reported in the literature is small, any general statement regarding the equivalence of these two scaling procedures must be regarded as highly tentative at the present time. However, existing findings suggest that the method of paired comparisons and the method of successive categories, both based upon Thurstone's scaling model, measure the same thing.

As we have noted earlier, the ultimate test of the usefulness of a measurement scale is whether values obtained using the scale are found to be lawfully related to other observable phenomena. Several tests of the predictive capacity of successive-category scale values in the area of food preferences have been reported by Bock and Jones (in press). In one study, for example, the preferences of a group of 254 subjects were scaled using the method of successive categories, and the resulting scale values were used to predict the relative frequencies with which different foods would be selected when subjects were presented with selections of three foods and asked to indicate their first choice. It was found that for any given set of three alternative foods the relative frequency with which each food was selected as a first choice by the 254 subjects could be predicted fairly accurately on the basis of the scale values assigned to those foods by the method of successive categories. Although the number of relevant studies and the range of phenomena investigated is limited at the present time, findings such as those reported by Bock and Jones attest in a preliminary manner to the significance of scale values provided by the method of successive categories.

DIRECT-ESTIMATE SCALES

In everyday discourse it is not unusual for individuals to phrase statements (verbal reports) concerning their sensations in terms of ratios. For example, an individual might describe the pain resulting from a given injury as being twice as great (or ten times as great) as that resulting from some other injury; similarly, statements to the effect that one light seems twice as bright as another, that one sound seems twice as loud as another, and so on, are not uncommon. Although it seems likely that such statements are frequently intended merely as figures of speech, there is a surprising degree of uniformity among the numbers used by different individuals to report the apparent ratios of sensations. For example, Hanes (1949) has found that, when subjects are instructed to adjust the brightness of one stimulus so that it is half as great or one-third as great as the brightness of a standard stimulus, the variation among the settings of different subjects is not much greater than when the subjects merely adjust one stimulus so that it appears equal to the other. Similarly, Ekman and Dahlbäck (1956), using a task in which subjects adjusted the velocity of a moving object, found that the variability among subjects when adjusting one velocity to appear half as great as another was only slightly more than when setting one velocity equal to another. Thus, in the case of certain types of judgments at least, it appears that the degree of uniformity obtained among subjects in adjusting stimuli so that the sensations produced by those stimuli are in some specified ratio compares favorably with what we might expect to be the limiting uniformity, that obtained in equating one stimulus with another.

In this section we shall consider four scaling methods based upon judgments of the apparent ratios among sensations. Although these methods differ somewhat in detail, they have in common that each of them presupposes that the judgments of subjects concerning apparent ratios of sensations have significant meaning. (The somewhat vague expression "significant meaning" is chosen advisedly, for it is not entirely clear what it means when a subject says that one sensation is, say, twice as great as another.) The four methods to be considered have been labeled by Stevens (1957, 1958) *ratio estimation, ratio production, magnitude estimation,* and *magnitude production.* As will become apparent from the descriptions of these procedures below, in using these scaling procedures the numerical values to be assigned to various sensations are obtained in a more direct manner than in the scaling methods considered previously;[6] accordingly, these methods are commonly referred to collectively as the *direct-estimate methods.*

In the method of ratio estimation the subject is presented with two fixed stimuli and is required to specify a number that describes the apparent ratio of the sensations produced by the two. For example, the subject might be presented with two lights of different brightness and required to indicate whether, compared to the dimmer of the two, the other seems twice as bright, three times as bright, or whatever.

---

[6] A possible exception is the method of equal-appearing intervals, in which the scaling procedure is also relatively direct.

In the method of ratio production the subject is presented with a fixed standard stimulus and a variable comparison stimulus and is instructed to adjust the variable stimulus so that the sensation it produces seems to bear a specified ratio to that produced by the fixed standard. For example, the subject might be instructed to adjust a variable light so that it appears to be half as bright, one-third as bright, or twice as bright as the standard.

In the method of magnitude estimation the subject is presented with a series of stimuli and is instructed to specify, for each stimulus, a number that describes the magnitude of the sensation produced by that stimulus. It is usually emphasized in the instructions to the subject that the numbers should be assigned to the stimuli in such a way as to indicate the apparent ratios among the corresponding sensations, i.e., that if the sensation produced by one stimulus seems twice as great as that produced by another, the number assigned to the first stimulus should be twice as great as that assigned the second. The subject may be presented with a standard reference stimulus that is assigned some arbitrary number, say 10. Thus, if one of the stimuli in the series seems twice as great as the standard, that stimulus would be assigned the value 20; if half as great, the value 5. It would seem that when a standard reference stimulus is employed, the task is virtually the same as that posed by the method of ratio estimation—the subject need only decide the apparent ratio to the standard stimulus of the stimulus being judged, and then multiply this ratio by the value of the standard. When no standard is provided by the experimenter, the judgment of each stimulus is presumably based upon the relationships between that stimulus and other stimuli in the series being judged, rather than upon the relationship of each of the stimuli to a single standard. Although this variation of the procedure may make the task somewhat more difficult for the subject, the nature of the task appears to be essentially the same as when a standard is provided by the experimenter. In effect, the use of a standard reference stimulus serves to fix the unit of measurement being employed; when no standard is provided, it is left to the subject to select his own unit of measurement.

The method of magnitude production is essentially the reverse of the method of magnitude estimation: in the method of magnitude production the experimenter specifies various values of apparent magnitude and the subject is required to adjust a variable stimulus so that the resulting sensations have the magnitudes specified by the experimenter.

PROTHETIC AND METATHETIC CONTINUA

Before examining some of the results obtained with the direct-estimate methods, it will be useful to note a classification of psychological continua proposed by Stevens and Galanter (1957). These investigators suggest that there are two basic kinds of psychological continua and have used the terms *prothetic* and *metathetic* to distinguish the two types.   The class of prothetic continua includes those involving variations of sensory intensity —for example, the brightness of lights, the loudness of tones, the intensity of odors, and the intensity of electric shocks.   Also included in the class of prothetic continua are such perceptual continua as the apparent length of lines, the apparent duration of temporal intervals, the apparent numerosity of collections of dots, and the apparent area of rectangles—continua that might be characterized as involving judgments of "how much" or "how many."   The class of metathetic continua, on the other hand, includes those involving judgments of sensory quality (e.g., the pitch of musical tones) or judgments of the position of objects in space (e.g., the position, from left to right, of a dot on a line, or the inclination of sloping lines).[7]

Although the number of experimental comparisons completed at the present time is limited, existing findings suggest the following tentative conclusions concerning the relationships between scale values obtained by direct-estimate methods and those obtained by other scaling procedures: on the one hand, for metathetic continua, scale values obtained by the direct-estimate methods agree fairly closely with scale values obtained by the method of equisection, by the method of equal-appearing intervals, and by summating jnd's; on the other hand, for prothetic continua, there appear to be consistent and systematic discrepancies between scale values obtained by the direct-estimate methods and those obtained by the other scaling procedures mentioned above.

Stevens (1957) suggests that the fundamental difference between metathetic and prothetic continua relates to the apparent size, as measured in direct-estimate scale units, of jnd's.   On metathetic continua the jnd is approximately the same, in direct-estimate units, throughout the scale. In other words, on a metathetic continuum an increase of, say, 20 units on a direct-estimate scale represents approximately the same number of jnd's at any point on the continuum—if, for example, there are ten jnd's between the stimulus having a direct-estimate scale value of 100 and the stimulus having a scale value of 120, there will be approximately the same number of jnd's between the stimuli having scale values of 200 and 220, between those having scale values of 300 and 320, and so on, throughout the scale.

On prothetic continua, on the other hand, as one progresses from the

---

[7] Concerning the choice of the labels *prothetic* and *metathetic*, Stevens and Galanter write: "Class I we label *prothetic*, because it includes, among other things, magnitudes like heaviness, loudness, brightness, etc., for which discrimination appears to be based on an additive mechanism by which excitation is added to excitation at the physiological level.   Class II we label *metathetic*, because it includes pitch, position, etc., for which discrimination behaves as though based on a substitutive mechanism at the physiological level" (Stevens and Galanter, 1957, p. 377).

low end of a continuum to the high end, successive jnd's represent larger and larger steps on a direct-estimate scale. The relationship between jnd and direct-estimate units is represented schematically in Figure 15-11.

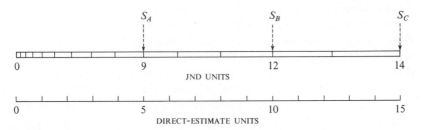

FIGURE 15-11 *Relationship of jnd and direct-estimate units on prothetic continua. Successive jnd's mark off steps of increasing size measured in relation to direct-estimate units.*

The increasing size of the jnd with increasing direct-estimate scale values reflects the fact that discriminability is not uniform throughout direct-estimate scales of prothetic continua. For example, although S_B is midway between S_A and S_C as distances are measured on the direct-estimate scale, measured in discrimination units S_B is closer to S_C (two jnd units) than to S_A (three jnd units). Consequently, if subjects were to make direct comparisons of the two intervals, as in the method of equisection, the interval between S_A and S_B would seem greater than that between S_B and S_C. Another consequence of the unequal sizes of jnd's is that the apparent ratio of two sensations as determined by direct-estimate methods does not correspond to the ratio between the corresponding scale values on a summated jnd scale. Consider, for example, S_A and S_C in Figure 15-11. These two stimuli are 9 jnd's and 14 jnd's, respectively, above the stimulus threshold; the corresponding scale values on the direct-estimate scale are 5 and 15, respectively. Thus, although S_C is less than twice as many jnd's above threshold as S_A, by direct-estimate procedures the sensation produced by S_C is judged to be three times as great as that produced by S_A. Discrepancies similar to those observed on prothetic continua between jnd scales and direct-estimate scales are also observed between direct-estimate scales and scales obtained by the method of equal-appearing intervals, although in the case of equal-appearing-interval scales the discrepancies are somewhat less extreme than in the case of jnd scales. That is to say, compared to direct-estimate units, units on an equal-appearing-interval scale increase in size as one progresses up the scale of measurement. Later in the chapter we shall consider the theoretical significance of the discrepancies between direct-estimate scales and scales of other kinds, but first we shall examine the nature of the psychophysical functions relating direct-estimate values to physical measures of stimulus intensity or magnitude.

PSYCHOPHYSICAL FUNCTIONS—THE POWER LAW

S. S. Stevens (1961) has called attention to the rather remarkable finding that for all prothetic continua that have been studied—over two dozen in all—the psychophysical function relating direct-estimate scale values to values on the corresponding stimulus continuum may be described by an equation of the same general form. Representing values on the psychological continuum by P and values on the stimulus continuum by S, this equation may be written as follows:

$$P = a(S - S_0)^b \qquad\qquad (15\text{-}4)$$

in which a, b, and S_0 are constants. The constant S_0 represents the physical value of the stimulus threshold, and the difference $S - S_0$ represents the physical values of stimuli expressed in terms of distance above the threshold. According to this equation, values on the psychological scale are directly proportional to the physical value of the stimulus—expressed in terms of distance above the threshold—raised to a constant power, b. The shape of the function described by Equation (15-4) depends upon the value of the constant b. When b is greater that 1, the psychophysical function is a positively accelerated curve having the general shape shown in the first part of Figure 15-12, i.e., rising slowly at first

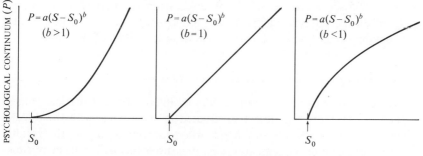

STIMULUS CONTINUUM (S)

FIGURE 15-12 *Variations in the power function relating direct-estimate scale values (P) to stimulus magnitude (S). The three curves differ in the value of the exponent b, as indicated.*

and then more rapidly; when b is equal to 1, the psychophysical function is a straight line such as shown in the middle part of Figure 15-12; when b is less than 1, the function is a negatively accelerated curve having the general shape shown in the third part of Figure 15-12, i.e., rising rapidly at first and then more slowly. Two continua for which the exponent b is greater than 1 are the apparent intensity of electric shock (Stevens, Carton, and Shickman, 1958) and the apparent heaviness of lifted weights

(Stevens and Galanter, 1957). In the case of both these continua—as in the case of all continua for which the exponent b is greater than 1—doubling the physical intensity of the stimulus more than doubles the value of the corresponding sensation (as scaled by direct-estimate methods). For example, when the physical intensity of an electric shock is doubled, the apparent intensity is increased more than ten times. Three continua for which the psychophysical function closely approximates a straight line ($b \approx 1$) are the apparent length of lines, the apparent duration of sounds, and the apparent area of rectangles (Stevens and Galanter, 1957). On each of these continua, doubling the value of the physical stimulus approximately doubles the value assigned on the corresponding psychological continuum. This finding is not too surprising in view of the fact that the scale of physical measurement of each of these stimulus properties is highly familiar from everyday experience: the findings referred to above would seem to indicate simply that subjects can make estimates of length, duration, and area that are in reasonably close agreement with actual measures of these characteristics of stimuli. Two continua for which the psychophysical function has the general form shown in the third part of Figure 15-12 ($b < 1$) are the apparent loudness of sounds and the apparent brightness of luminous objects (Stevens and Galanter, 1957). On continua having this form of psychophysical function, doubling the intensity of the physical stimulus results in less than a doubling of the intensity of the corresponding sensation (as scaled by direct-estimate methods). For example, when the physical intensity of a sound is doubled, the value of the corresponding sensation is increased somewhat less than 25 per cent.

THE MEANING OF DIRECT-ESTIMATE SCALE VALUES

Finally, let us turn to the question of how to interpret the numerical values assigned to sensations by subjects instructed in accordance with the direct-estimate methods. On the one hand, when individuals report the results of various physical measurements—e.g., measurements of length or of time —we know exactly what such values mean, for there are explicit sets of rules (measurement procedures) for obtaining such values. On the other hand, when individuals report their direct estimates of the magnitudes of sensations, the meaning of the values reported is not immediately evident, for there are no well-defined rules, agreed upon by convention, for obtaining such values. Clearly, the capacity to assess sensations numerically is not inborn—such a capacity must somehow be an outcome of learning. It is equally clear that for many of the sensory attributes that have been scaled by the direct-estimate methods, individuals do not receive any direct training in the assignment of numerical values to sensations—for example, there is nothing in the everyday experience of most individuals that would teach them to recognize when one tone seems, say, twice as loud as another or when one light seems twice as bright as another.   It would seem, therefore, that such judgments by subjects must rest upon an analogy to situations in which the use and meaning of numbers is familiar—very likely, situations involving the measurement of such familiar variables as the lengths of lines or the durations of temporal intervals.   In other words, the use of numbers—or, more precisely, the use of verbal responses that refer to numbers—to describe sensations of loudness, brightness, etc., would seem to be an example of metaphorical extension, a phenomenon considered in a somewhat different context in Chapter 11.   This view— that the numerical judgments obtained in the direct-estimate scaling methods rest upon an analogy to the use of numbers in connection with familiar quantities such as length and time—is consistent with the fact, cited in the preceding subsection, that when the direct-estimate methods are applied to judgments of apparent length and apparent temporal duration, the resulting psychological values correspond almost directly to actual physical measures of the stimuli in question.

Earlier in the chapter the same assumption was made in connection with the method of equal-appearing intervals, i.e., it was assumed that the judgments obtained using that procedure are also based upon an analogy to familiar measurements such as of length and time.   The question therefore arises, if the direct-estimate methods and the method of equal-appearing intervals both rest upon an analogy to the same types of measures, why are the results of the two methods not in agreement?   Two alternative points of view with respect to this question will be considered briefly.

One point of view—that favored by Stevens—derives from the general position that the discriminability of stimuli and the apparent magnitude of sensations are two distinct and separate concepts.   According to this point of view, although it may be meaningful, and for certain purposes useful, to locate sensations on a continuum with respect to the discriminability of the corresponding stimuli—e.g., by counting off jnd's from some arbitrary reference point—the resulting scale values do not necessarily reflect the apparent magnitude of the corresponding sensations.[8]   Stated differently, equal steps on a scale of apparent magnitude may or may not be equally discriminable, depending upon whether the size of the jnd, measured in units of apparent magnitude, is constant throughout the continuum or

---

[8] Although adherence to this general point of view does not necessarily entail acceptance of Thurstone's scaling model, Thurstone's model affords one way of formulating a distinction between apparent magnitude and discriminability.   The apparent magnitude of the sensation associated with a given stimulus is the value of μ, the mean sensory reaction to that stimulus.   The discriminability of two stimuli—as indicated, for example, by the frequency with which one is mistaken for the other— depends not only upon the separation between the corresponding values of μ, but also upon the variability of the corresponding distributions of sensory reactions.   For example, given that $\mu_A = 5$ and $\mu_B = 10$, the two stimuli in question, S_A and S_B, may be more or less discriminable depending upon whether the values of σ_A and σ_B are small or large.

varies with apparent magnitude—for example, as shown in Figure 15-11. Stevens (1957) suggests that direct-estimate methods of scaling measure the apparent magnitude of sensations, whereas the method of equal-appearing intervals measures—or at least is considerably influenced by—the discriminability of stimuli. Thus, because these two approaches to scaling measure different aspects of sensory reactions, they do not necessarily agree in all cases.

An alternative hypothesis suggested by Torgerson (1960) is that the method of equal-appearing intervals and the direct-estimate approach to scaling both reflect the discriminability of stimuli, but that on equal-appearing-interval scales equally discriminable differences between stimuli are represented by equal differences in scale values, whereas on direct-estimate scales equally discriminable differences are represented by equal ratios. To illustrate, let us suppose that S_A, S_B, S_C, S_D, and S_E represent a series of gray papers differing in lightness and selected in such a way that there are five jnd's between S_A and S_B, five jnd's between S_B and S_C, and so on. According to Torgerson's hypothesis, subjects instructed in accordance with the method of equal-appearing intervals would assign numbers to these stimuli in such a way that successive pairs of stimuli are separated by equal differences. For example, the five stimuli might be assigned the numbers 1, 2, 3, 4, and 5, respectively. (Depending upon the details of the instructions and other stimuli included in the series to be rated, other sets of numbers separated by equal differences might be employed, e.g., the series 3, 4, 5, 6, 7, or the series 1, 3, 5, 7, 9, to mention but two possibilities.) On the other hand—according to Torgerson's hypothesis—given the five stimuli described above, subjects instructed in accordance with the method of magnitude estimation would assign numbers in such a way that each number is a constant multiple of the one preceding it in the series. For example, assuming that S_A is assigned the value 8 and that each increment of five jnd's results in a doubling of the value assigned, the five stimuli would be assigned the values 8, 16, 32, 64, and 128, respectively. (It should be noted that the assumption that each successive increment of five jnd's results in a doubling of the value assigned is made only for purposes of illustration; it is possible, of course, that five jnd's might result in increases by some multiple other than 2. If, for example, each increment of five jnd's resulted in an increase by a multiple of 1.5, the values assigned the five stimuli in the above example would be 8, 12, 18, 27, and 40.5, respectively. Unfortunately, the factors determining the ratio corresponding to any given number of jnd's are not well understood at the present time.)

There are several considerations to recommend the hypothesis that despite some apparent indications to the contrary, direct-estimate methods measure the discriminability of stimuli. First, in relating direct-estimate judgments to the phenomenon of discrimination, this hypothesis considerably lessens the mystery of how subjects can, without specific training, assign numerical values to their sensations in consistent and apparently lawful ways. Moreover, the mathematical implications of this hypothesis appear to be consistent with some of the major empirical findings concerning scale values obtained by direct-estimate methods. For one thing, this hypothesis appears to be consistent with the general finding that direct-estimate scale values are related to physical measures of stimulus magnitude by a power function such as described in Equation (15-4).[9] For another, as we have shown in a very general way in the example in the preceding paragraph, and as Torgerson (1960) has demonstrated in somewhat greater detail, the general form of the relationship between scale values obtained by the method of equal-appearing intervals and those obtained by direct-estimate methods appears to be consistent with this hypothesis. More generally, in relating direct-estimate scales to stimulus discriminability, this hypothesis holds promise of making it possible to account in detail for the relationships between direct-estimate scales and scales obtained by other methods described in this chapter, thus serving to unify to a considerable extent experimental findings in the field of sensory scaling. The question of whether this promise is realized must find an answer in future experimental work and theoretical analysis.

PROBLEMS

1. Using the simplified version of the method of paired comparisons described in this chapter, a wine-taster judged each of four comparison wines (S_W, S_X, S_Y, and S_Z) in relation to a single standard wine (S_A) a large number of times. (We will assume the tests were made blindfolded so that the wines had to be evaluated solely on the basis of taste.) The following table gives the proportion of trials on which each of the four comparison wines was judged sweeter or drier (less sweet) than the standard:

Comparison Stimulus	S_W	S_X	S_Y	S_Z
Proportion of "Sweeter" Judgments	.80	.15	.50	.75
Proportion of "Drier" Judgments	.20	.85	.50	.25

(a) Assuming $\sigma_W = \sigma_X = \sigma_Y = \sigma_Z = 1$, determine the position on the psychological continuum, relative to μ_A, of μ_W, μ_X, μ_Y, and μ_Z. Assign values in such a way that sweet wines are assigned high numbers; dry wines, low numbers. (Use Table A-3 to obtain values of z.) (b) Assuming the driest wine in the series is assigned a scale value of 0, what scale value is assigned to each of the other wines?

[9] This is shown by Stevens (1957, pp. 172–173). Although the hypothesis upon which Stevens' mathematical derivation is based differs somewhat from Torgerson's hypothesis described above, the two hypotheses have certain mathematical implications in common, among them the derivation of the power function described in Equation (15-4).

2. Using the method of successive categories, and employing four categories for classifying stimuli, 100 subjects each rated several specimens of handwriting for legibility. The distributions of ratings assigned to two of the specimens are given below.

SPECIMEN	CATEGORY			
	Poor	Fair	Good	Very Good
S_A	34	28	24	14
S_B	10	21	29	40

Assuming $\sigma_A = \sigma_B = 1$, and using the scaling procedure described in this chapter in connection with the method of successive categories, determine the separation on the psychological continuum, in σ units, between μ_A and μ_B, taking as the point of reference the category boundary (a) between the first and second categories, (b) between the second and third categories, and (c) between the third and fourth categories. (Obtain approximate values of z from Table A-2, using tabled values closest to the values required.) (d) What is the overall estimate of the separation between μ_A and μ_B based upon the above data?

3. Each of four shades of gray were rated as *dark* or *light* by 100 subjects, with the following results:

SPECIMEN	CATEGORY	
	Dark	Light
S_A	85	15
S_B	60	40
S_C	30	70
S_D	10	90

(a) Assuming $\sigma_A = \sigma_B = \sigma_C = \sigma_D = 1$, and using the scaling method described in this chapter in connection with the method of successive categories, determine the position of μ_A, μ_B, μ_C, and μ_D relative to the boundary separating the two categories. (Obtain the appropriate values of z from Table A-3.) (b) If μ_A is arbitrarily assigned a scale value of 1, what are the scale values assigned to the remaining specimens?

REFERENCES

BOCK, R. D. and L. V. JONES. *The measurement and prediction of judgment and choice.* San Francisco: Holden-Day, in press.

EDWARDS, A. L. and L. L. THURSTONE. An internal consistency check for scale values determined by the method of successive intervals. *Psychometrika,* 1952, **17,** 169–180.

EKMAN, G. and B. DAHLBÄCK. A subjective scale of velocity. Report from the Psychological Laboratory, Univ. of Stockholm, No. 31, February 1956. Cited by Stevens (1957, p. 170).

GUILFORD, J. P. *Psychometric methods* (2d ed.). New York: McGraw-Hill, 1954.

HANES, R. M. A scale of subjective brightness. *J. exp. Psychol.,* 1949, **39,** 438–452.

JONES, L. V. and L. L. THURSTONE. The psychophysics of semantics: an experimental investigation. *J. appl. Psychol.,* 1955, **39,** 31–36.

MUNSELL, A. E. O., L. L. SLOAN, and I. H. GODLOVE. Neutral value scales. I. Munsell neutral value scale. *J. opt. Soc. Amer.,* 1933, **23,** 394–411.

SHEPARD, R. Similarity of stimuli and metric properties of behavioral data. In H. Gulliksen and S. Messick (eds.), *Psychological scaling: theory and applications.* New York: Wiley, 1960. Pp. 33–43.

STEVENS, S. S. On the psychophysical law. *Psychol. Rev.,* 1957, **64,** 153–181.

———. Problems and methods of psychophysics. *Psychol. Bull.,* 1958, **55,** 177–196.

———. The psychophysics of sensory function. In W. A. Rosenblith (ed.), *Sensory communication.* Cambridge: M.I.T. Press. New York: Wiley, 1961. Pp. 1–33.

STEVENS, S. S., A. S. CARTON, and G. M. SHICKMAN. A scale of apparent intensity of electric shock. *J. exp. Psychol.,* 1958, **56,** 328–334.

STEVENS, S. S. and E. H. GALANTER. Ratio scales and category scales for a dozen perceptual continua. *J. exp. Psychol.,* 1957, **54,** 377–411.

STEVENS, S. S. and J. VOLKMANN. The relation of pitch to frequency: a revised scale. *Amer. J. Psychol.,* 1940, **53,** 329–353.

STEVENS, S. S., J. VOLKMANN, and E. B. NEWMAN. A scale for the measurement of the psychological magnitude pitch. *J. acoust. Soc. Amer.,* 1937, **8,** 185–190.

THURSTONE, L. L. Psychophysical analysis. *Amer. J. Psychol.,* 1927, **38,** 368–389.

———. Fechner's law and the method of equal-appearing intervals. *J. exp. Psychol.,* 1929, **12,** 214–224.

TORGERSON, W. S. *Theory and methods of scaling.* New York: Wiley, 1958.

———. Quantitative judgment scales. In H. Gulliksen and S. Messick (eds.), *Psychological scaling: theory and applications.* New York: Wiley, 1960. Pp. 21–31.

ADDITIONAL READINGS

GALANTER, E. Contemporary psychophysics. In T. M. Newcomb (ed.), *New directions in psychology.* New York: Holt, Rinehart, and Winston, 1962. Pp. 87–156. Includes a simplified discussion of scaling, with emphasis on equal-appearing-interval (category) scales and direct-estimate scales.

GRAHAM, C. H. and P. RATOOSH. Notes on some interrelations of sensory psychology, perception, and behavior. In S. Koch (ed.), *Psychology: a study of a science.* Vol. 4. New York: McGraw-Hill, 1962. Pp. 483–514. Includes a discussion of certain conceptual difficulties underlying direct-estimate scaling procedures and analyzes the interpretation of responses having numerical form. The distinction between sensation and perception is also discussed from a behavioristic point of view.

LUCE, R. D. and E. GALANTER. Psychophysical scaling. In R. D. Luce, R. R. Bush, and E. Galanter (eds.), *Handbook of mathematical psychology.* New York: Wiley, 1963. Pp. 245–307. A technical discussion of the mathematical theory underlying sensory scaling.

STEVENS, S. S. The surprising simplicity of sensory metrics. *Amer. Psychologist,* 1962, **17,** 29–39. A very readable account of recent results obtained using direct-estimate methods of scaling. Includes a description of a newly developed technique, so-called *cross-modality comparisons.*

WOODWORTH, R. S. and H. SCHLOSBERG. *Experimental psychology* (rev. ed.). New York: Holt, 1954. Chap. 9. Presents a rather detailed review of some of the major experimental findings in the field of sensory scaling.

answers to problems

CHAPTER 2

1. Continuous: c, d, f, g, i. Discrete: a, b, e, h.
2. (a) Class frequencies: 1, 3, 2, 2, 1, 0, 1, respectively.
   (b) Class boundaries (in sec.): 4.95, 9.95, 14.95, 19.95, $\cdots$
   (c) Class interval: 5 sec.
3. Class frequencies: 1, 2, 3, 2, 0, 1, 1, respectively.
4. (a) $P_{25} = 6$ sec.; $P_{75} = 8.5$ sec. (b) The percentile rank of 7 sec. is 50; the percentile rank of 9.5 sec. is 84.4.
5. (a) $D_1 = 7$, $D_2 = 11.5$, $D_3 = 13$, $D_4 = 14.5$, $D_5 = 16$, $D_6 = 17.5$, $D_7 = 20.5$, $D_8 = 25$, $D_9 = 29.5$. (Note that D_1 could be located anywhere in the interval between 5.5 and 8.5; by convention, this decile is assigned the value of the midpoint of the interval.) (b) $Q_1 = 12.25$, $Q_2 = 16$, $Q_3 = 23.5$. (c) A score of 10 has a percentile rank of 15; a score of 13 has a percentile rank of 30.

CHAPTER 3

1. $\overline{X} \approx 7.17$; $P_{50} = 6.75$; Mode $= 6$.
2. $\overline{X} = 7.00$; $P_{50} = 5.05$; Mode $= 4$.
3. $\overline{X} = 14.0$; $P_{50} = 10.5$; Mode $= 7$.
4. $\overline{X} = 25.5$; $P_{50} = 22$; Mode $= 14.5$.
5. (a) Interquartile range ≈ 10.83. (b) Interquartile range ≈ 24.67.
6. $s^2 = 6.8$; $s \approx 2.61$.
7. $s^2 \approx 6.04$; $s \approx 2.46$.
8. (a) $s^2 = 15.2$; $s \approx 3.90$. (b) The results are the same, since subtracting a constant does not change the standard deviation (or variance).
9. $s^2 \approx 2.85$; $s \approx 1.69$; subtracting a constant does not alter these values.
10. (a) $\overline{X} = 14$; $s_V \approx 2.5$, $s_X \approx 12.5$. (b) $\overline{X} = 25.5$; $s_V = 1.86$, $s_X \approx 18.6$.
11. (a) $\overline{V} = 60$, $s_V = 12$. (b) $\overline{V} = 41$, $s_V = 6$. (c) $\overline{V} = 30$, $s_V = 6$.
12. $Z = 40$, $Z = 45$, $Z = 55$; upward.
13. $Z = 80$, $Z = 90$, $Z = 110$.

CHAPTER 4

1. The four possible outcomes are HH, HT, TH, TT. The probability of each is .25.
2. The probabilities of values of X equal to 0, 1, and 2 are .25, .50, and .25, respectively.
3. $\mu = 1$, $\sigma^2 = .50$.

4. Jack would win approximately 25 times; Tom, approximately 75 times.
5. (*a*) There are 36 possible outcomes: 1 and 1, 1 and 2, 1 and 3, $\cdots$, 6 and 6.   (*b*) All 36 outcomes are equally likely; the probability of each is 1/36.   (*c*) The possible values of S are $S = 2$ (one outcome), $S = 3$ (two outcomes), $S = 4$ (three outcomes), $S = 5$ (four outcomes), $S = 6$ (five outcomes), $S = 7$ (six outcomes), $S = 8$ (five outcomes), $S = 9$ (four outcomes), $S = 10$ (three outcomes), $S = 11$ (two outcomes), and $S = 12$ (one outcome).   (*d*) The probability distribution of S is as follows:

S	2	3	4	5	6	7	8	9	10	11	12
Probability	$\frac{1}{36}$	$\frac{2}{36}$	$\frac{3}{36}$	$\frac{4}{36}$	$\frac{5}{36}$	$\frac{6}{36}$	$\frac{5}{36}$	$\frac{4}{36}$	$\frac{3}{36}$	$\frac{2}{36}$	$\frac{1}{36}$

(*e*) $\mu = 7$, $\sigma^2 = 5\frac{5}{6}$.
6. (*a*) Stratified sampling.   (*b*) Simple random sampling.   (*c*) Systematic sampling.   (*d*) Sampling in two stages.
7. (*a*) $\sigma_\epsilon^2 = 25$, $\sigma_\tau^2 = 100$, $\sigma^2 = \sigma_\epsilon^2 + \sigma_\tau^2 = 125$.   (*b*) $\sigma^2 = 125$.   (*c*) The sample variance would approximate $\sigma_\epsilon^2 = 25$.   (*d*) The sample variance would approximate $\sigma^2 = 125$.

CHAPTER 5

1. (*a*) .50.   (*b*) .0668.   (*c*) .4332.   (*d*) Approximately 433.
2. (*a*) .9332.   (*b*) $P_{30} = 76.856$.   (*c*) $X = 74.948$ and $X = 85.052$.   (*d*) .8185.
3. (*a*) $X = 80.4$ and $X = 119.6$.   (*b*) .05.   (*c*) $X = 74.24$ and $X = 125.76$.   (*d*) .01.
4. T scores corresponding to the various values of X are as follows:

X	3	4	5	6	7	8	9	10
T	27	31	34	40	46	52	59	68

CHAPTER 6

1. (*a*) The sampling distribution of $\overline{X}$ is as follows:

$\overline{X}$	1.0	1.5	2.0	2.5	3.0	3.5	4.0	4.5	5.0	5.5	6.0
Probability	$\frac{1}{36}$	$\frac{2}{36}$	$\frac{3}{36}$	$\frac{4}{36}$	$\frac{5}{36}$	$\frac{6}{36}$	$\frac{5}{36}$	$\frac{4}{36}$	$\frac{3}{36}$	$\frac{2}{36}$	$\frac{1}{36}$

(*b*) $3/36 + 2/36 + 1/36 = 1/6$.   (*c*) $\mu_{\overline{X}} = 3.5$, $\sigma_{\overline{X}}^2 = 1\frac{11}{24}$.   (*d*) The values are the same as obtained by direct calculation.
2. For the first alternative, $\sigma_{\overline{X}} = 1.0$; for the second, $\sigma_{\overline{X}} = .8$.   Thus, greater precision of $\overline{X}$ is afforded by the second alternative.
3. (*a*) $p = .8664$.   (*b*) 76.08 and 83.92.
4. (*a*) $p = .9974$.   (*b*) 78.04 and 81.96.
5. $p = .6826$.
6. $p = .7888$.
7. (*a*) The class distribution constitutes an empirical approximation of the sampling distribution of $\overline{X}$ for samples of ten cases.   (*b*) The mean of the class distribution will approximate $\mu_{\overline{X}} = 30$.   (*c*) The variance of the class distribution will approximate $\sigma_{\overline{X}}^2 = 5$.

8. (a) The class distribution constitutes an empirical approximation of the sampling distribution of s^2 for samples of ten cases. (b) The mean of the class distribution will approximate $\mu_{s^2} = \sigma^2 = 50$.

CHAPTER 7 *

1. (a) Critical values are $\bar{X} = 72.16$ and $\bar{X} = 87.84$. (b) Reject hypothesis that $\mu = 80$.
2. (a) Critical values of $\bar{X}$ are 194.12 and 205.88. (b) $\beta \approx .8992$. (c) $1 - \beta \approx .1008$.
3. (a) Critical values of $\bar{X}$ are 192.27 and 207.73. (b) $1 - \beta \approx .0293$. (c) Other factors being equal, reducing α decreases power.
4. (a) Critical values of $\bar{X}$ are 196.08 and 203.92. (b) $1 - \beta \approx .1727$. (c) Other factors being equal, increasing n increases power.
5. (a) Critical values of $\bar{X}$ are 194.12 and 205.88. (b)$1 - \beta \approx .3821$. (c) Other factors being equal, the greater the discrepancy between the actual value of μ and the value specified by the hypothesis being tested, the greater is the power of the test to reject the hypothesis. (d) As μ_A approaches μ_0, power approaches a minimum value of α; as the discrepancy between μ_A and μ_0 increases, power approaches 1.00.
6. (a) $z = -2.25$. (b) Critical values of z for a test at the .05 level are -1.960 and 1.960; thus, the hypothesis is rejected at the .05 level. (c) Critical values of z for a test at the .01 level are -2.576 and 2.576; thus, the hypothesis is accepted if the .01 level of significance is adopted.
7. $t \approx 2.12$ $(df = 4)$. Critical values of t for a test at the .05 level are -2.776 and 2.776; accordingly, the hypothesis is accepted.
8. $t \approx 4.38$ $(df = 3)$. Critical values of t for a test at the .05 level are -3.182 and 3.182; accordingly, the hypothesis is rejected.
9. (a) -2.132. (b) 4.541.
10. (a) 93.07 and 100.93. (b) 90.49 and 103.51.
11. (a) 5.09 and 10.91. (b) 2.67 and 13.33.

CHAPTER 8

1. $\mu_{X_1-X_2} = 10$, $\sigma_{X_1-X_2}^2 = 150$.
2. (a) The sampling distribution of $\bar{X}_1 - \bar{X}_2$. (b) $\mu_{\bar{X}_1-\bar{X}_2} = 10$. (c) $\sigma_{\bar{X}_1-\bar{X}_2}^2 = 23$.
3. (a) $s_p^2 = 5.5$, $t \approx 6/1.92 \approx 3.13$. (b) $df = 4$. (c) Critical values of t are ± 2.776. (Thus, $t \approx 3.13$ is significant.) (d) Unequal.
4. (a) $s_D^2 = 9$, $t \approx 8/1.73 \approx 4.62$. (b) $df = 2$. (c) Critical values of t are ± 4.303. (Thus, $t \approx 4.62$ is significant.) (d) Unequal.
5. $t \approx 5.4/1.89 \approx 2.86$ $(df = 8)$. The difference is significant at the .05 level.
6. $t \approx 9.25/4.61 \approx 2.01$ $(df = 3)$. The difference is not significant at the .05 level.
7. (a) $\sigma_{\bar{X}_1-\bar{X}_2}^2 = 25$. (b) $\sigma_{\bar{D}}^2 = 5$.

* In all problems involving the normal distribution in which it is required to find a value of z corresponding to an area whose exact value is not given in Table A-2 or Table A-3, the value of z used is the value listed in Table A-2 corresponding to the tabled area nearest in value to the area required.

8. Ninety-five per cent confidence limits: (a) .68 and 11.32; (b) .55 and 15.45; (c) 1.05 and 9.75; (d) −5.41 and 23.91.
9. $R_1 = 26$. (If the observations are ranked from high to low, $R_1 = 52$.) Critical values of R_1 for $n_1 = n_2 = 6$ and $\alpha = .05$ are 26 and 52; accordingly, the hypothesis that the two population distributions are the same is rejected at the .05 level of significance.
10. $T = 3.5$. Critical values of T for $n = 7$ and $\alpha = .05$ are 2 and 26; accordingly, the null hypothesis is accepted.

CHAPTER 9

2. (a) $\Sigma x^2 = 60$, $\Sigma y^2 = 1,608$, $\Sigma xy = -240$. (b) $\hat{Y}_X = 100 - 4(X - 20)$.
   (c) $\hat{Y}_{17} = 112$, $\hat{Y}_{22} = 92$.
4. (a) $\Sigma x^2 = 28$, $\Sigma y^2 \approx 23.43$, $\Sigma xy = 17$. (b) $\hat{Y}_X \approx 3.3 + .61(X - 3)$.
   (c) $\hat{Y}_1 \approx 2.08$, $\hat{Y}_4 \approx 3.91$.
5. (a) $\Sigma c^2 = 960$, $\Sigma d^2 = 648$. (b) Proportion due to regression $= \Sigma c^2/\Sigma y^2 \approx$ .60. Residual proportion $= \Sigma d^2/\Sigma y^2 \approx$ .40.
7. $\Sigma c^2 \approx 10.32$; $\Sigma d^2 \approx 13.11$; $\Sigma c^2/\Sigma y^2 \approx .44$; $\Sigma d^2/\Sigma y^2 \approx .56$.
8. $s_{Y \cdot X}^2 \approx 92.6$.
9. $s_{Y \cdot X}^2 \approx 2.62$.
10. $s_b^2 \approx 1.54$, $t \approx -3.22$ $(df = 7)$. Reject hypothesis that $B = 0$.
11. $s_b^2 \approx .0936$, $t \approx 1.99$ $(df = 5)$. Accept hypothesis that $B = 0$.
12. (a) $b_{Y \cdot X} = .4875$, $b_{X \cdot Y} = 1.95$.
    (b) $\Sigma c_Y^2/\Sigma y^2 \approx .95$; $\Sigma c_X^2/\Sigma x^2 \approx .95$. The two proportions are the same.
13. (a) $b_{Y \cdot X} = 1.4625$, $b_{X \cdot Y} = .65$. (b) $\Sigma c_Y^2/\Sigma y^2 \approx .95$. The result is the same as in Problem 12.
14. $s_X = 4$, $s_Y = 2$; $b_{V \cdot U} = b_{U \cdot V} = .975$.
15. $r = .975$.
16. $r^2 \approx .95$, the same as the value computed in Problem 12.
17. $t \approx 8.72$ $(df = 4)$. Reject hypothesis at .01 level.
18. (a) $\sigma^2 = 20$. (b) $R = .90$.
19. $R = .80$.
20. $r \approx .82$.
21. $r_S \approx .971$. Reject hypothesis of independence at .05 level.

CHAPTER 10

1. $\chi_c^2 = 2.45$ $(df = 1)$. The critical value of chi square for a one-sided test at the .05 level of significance is 2.706; therefore, accept the hypothesis that he cannot distinguish the two brands. Either Formula (10-4) or Formula (10-5) can be used to compute χ_c^2.
2. $\chi_c^2 \approx 6.02$ $(df = 1)$. Reject. Note that Formulae (10-3) and (10-5), which test the hypothesis that $p = q = .5$, cannot be used in this problem.
3. $\chi^2 = 15.0$ $(df = 3)$. Reject at .01 level.
4. $\chi^2 = 11.62$ $(df = 5)$. Reject at .05 level.
5. $\chi_c^2 \approx 39.0$ $(df = 1)$. Reject at .01 level.
6. $\chi_c^2 \approx 3.02$ $(df = 1)$. The data do not warrant rejection at the .05 level of the hypothesis that use of the product is independent of viewing habits.
7. $\chi_c^2 = 9.8$ $(df = 1)$. Reject at the .01 level the hypothesis that the two population distributions are identical.
8. $\chi^2 = 13.15$ $(df = 8)$. This value of chi square falls slightly short of the critical value for a test at the .05 level.

9. $\chi_c^2 = 4.05$ $(df = 1)$.   The difference is significant at the .05 level.
10. $\chi_c^2 = 9.025$ $(df = 1)$.   The difference is significant at the .01 level.
11. $\mu = .80$, $\sigma^2 = .16$.
12. $\mu_{\bar{x}} = .80$, $\sigma_{\bar{x}}^2 = .004$.
13. Problem 1: $z \approx 1.79$.   Problem 2: $z \approx 2.58$.   Problem 5: $z \approx 6.32$.
    Problem 6: $z \approx 1.87$.

CHAPTER 13

1. (a) Subject A: PSE ≈ 48.17.   Subject B: PSE $= 48.25$.   (b) Subject A:
   CE $\approx 48.17 - 50 = -1.83$.   Subject B: CE $= 48.25 - 50 = -1.75$.   (c)
   Subject A: semi-interquartile range $= 1.25$.   Subject B: semi-interquartile
   range $= 3.25$.   (d) Subject A has finer discriminative capacity, indicated by
   a smaller semi-interquartile range (jnd).
2. (a) 1.0.   (b) PSE $= 48.5$.   (c) CE $= -1.5$.
3. The subject whose data are presented in Problem 3 has finer discrimination.
   (His jnd is only .5, compared with a value of 1.0 for the first subject.   The
   difference is also apparent from the greater steepness of the graph based
   upon the data presented in Problem 3.)
4. (a) Mean   LL $= 46.5$,   mean   UL $= 50.5$.   (b) IU $= 4.0$.   (c) jnd $=$
   $4.0/2 = 2.0$.   (d) PSE $= 48.5$.   (e) CE $= -1.5$.
5. (a) 8 intensity units.   (b) 40 intensity units.   (These values are based
   upon the estimated value $k = .04$ determined from the data given.)

CHAPTER 15

1. (a) To two decimal places, μ_W is 1.19 units above μ_A, μ_X is 1.47 units below μ_A, μ_Y is equal to μ_A, μ_Z is .95 units above μ_A.   (b) Letting $\mu_X = 0$,
   the remaining scale values are as follows: $\mu_A = 1.47$, $\mu_W = 2.66$, $\mu_Y = 1.47$,
   $\mu_Z = 2.42$.
2. (a) .90.   (b) .80.   (c) .85.   (d) .85, the mean of the three estimates.
3. μ_A, μ_B, μ_C, and μ_D are, respectively, 1.036 units below, .253 units below,
   .524 units above, and 1.282 units above the boundary separating the two
   categories.   (b) Letting $\mu_A = 1$, the values assigned to the remaining specimens are as follows: $\mu_B = 1.783$, $\mu_C = 2.560$, $\mu_D = 3.318$.

appendix a:

statistical tables

TABLE A-1

Random Numbers

10 09 73 25 33	76 52 01 35 86	34 67 35 48 76	80 95 90 91 17	39 29 27 49 45
37 54 20 48 05	64 89 47 42 96	24 80 52 40 37	20 63 61 04 02	00 82 29 16 65
08 42 26 89 53	19 64 50 93 03	23 20 90 25 60	15 95 33 47 64	35 08 03 36 06
99 01 90 25 29	09 37 67 07 15	38 31 13 11 65	88 67 67 43 97	04 43 62 76 59
12 80 79 99 70	80 15 73 61 47	64 03 23 66 53	98 95 11 68 77	12 17 17 68 33
66 06 57 47 17	34 07 27 68 50	36 69 73 61 70	65 81 33 98 85	11 19 92 91 70
31 06 01 08 05	45 57 18 24 06	35 30 34 26 14	86 79 90 74 39	23 40 30 97 32
85 26 97 76 02	02 05 16 56 92	68 66 57 48 18	73 05 38 52 47	18 62 38 85 79
63 57 33 21 35	05 32 54 70 48	90 55 35 75 48	28 46 82 87 09	83 49 12 56 24
73 79 64 57 53	03 52 96 47 78	35 80 83 42 82	60 93 52 03 44	35 27 38 84 35
98 52 01 77 67	14 90 56 86 07	22 10 94 05 58	60 97 09 34 33	50 50 07 39 98
11 80 50 54 31	39 80 82 77 32	50 72 56 82 48	29 40 52 42 01	52 77 56 78 51
83 45 29 96 34	06 28 89 80 83	13 74 67 00 78	18 47 54 06 10	68 71 17 78 17
88 68 54 02 00	86 50 75 84 01	36 76 66 79 51	90 36 47 64 93	29 60 91 10 62
99 59 46 73 48	87 51 76 49 69	91 82 60 89 28	93 78 56 13 68	23 47 83 41 13
65 48 11 76 74	17 46 85 09 50	58 04 77 69 74	73 03 95 71 86	40 21 81 65 44
80 12 43 56 35	17 72 70 80 15	45 31 82 23 74	21 11 57 82 53	14 38 55 37 63
74 35 09 98 17	77 40 27 72 14	43 23 60 02 10	45 52 16 42 37	96 28 60 26 55
69 91 62 68 03	66 25 22 91 48	36 93 68 72 03	76 62 11 39 90	94 40 05 64 18
09 89 32 05 05	14 22 56 85 14	46 42 75 67 88	96 29 77 88 22	54 38 21 45 98
91 49 91 45 23	68 47 92 76 86	46 16 28 35 54	94 75 08 99 23	37 08 92 00 48
80 33 69 45 98	26 94 03 68 58	70 29 73 41 35	53 14 03 33 40	42 05 08 23 41
44 10 48 19 49	85 15 74 79 54	32 97 92 65 75	57 60 04 08 81	22 22 20 64 13
12 55 07 37 42	11 10 00 20 40	12 86 07 46 97	96 64 48 94 39	28 70 72 58 15
63 60 64 93 29	16 50 53 44 84	40 21 95 25 63	43 65 17 70 82	07 20 73 17 90
61 19 69 04 46	26 45 74 77 74	51 92 43 37 29	65 39 45 95 93	42 58 26 05 27
15 47 44 52 66	95 27 07 99 53	59 36 78 38 48	82 39 61 01 18	33 21 15 94 66
94 55 72 85 73	67 89 75 43 87	54 62 24 44 31	91 19 04 25 92	92 92 74 59 73
42 48 11 62 13	97 34 40 87 21	16 86 84 87 67	03 07 11 20 59	25 70 14 66 70
23 52 37 83 17	73 20 88 98 37	68 93 59 14 16	26 25 22 96 63	05 52 28 25 62
04 49 35 24 94	75 24 63 38 24	45 86 25 10 25	61 96 27 93 35	65 33 71 24 72
00 54 99 76 54	64 05 18 81 59	96 11 96 38 96	54 69 28 23 91	23 28 72 95 29
35 96 31 53 07	26 89 80 93 54	33 35 13 54 62	77 97 45 00 24	90 10 33 93 33
59 80 80 83 91	45 42 72 68 42	83 60 94 97 00	13 02 12 48 92	78 56 52 01 06
46 05 88 52 36	01 39 09 22 86	77 28 14 40 77	93 91 08 36 47	70 61 74 29 41
32 17 90 05 97	87 37 92 52 41	05 56 70 70 07	86 74 31 71 57	85 39 41 18 38
69 23 46 14 06	20 11 74 52 04	15 95 66 00 00	18 74 39 24 23	97 11 89 63 38
19 56 54 14 30	01 75 87 53 79	40 41 92 15 85	66 67 43 68 06	84 96 28 52 07
45 15 51 49 38	19 47 60 72 46	43 66 79 45 43	59 04 79 00 33	20 82 66 95 41
94 86 43 19 94	36 16 81 08 51	34 88 88 15 53	01 54 03 54 56	05 01 45 11 76
98 08 62 48 26	45 24 02 84 04	44 99 90 88 96	39 09 47 34 07	35 44 13 18 80
33 18 51 62 32	41 94 15 09 49	89 43 54 85 81	88 69 54 19 94	37 54 87 30 43
80 95 10 04 06	96 38 27 07 74	20 15 12 33 87	25 01 62 52 98	94 62 46 11 71
79 75 24 91 40	71 96 12 82 96	69 86 10 25 91	74 85 22 05 39	00 38 75 95 79
18 63 33 25 37	98 14 50 65 71	31 01 02 46 74	05 45 56 14 27	77 93 89 19 36
74 02 94 39 02	77 55 73 22 70	97 79 01 71 19	52 52 75 80 21	80 81 45 17 48
54 17 84 56 11	80 99 33 71 43	05 33 51 29 69	56 12 71 92 55	36 04 09 03 24
11 66 44 98 83	52 07 98 48 27	59 38 17 15 39	09 97 33 34 40	88 46 12 33 56
48 32 47 79 28	31 24 96 47 10	02 29 53 68 70	32 30 75 75 46	15 02 00 99 94
69 07 49 41 38	87 63 79 19 76	35 58 40 44 01	10 51 82 16 15	01 84 87 69 38

TABLE A-2

Areas of the Normal Distribution Corresponding to Selected Values of z

z	Area	z	Area	z	Area
3.25	.9994	1.00	.8413	−1.05	.1469
3.20	.9993	.95	.8289	−1.10	.1357
3.15	.9992	.90	.8159	−1.15	.1251
3.10	.9990	.85	.8023	−1.20	.1151
3.05	.9989	.80	.7881	−1.25	.1056
3.00	.9987	.75	.7734	−1.30	.0968
2.95	.9984	.70	.7580	−1.35	.0885
2.90	.9981	.65	.7422	−1.40	.0808
2.85	.9978	.60	.7257	−1.45	.0735
2.80	.9974	.55	.7088	−1.50	.0668
2.75	.9970	.50	.6915	−1.55	.0606
2.70	.9965	.45	.6736	−1.60	.0548
2.65	.9960	.40	.6554	−1.65	.0495
2.60	.9953	.35	.6368	−1.70	.0446
2.55	.9946	.30	.6179	−1.75	.0401
2.50	.9938	.25	.5987	−1.80	.0359
2.45	.9929	.20	.5793	−1.85	.0322
2.40	.9918	.15	.5596	−1.90	.0287
2.35	.9906	.10	.5398	−1.95	.0256
2.30	.9893	.05	.5199	−2.00	.0228
2.25	.9878			−2.05	.0202
2.20	.9861			−2.10	.0179
2.15	.9842	.00	.5000	−2.15	.0158
2.10	.9821			−2.20	.0139
2.05	.9798			−2.25	.0122
2.00	.9772	− .05	.4801	−2.30	.0107
1.95	.9744	− .10	.4602	−2.35	.0094
1.90	.9713	− .15	.4404	−2.40	.0082
1.85	.9678	− .20	.4207	−2.45	.0071
1.80	.9641	− .25	.4013	−2.50	.0062
1.75	.9599	− .30	.3821	−2.55	.0054
1.70	.9554	− .35	.3632	−2.60	.0047
1.65	.9505	− .40	.3446	−2.65	.0040
1.60	.9452	− .45	.3264	−2.70	.0035
1.55	.9394	− .50	.3085	−2.75	.0030
1.50	.9332	− .55	.2912	−2.80	.0026
1.45	.9265	− .60	.2743	−2.85	.0022
1.40	.9192	− .65	.2578	−2.90	.0019
1.35	.9115	− .70	.2420	−2.95	.0016
1.30	.9032	− .75	.2266	−3.00	.0013
1.25	.8944	− .80	.2119	−3.05	.0011
1.20	.8849	− .85	.1977	−3.10	.0010
1.15	.8749	− .90	.1841	−3.15	.0008
1.10	.8643	− .95	.1711	−3.20	.0007
1.05	.8531	−1.00	.1587	−3.25	.0006

The values specified are areas below (to the left of) the corresponding values of *z*. From W. J. Dixon and F. J. Massey, Jr., *Introduction to statistical analysis* (2d ed.), New York, McGraw-Hill, 1957. By permission of the authors and publisher.

TABLE A-3

Values of z Corresponding to Selected Areas of the Normal Distribution

Area	z
.99999	4.265
.9999	3.719
.999	3.090
.995	2.576
.99	2.326
.98	2.054
.975	1.960
.97	1.881
.96	1.751
.95	1.645
.94	1.555
.93	1.476
.92	1.405
.91	1.341
.90	1.282
.85	1.036
.80	.842
.75	.674
.70	.524
.65	.385
.60	.253
.55	.126
.50	0.000
.45	− .126
.40	− .253
.35	− .385
.30	− .524
.25	− .674
.20	− .842
.15	−1.036
.10	−1.282
.09	−1.341
.08	−1.405
.07	−1.476
.06	−1.555
.05	−1.645
.04	−1.751
.03	−1.881
.025	−1.960
.02	−2.054
.01	−2.326
.005	−2.576
.001	−3.090
.0001	−3.719
.00001	−4.265

The values of z given are those below which the corresponding areas are located. From W. J. Dixon and F. J. Massey, Jr., *Introduction to statistical analysis* (2d ed.), New York, McGraw-Hill, 1957. By permission of the authors and publisher.

TABLE A-4

Critical Values of t for Selected Values of α

df	Probability (α)			
	.10	.05	.02	.01
1	6.314	12.706	31.821	63.657
2	2.920	4.303	6.965	9.925
3	2.353	3.182	4.541	5.841
4	2.132	2.776	3.747	4.604
5	2.015	2.571	3.365	4.032
6	1.943	2.447	3.143	3.707
7	1.895	2.365	2.998	3.499
8	1.860	2.306	2.896	3.355
9	1.833	2.262	2.821	3.250
10	1.812	2.228	2.764	3.169
11	1.796	2.201	2.718	3.106
12	1.782	2.179	2.681	3.055
13	1.771	2.160	2.650	3.012
14	1.761	2.145	2.624	2.977
15	1.753	2.131	2.602	2.947
16	1.746	2.120	2.583	2.921
17	1.740	2.110	2.567	2.898
18	1.734	2.101	2.552	2.878
19	1.729	2.093	2.539	2.861
20	1.725	2.086	2.528	2.845
21	1.721	2.080	2.518	2.831
22	1.717	2.074	2.508	2.819
23	1.714	2.069	2.500	2.807
24	1.711	2.064	2.492	2.797
25	1.708	2.060	2.485	2.787
26	1.706	2.056	2.479	2.779
27	1.703	2.052	2.473	2.771
28	1.701	2.048	2.467	2.763
29	1.699	2.045	2.462	2.756
30	1.697	2.042	2.457	2.750
40	1.684	2.021	2.423	2.704
60	1.671	2.000	2.390	2.660
120	1.658	1.980	2.358	2.617
∞	1.645	1.960	2.326	2.576

Table A-4 is abridged from Table III of Fisher & Yates: *Statistical Tables for Biological, Agricultural and Medical Research*, published by Oliver & Boyd Ltd., Edinburgh, and by permission of the authors and publishers.

TABLE A-5

Critical Values of the Rank Sum, R
(.05 Level of Significance)

n_1	n_2	$R_{.025}$	$R_{.975}$	n_1	n_2	$R_{.025}$	$R_{.975}$	n_1	n_2	$R_{.025}$	$R_{.975}$
2	8	3	19	5	7	20	45	8	13	60	116
2	9	3	21	5	8	21	49	8	14	63	121
2	10	3	23	5	9	22	53	8	15	65	127
2	11	4	24	5	10	23	57	9	9	63	108
2	12	4	26	5	11	24	61	9	10	65	115
2	13	4	28	5	12	26	64	9	11	68	121
2	14	4	30	5	13	27	68	9	12	71	127
2	15	4	32	5	14	28	72	9	13	73	134
3	5	6	21	5	15	29	76	9	14	76	140
3	6	7	23	6	6	26	52	9	15	79	146
3	7	7	26	6	7	27	57	10	10	78	132
3	8	8	28	6	8	29	61	10	11	81	139
3	9	8	31	6	9	31	65	10	12	85	145
3	10	9	33	6	10	32	70	10	13	88	152
3	11	9	36	6	11	34	74	10	14	91	159
3	12	10	38	6	12	35	79	10	15	94	166
3	13	10	41	6	13	37	83	11	11	96	157
3	14	11	43	6	14	38	88	11	12	99	165
3	15	11	46	6	15	40	92	11	13	103	172
4	4	10	26	7	7	36	69	11	14	106	180
4	5	11	29	7	8	38	74	11	15	110	187
4	6	12	32	7	9	40	79	12	12	115	185
4	7	13	35	7	10	42	84	12	13	119	193
4	8	14	38	7	11	44	89	12	14	123	201
4	9	15	41	7	12	46	94	12	15	127	209
4	10	15	45	7	13	48	99	13	13	137	214
4	11	16	48	7	14	50	104	13	14	141	223
4	12	17	51	7	15	52	109	13	15	145	232
4	13	18	54	8	8	49	87	14	14	160	246
4	14	19	57	8	9	51	93	14	15	164	256
4	15	20	60	8	10	53	99	15	15	185	280
5	5	17	38	8	11	55	105				
5	6	18	42	8	12	58	110				

Critical values are for R_1, the sum of ranks for the smaller of two groups. For a two-sided test at the .05 level of significance, reject the null hypothesis if R_1 is equal to or less than $R_{.025}$ or if R_1 is equal to or greater than $R_{.975}$. Because the distribution of R_1 is discrete, the indicated value of α is approximate—the actual value of α is equal to or less than .05.

Based upon critical values from C. White, "The use of ranks in a test of significance for comparing two treatments," *Biometrics*, 1952, **8**, 33–41. By permission of the author and editor.

TABLE A-5 (*Cont.*)

Critical Values of the Rank Sum, R
(*.01 Level of Significance*)

n_1	n_2	$R_{.005}$	$R_{.995}$	n_1	n_2	$R_{.005}$	$R_{.995}$	n_1	n_2	$R_{.005}$	$R_{.995}$
3	9	6	33	6	6	23	55	9	10	58	122
3	10	6	36	6	7	24	60	9	11	61	128
3	11	6	39	6	8	25	65	9	12	63	135
3	12	7	41	6	9	26	70	9	13	65	142
3	13	7	44	6	10	27	75	9	14	67	149
3	14	7	47	6	11	28	80	9	15	70	155
3	15	8	49	6	12	30	84	10	10	71	139
4	6	10	34	6	13	31	89	10	11	74	146
4	7	10	38	6	14	32	94	10	12	76	154
4	8	11	41	6	15	33	99	10	13	79	161
4	9	11	45	7	7	32	73	10	14	81	169
4	10	12	48	7	8	34	78	10	15	84	176
4	11	12	52	7	9	35	84	11	11	87	166
4	12	13	55	7	10	37	89	11	12	90	174
4	13	14	58	7	11	38	95	11	13	93	182
4	14	14	62	7	12	40	100	11	14	96	190
4	15	15	65	7	13	41	106	11	15	99	198
5	5	15	40	7	14	43	111	12	12	106	194
5	6	16	44	7	15	44	117	12	13	109	203
5	7	17	48	8	8	43	93	12	14	112	212
5	8	17	53	8	9	45	99	12	15	115	221
5	9	18	57	8	10	47	105	13	13	125	226
5	10	19	61	8	11	49	111	13	14	129	235
5	11	20	65	8	12	51	117	13	15	133	244
5	12	21	69	8	13	53	123	14	14	147	259
5	13	22	73	8	14	54	130	14	15	151	269
5	14	22	78	8	15	56	136	15	15	171	294
5	15	23	82	9	9	56	115				

Critical values are for R_1, the sum of ranks for the smaller of two groups. For a two-sided test at the .01 level of significance, reject the null hypothesis if R_1 is equal to or less than $R_{.005}$ or if R_1 is equal to or greater than $R_{.995}$. Because the distribution of R_1 is discrete, the indicated value of α is approximate—the actual value of α is equal to or less than .01.

Based upon critical values from C. White, "The use of ranks in a test of significance for comparing two treatments," *Biometrics*, 1952, **8**, 33–41. By permission of the author and editor.

TABLE A-6

Critical Values of T, the Signed-Rank Statistic

Number of Pairs	.05 Level of Significance		.01 Level of Significance	
	$T_{.025}$	$T_{.975}$	$T_{.005}$	$T_{.995}$
6	0	21	—	—
7	2	26	—	—
8	3	33	0	36
9	5	40	1	44
10	8	47	3	52
11	10	56	5	61
12	13	65	7	71
13	17	74	10	81
14	21	84	13	92
15	25	95	16	104
16	30	106	20	116
17	35	118	24	129
18	40	131	28	143
19	46	144	33	157
20	52	158	38	172

For a two-sided test at the level of significance indicated, reject the null hypothesis if T is equal to or less than the lower critical value, or if T is equal to or greater than the higher critical value. Because the distribution of T is discrete, the indicated values of α are approximate—the actual value of α is equal to or less than that stated at the top of the table.

Based upon Table A-19 of W. J. Dixon and F. J. Massey, Jr., *Introduction to statistical analysis* (2d ed.), New York, McGraw-Hill, 1957. By permission of the authors and publisher.

TABLE A-7

Critical Values of r_s, the Rank Correlation Coefficient

n	Probability (α)			
	.10	.05	.02	.01
5	.900	1.000	1.000	
6	.829	.886	.943	1.000
7	.714	.786	.893	.929
8	.643	.738	.833	.881
9	.600	.683	.783	.833
10	.564	.648	.745	.794
11	.520	.620	.735	.815
12	.496	.591	.701	.777
13	.475	.566	.671	.744
14	.456	.544	.645	.715
15	.440	.524	.622	.688
16	.425	.506	.601	.665
17	.411	.490	.582	.644
18	.399	.475	.564	.625
19	.388	.462	.548	.607
20	.377	.450	.534	.591

Computed with permission from values of ΣD^2 from E. G. Olds, "Distributions of sums of squares of rank differences for small numbers of individuals," *Ann. Math. Statist.*, 1938, **9**, 133–148, and from E. G. Olds, "The 5% significance levels for sums of squares of rank differences and a correction," *Ann. Math. Statist.*, 1949, **20**, 117–118.

Critical values of ΣD^2 for $n = 12$ presented in Table V of Olds' 1938 article were found to be in error, apparently as a result of a computational error. Values of r_s presented above for $n = 12$ are computed from corrected values of ΣD^2 obtained using the approximation described by Olds.

The inversion, between $n = 10$ and $n = 11$ in the .01 column, in the trend toward decreasing values of r_s is apparently an artifact arising from the fact that a different approximation function was used for values of n equal to or less than 10 and values of n equal to or greater than 11.

TABLE A-8

Critical Values of χ^2 for Selected Values of α

df	Probability (α)			
	.10	.05	.02	.01
1	2.706	3.841	5.412	6.635
2	4.605	5.991	7.824	9.210
3	6.251	7.815	9.837	11.345
4	7.779	9.488	11.668	13.277
5	9.236	11.070	13.388	15.086
6	10.645	12.592	15.033	16.812
7	12.017	14.067	16.622	18.475
8	13.362	15.507	18.168	20.090
9	14.684	16.919	19.679	21.666
10	15.987	18.307	21.161	23.209
11	17.275	19.675	22.618	24.725
12	18.549	21.026	24.054	26.217
13	19.812	22.362	25.472	27.688
14	21.064	23.685	26.873	29.141
15	22.307	24.996	28.259	30.578
16	23.542	26.296	29.633	32.000
17	24.769	27.587	30.995	33.409
18	25.989	28.869	32.346	34.805
19	27.204	30.144	33.687	36.191
20	28.412	31.410	35.020	37.566
21	29.615	32.671	36.343	38.932
22	30.813	33.924	37.659	40.289
23	32.007	35.172	38.968	41.638
24	33.196	36.415	40.270	42.980
25	34.382	37.652	41.566	44.314
26	35.563	38.885	42.856	45.642
27	36.741	40.113	44.140	46.963
28	37.916	41.337	45.419	48.278
29	39.087	42.557	46.693	49.588
30	40.256	43.773	47.962	50.892
32	42.585	46.194	50.487	53.486
34	44.903	48.602	52.995	56.061
36	47.212	50.999	55.489	58.619
38	49.513	53.384	57.969	61.162
40	51.805	55.759	60.436	63.691

Table A-8 is abridged from Table IV of Fisher & Yates: *Statistical Tables for Biological, Agricultural and Medical Research*, published by Oliver & Boyd Ltd., Edinburgh, and by permission of the authors and publishers.

TABLE A-9

Squares and Square Roots

n	n^2	$\sqrt{n}$	$\sqrt{10n}$	n	n^2	$\sqrt{n}$	$\sqrt{10n}$
1.00	1.0000	1.00000	3.16228	1.50	2.2500	1.22474	3.87298
1.01	1.0201	1.00499	3.17805	1.51	2.2801	1.22882	3.88587
1.02	1.0404	1.00995	3.19374	1.52	2.3104	1.23288	3.89872
1.03	1.0609	1.01489	3.20936	1.53	2.3409	1.23693	3.91152
1.04	1.0816	1.01980	3.22490	1.54	2.3716	1.24097	3.92428
1.05	1.1025	1.02470	3.24037	1.55	2.4025	1.24499	3.93700
1.06	1.1236	1.02956	3.25576	1.56	2.4336	1.24900	3.94968
1.07	1.1449	1.03441	3.27109	1.57	2.4649	1.25300	3.96232
1.08	1.1664	1.03923	3.28634	1.58	2.4964	1.25698	3.97492
1.09	1.1881	1.04403	3.30151	1.59	2.5281	1.26095	3.98748
1.10	1.2100	1.04881	3.31662	1.60	2.5600	1.26491	4.00000
1.11	1.2321	1.05357	3.33167	1.61	2.5921	1.26886	4.01248
1.12	1.2544	1.05830	3.34664	1.62	2.6244	1.27279	4.02492
1.13	1.2769	1.06301	3.36155	1.63	2.6569	1.27671	4.03733
1.14	1.2996	1.06771	3.37639	1.64	2.6896	1.28062	4.04969
1.15	1.3225	1.07238	3.39116	1.65	2.7225	1.28452	4.06202
1.16	1.3456	1.07703	3.40588	1.66	2.7556	1.28841	4.07431
1.17	1.3689	1.08167	3.42053	1.67	2.7889	1.29228	4.08656
1.18	1.3924	1.08628	3.43511	1.68	2.8224	1.29615	4.09878
1.19	1.4161	1.09087	3.44964	1.69	2.8561	1.30000	4.11096
1.20	1.4400	1.09545	3.46410	1.70	2.8900	1.30384	4.12311
1.21	1.4641	1.10000	3.47851	1.71	2.9241	1.30767	4.13521
1.22	1.4884	1.10454	3.49285	1.72	2.9584	1.31149	4.14729
1.23	1.5129	1.10905	3.50714	1.73	2.9929	1.31529	4.15933
1.24	1.5376	1.11355	3.52136	1.74	3.0276	1.31909	4.17133
1.25	1.5625	1.11803	3.53553	1.75	3.0625	1.32288	4.18330
1.26	1.5876	1.12250	3.54965	1.76	3.0976	1.32665	4.19524
1.27	1.6129	1.12694	3.56371	1.77	3.1329	1.33041	4.20714
1.28	1.6384	1.13137	3.57771	1.78	3.1684	1.33417	4.21900
1.29	1.6641	1.13578	3.59166	1.79	3.2041	1.33791	4.23084
1.30	1.6900	1.14018	3.60555	1.80	3.2400	1.34164	4.24264
1.31	1.7161	1.14455	3.61939	1.81	3.2761	1.34536	4.25441
1.32	1.7424	1.14891	3.63318	1.82	3.3124	1.34907	4.26615
1.33	1.7689	1.15326	3.64692	1.83	3.3489	1.35277	4.27785
1.34	1.7956	1.15758	3.66060	1.84	3.3856	1.35647	4.28952
1.35	1.8225	1.16190	3.67423	1.85	3.4225	1.36015	4.30116
1.36	1.8496	1.16619	3.68782	1.86	3.4596	1.36382	4.31277
1.37	1.8769	1.17047	3.70135	1.87	3.4969	1.36748	4.32435
1.38	1.9044	1.17473	3.71484	1.88	3.5344	1.37113	4.33590
1.39	1.9321	1.17898	3.72827	1.89	3.5721	1.37477	4.34741
1.40	1.9600	1.18322	3.74166	1.90	3.6100	1.37840	4.35890
1.41	1.9881	1.18743	3.75500	1.91	3.6481	1.38203	4.37035
1.42	2.0164	1.19164	3.76829	1.92	3.6864	1.38564	4.38178
1.43	2.0449	1.19583	3.78153	1.93	3.7249	1.38924	4.39318
1.44	2.0736	1.20000	3.79473	1.94	3.7636	1.39284	4.40454
1.45	2.1025	1.20416	3.80789	1.95	3.8025	1.39642	4.41588
1.46	2.1316	1.20830	3.82099	1.96	3.8416	1.40000	4.42719
1.47	2.1609	1.21244	3.83406	1.97	3.8809	1.40357	4.43847
1.48	2.1904	1.21655	3.84708	1.98	3.9204	1.40712	4.44972
1.49	2.2201	1.22066	3.86005	1.99	3.9601	1.41067	4.46094

The use of this table is explained in Appendix B.

TABLE A-9 (*Cont.*)

Squares and Square Roots

n	n²	√n	√10n	n	n²	√n	√10n
2.00	4.0000	1.41421	4.47214	2.50	6.2500	1.58114	5.00000
2.01	4.0401	1.41774	4.48330	2.51	6.3001	1.58430	5.00999
2.02	4.0804	1.42127	4.49444	2.52	6.3504	1.58745	5.01996
2.03	4.1209	1.42478	4.50555	2.53	6.4009	1.59060	5.02991
2.04	4.1616	1.42829	4.51664	2.54	6.4516	1.59374	5.03984
2.05	4.2025	1.43178	4.52769	2.55	6.5025	1.59687	5.04975
2.06	4.2436	1.43527	4.53872	2.56	6.5536	1.60000	5.05964
2.07	4.2849	1.43875	4.54973	2.57	6.6049	1.60312	5.06952
2.08	4.3264	1.44222	4.56070	2.58	6.6564	1.60624	5.07937
2.09	4.3681	1.44568	4.57165	2.59	6.7081	1.60935	5.08920
2.10	4.4100	1.44914	4.58258	2.60	6.7600	1.61245	5.09902
2.11	4.4521	1.45258	4.59347	2.61	6.8121	1.61555	5.10882
2.12	4.4944	1.45602	4.60435	2.62	6.8644	1.61864	5.11859
2.13	4.5369	1.45945	4.61519	2.63	6.9169	1.62173	5.12835
2.14	4.5796	1.46287	4.62601	2.64	6.9696	1.62481	5.13809
2.15	4.6225	1.46629	4.63681	2.65	7.0225	1.62788	5.14782
2.16	4.6656	1.46969	4.64758	2.66	7.0756	1.63095	5.15752
2.17	4.7089	1.47309	4.65833	2.67	7.1289	1.63401	5.16720
2.18	4.7524	1.47648	4.66905	2.68	7.1824	1.63707	5.17687
2.19	4.7961	1.47986	4.67974	2.69	7.2361	1.64012	5.18652
2.20	4.8400	1.48324	4.69042	2.70	7.2900	1.64317	5.19615
2.21	4.8841	1.48661	4.70106	2.71	7.3441	1.64621	5.20577
2.22	4.9284	1.48997	4.71169	2.72	7.3984	1.64924	5.21536
2.23	4.9729	1.49332	4.72229	2.73	7.4529	1.65227	5.22494
2.24	5.0176	1.49666	4.73286	2.74	7.5076	1.65529	5.23450
2.25	5.0625	1.50000	4.74342	2.75	7.5625	1.65831	5.24404
2.26	5.1076	1.50333	4.75395	2.76	7.6176	1.66132	5.25357
2.27	5.1529	1.50665	4.76445	2.77	7.6729	1.66433	5.26308
2.28	5.1984	1.50997	4.77493	2.78	7.7284	1.66733	5.27257
2.29	5.2441	1.51327	4.78539	2.79	7.7841	1.67033	5.28205
2.30	5.2900	1.51658	4.79583	2.80	7.8400	1.67332	5.29150
2.31	5.3361	1.51987	4.80625	2.81	7.8961	1.67631	5.30094
2.32	5.3824	1.52315	4.81664	2.82	7.9524	1.67929	5.31037
2.33	5.4289	1.52643	4.82701	2.83	8.0089	1.68226	5.31977
2.34	5.4756	1.52971	4.83735	2.84	8.0656	1.68523	5.32917
2.35	5.5225	1.53297	4.84768	2.85	8.1225	1.68819	5.33854
2.36	5.5696	1.53623	4.85798	2.86	8.1796	1.69115	5.34790
2.37	5.6169	1.53948	4.86826	2.87	8.2369	1.69411	5.35724
2.38	5.6644	1.54272	4.87852	2.88	8.2944	1.69706	5.36656
2.39	5.7121	1.54596	4.88876	2.89	8.3521	1.70000	5.37587
2.40	5.7600	1.54919	4.89898	2.90	8.4100	1.70294	5.38516
2.41	5.8081	1.55242	4.90918	2.91	8.4681	1.70587	5.39444
2.42	5.8564	1.55563	4.91935	2.92	8.5264	1.70880	5.40370
2.43	5.9049	1.55885	4.92950	2.93	8.5849	1.71172	5.41295
2.44	5.9536	1.56205	4.93964	2.94	8.6436	1.71464	5.42218
2.45	6.0025	1.56525	4.94975	2.95	8.7025	1.71756	5.43139
2.46	6.0516	1.56844	4.95984	2.96	8.7616	1.72047	5.44059
2.47	6.1009	1.57162	4.96991	2.97	8.8209	1.72337	5.44977
2.48	6.1504	1.57480	4.97996	2.98	8.8804	1.72627	5.45894
2.49	6.2001	1.57797	4.98999	2.99	8.9401	1.72916	5.46809

TABLE A-9 (*Cont.*)

Squares and Square Roots

n	n^2	$\sqrt{n}$	$\sqrt{10n}$	n	n^2	$\sqrt{n}$	$\sqrt{10n}$
3.00	9.0000	1.73205	5.47723	3.50	12.2500	1.87083	5.91608
3.01	9.0601	1.73494	5.48635	3.51	12.3201	1.87350	5.92453
3.02	9.1204	1.73781	5.49545	3.52	12.3904	1.87617	5.93296
3.03	9.1809	1.74069	5.50454	3.53	12.4609	1.87883	5.94138
3.04	9.2416	1.74356	5.51362	3.54	12.5316	1.88149	5.94979
3.05	9.3025	1.74642	5.52268	3.55	12.6025	1.88414	5.95819
3.06	9.3636	1.74929	5.53173	3.56	12.6736	1.88680	5.96657
3.07	9.4249	1.75214	5.54076	3.57	12.7449	1.88944	5.97495
3.08	9.4864	1.75499	5.54977	3.58	12.8164	1.89209	5.98331
3.09	9.5481	1.75784	5.55878	3.59	12.8881	1.89473	5.99166
3.10	9.6100	1.76068	5.56776	3.60	12.9600	1.89737	6.00000
3.11	9.6721	1.76352	5.57674	3.61	13.0321	1.90000	6.00833
3.12	9.7344	1.76635	5.58570	3.62	13.1044	1.90263	6.01664
3.13	9.7969	1.76918	5.59464	3.63	13.1769	1.90526	6.02495
3.14	9.8596	1.77200	5.60357	3.64	13.2496	1.90788	6.03324
3.15	9.9225	1.77482	5.61249	3.65	13.3225	1.91050	6.04152
3.16	9.9856	1.77764	5.62139	3.66	13.3956	1.91311	6.04979
3.17	10.0489	1.78045	5.63028	3.67	13.4689	1.91572	6.05805
3.18	10.1124	1.78326	5.63915	3.68	13.5424	1.91833	6.06630
3.19	10.1761	1.78606	5.64801	3.69	13.6161	1.92094	6.07454
3.20	10.2400	1.78885	5.65685	3.70	13.6900	1.92354	6.08276
3.21	10.3041	1.79165	5.66569	3.71	13.7641	1.92614	6.09098
3.22	10.3684	1.79444	5.67450	3.72	13.8384	1.92873	6.09918
3.23	10.4329	1.79722	5.68331	3.73	13.9129	1.93132	6.10737
3.24	10.4976	1.80000	5.69210	3.74	13.9876	1.93391	6.11555
3.25	10.5625	1.80278	5.70088	3.75	14.0625	1.93649	6.12372
3.26	10.6276	1.80555	5.70964	3.76	14.1376	1.93907	6.13188
3.27	10.6929	1.80831	5.71839	3.77	14.2129	1.94165	6.14003
3.28	10.7584	1.81108	5.72713	3.78	14.2884	1.94422	6.14817
3.29	10.8241	1.81384	5.73585	3.79	14.3641	1.94679	6.15630
3.30	10.8900	1.81659	5.74456	3.80	14.4400	1.94936	6.16441
3.31	10.9561	1.81934	5.75326	3.81	14.5161	1.95192	6.17252
3.32	11.0224	1.82209	5.76194	3.82	14.5924	1.95448	6.18061
3.33	11.0889	1.82483	5.77062	3.83	14.6689	1.95704	6.18870
3.34	11.1556	1.82757	5.77927	3.84	14.7456	1.95959	6.19677
3.35	11.2225	1.83030	5.78792	3.85	14.8225	1.96214	6.20484
3.36	11.2896	1.83303	5.79655	3.86	14.8996	1.96469	6.21289
3.37	11.3569	1.83576	5.80517	3.87	14.9769	1.96723	6.22093
3.38	11.4244	1.83848	5.81378	3.88	15.0544	1.96977	6.22896
3.39	11.4921	1.84120	5.82237	3.89	15.1321	1.97231	6.23699
3.40	11.5600	1.84391	5.83095	3.90	15.2100	1.97484	6.24500
3.41	11.6281	1.84662	5.83952	3.91	15.2881	1.97737	6.25300
3.42	11.6964	1.84932	5.84808	3.92	15.3664	1.97990	6.26099
3.43	11.7649	1.85203	5.85662	3.93	15.4449	1.98242	6.26897
3.44	11.8336	1.85472	5.86515	3.94	15.5236	1.98494	6.27694
3.45	11.9025	1.85742	5.87367	3.95	15.6025	1.98746	6.28490
3.46	11.9716	1.86011	5.88218	3.96	15.6816	1.98997	6.29285
3.47	12.0409	1.86279	5.89067	3.97	15.7609	1.99249	6.30079
3.48	12.1104	1.86548	5.89915	3.98	15.8408	1.99499	6.30872
3.49	12.1801	1.86815	5.90762	3.99	15.9201	1.99750	6.31664

TABLE A-9   (*Cont.*)

Squares and Square Roots

n	n²	√n	√10n	n	n²	√n	√10n
4.00	16.0000	2.00000	6.32456	4.50	20.2500	2.12132	6.70820
4.01	16.0801	2.00250	6.33246	4.51	20.3401	2.12368	6.71565
4.02	16.1604	2.00499	6.34035	4.52	20.4304	2.12603	6.72309
4.03	16.2409	2.00749	6.34823	4.53	20.5209	2.12838	6.73053
4.04	16.3216	2.00998	6.35610	4.54	20.6116	2.13073	6.73795
4.05	16.4025	2.01246	6.36396	4.55	20.7025	2.13307	6.74537
4.06	16.4836	2.01494	6.37181	4.56	20.7936	2.13542	6.75278
4.07	16.5649	2.01742	6.37966	4.57	20.8849	2.13776	6.76018
4.08	16.6464	2.01990	6.38749	4.58	20.9764	2.14009	6.76757
4.09	16.7281	2.02237	6.39531	4.59	21.0681	2.14243	6.77495
4.10	16.8100	2.02485	6.40312	4.60	21.1600	2.14476	6.78233
4.11	16.8921	2.02731	6.41093	4.61	21.2521	2.14709	6.78970
4.12	16.9744	2.02978	6.41872	4.62	21.3444	2.14942	6.79706
4.13	17.0569	2.03224	6.42651	4.63	21.4369	2.15174	6.80441
4.14	17.1396	2.03470	6.43428	4.64	21.5296	2.15407	6.81175
4.15	17.2225	2.03715	6.44205	4.65	21.6225	2.15639	6.81909
4.16	17.3056	2.03961	6.44981	4.66	21.7156	2.15870	6.82642
4.17	17.3889	2.04206	6.45755	4.67	21.8089	2.16102	6.83374
4.18	17.4724	2.04450	6.46529	4.68	21.9024	2.16333	6.84105
4.19	17.5561	2.04695	6.47302	4.69	21.9961	2.16564	6.84836
4.20	17.6400	2.04939	6.48074	4.70	22.0900	2.16795	6.85565
4.21	17.7241	2.05183	6.48845	4.71	22.1841	2.17025	6.86294
4.22	17.8084	2.05426	6.49615	4.72	22.2784	2.17256	6.87023
4.23	17.8929	2.05670	6.50384	4.73	22.3729	2.17486	6.87750
4.24	17.9776	2.05913	6.51153	4.74	22.4676	2.17715	6.88477
4.25	18.0625	2.06155	6.51920	4.75	22.5625	2.17945	6.89202
4.26	18.1476	2.06398	6.52687	4.76	22.6576	2.18174	6.89928
4.27	18.2329	2.06640	6.53452	4.77	22.7529	2.18403	6.90652
4.28	18.3184	2.06882	6.54217	4.78	22.8484	2.18632	6.91375
4.29	18.4041	2.07123	6.54981	4.79	22.9441	2.18861	6.92098
4.30	18.4900	2.07364	6.55744	4.80	23.0400	2.19089	6.92820
4.31	18.5761	2.07605	6.56506	4.81	23.1361	2.19317	6.93542
4.32	18.6624	2.07846	6.57267	4.82	23.2324	2.19545	6.94262
4.33	18.7489	2.08087	6.58027	4.83	23.3289	2.19773	6.94982
4.34	18.8356	2.08327	6.58787	4.84	23.4256	2.20000	6.95701
4.35	18.9225	2.08567	6.59545	4.85	23.5225	2.20227	6.96419
4.36	19.0096	2.08806	6.60303	4.86	23.6196	2.20454	6.97137
4.37	19.0969	2.09045	6.61060	4.87	23.7169	2.20681	6.97854
4.38	19.1844	2.09284	6.61816	4.88	23.8144	2.20907	6.98570
4.39	19.2721	2.09523	6.62571	4.89	23.9121	2.21133	6.99285
4.40	19.3600	2.09762	6.63325	4.90	24.0100	2.21359	7.00000
4.41	19.4481	2.10000	6.64078	4.91	24.1081	2.21585	7.00714
4.42	19.5364	2.10238	6.64831	4.92	24.2064	2.21811	7.01427
4.43	19.6249	2.10476	6.65582	4.93	24.3049	2.22036	7.02140
4.44	19.7136	2.10713	6.66333	4.94	24.4036	2.22261	7.02851
4.45	19.8025	2.10950	6.67083	4.95	24.5025	2.22486	7.03562
4.46	19.8916	2.11187	6.67832	4.96	24.6016	2.22711	7.04273
4.47	19.9809	2.11424	6.68581	4.97	24.7009	2.22935	7.04982
4.48	20.0704	2.11660	6.69328	4.98	24.8004	2.23159	7.05691
4.49	20.1601	2.11896	6.70075	4.99	24.9001	2.23383	7.06399

TABLE A-9 *(Cont.)*

Squares and Square Roots

n	n^2	$\sqrt{n}$	$\sqrt{10n}$	n	n^2	$\sqrt{n}$	$\sqrt{10n}$
5.00	25.0000	2.23607	7.07107	5.50	30.2500	2.34521	7.41620
5.01	25.1001	2.23830	7.07814	5.51	30.3601	2.34734	7.42294
5.02	25.2004	2.24054	7.08520	5.52	30.4704	2.34947	7.42967
5.03	25.3009	2.24277	7.09225	5.53	30.5809	2.35160	7.43640
5.04	25.4016	2.24499	7.09930	5.54	30.6916	2.35372	7.44312
5.05	25.5025	2.24722	7.10634	5.55	30.8025	2.35584	7.44983
5.06	25.6036	2.24944	7.11337	5.56	30.9136	2.35797	7.45654
5.07	25.7049	2.25167	7.12039	5.57	31.0249	2.36008	7.46324
5.08	25.8064	2.25389	7.12741	5.58	31.1364	2.36220	7.46994
5.09	25.9081	2.25610	7.13442	5.59	31.2481	2.36432	7.47663
5.10	26.0100	2.25832	7.14143	5.60	31.3600	2.36643	7.48331
5.11	26.1121	2.26053	7.14843	5.61	31.4721	2.36854	7.48999
5.12	26.2144	2.26274	7.15542	5.62	31.5844	2.37065	7.49667
5.13	26.3169	2.26495	7.16240	5.63	31.6969	2.37276	7.50333
5.14	26.4196	2.26716	7.16938	5.64	31.8096	2.37487	7.50999
5.15	26.5225	2.26936	7.17635	5.65	31.9225	2.37697	7.51665
5.16	26.6256	2.27156	7.18331	5.66	32.0356	2.37908	7.52330
5.17	26.7289	2.27376	7.19027	5.67	32.1489	2.38118	7.52994
5.18	26.8324	2.27596	7.19722	5.68	32.2624	2.38328	7.53658
5.19	26.9361	2.27816	7.20417	5.69	32.3761	2.38537	7.54321
5.20	27.0400	2.28035	7.21110	5.70	32.4900	2.38747	7.54983
5.21	27.1441	2.28254	7.21803	5.71	32.6041	2.38956	7.55645
5.22	27.2484	2.28473	7.22496	5.72	32.7184	2.39165	7.56307
5.23	27.3529	2.28692	7.23187	5.73	32.8329	2.39374	7.56968
5.24	27.4576	2.28910	7.23878	5.74	32.9476	2.39583	7.57628
5.25	27.5625	2.29129	7.24569	5.75	33.0625	2.39792	7.58288
5.26	27.6676	2.29347	7.25259	5.76	33.1776	2.40000	7.58947
5.27	27.7729	2.29565	7.25948	5.77	33.2929	2.40208	7.59605
5.28	27.8784	2.29783	7.26636	5.78	33.4084	2.40416	7.60263
5.29	27.9841	2.30000	7.27324	5.79	33.5241	2.40624	7.60920
5.30	28.0900	2.30217	7.28011	5.80	33.6400	2.40832	7.61577
5.31	28.1961	2.30434	7.28697	5.81	33.7561	2.41039	7.62234
5.32	28.3024	2.30651	7.29383	5.82	33.8724	2.41247	7.62889
5.33	28.4089	2.30868	7.30068	5.83	33.9889	2.41454	7.63544
5.34	28.5156	2.31084	7.30753	5.84	34.1056	2.41661	7.64199
5.35	28.6225	2.31301	7.31437	5.85	34.2225	2.41868	7.64853
5.36	28.7296	2.31517	7.32120	5.86	34.3396	2.42074	7.65506
5.37	28.8369	2.31733	7.32803	5.87	34.4569	2.42281	7.66159
5.38	28.9444	2.31948	7.33485	5.88	34.5744	2.42487	7.66812
5.39	29.0521	2.32164	7.34166	5.89	34.6921	2.42693	7.67463
5.40	29.1600	2.32379	7.34847	5.90	34.8100	2.42899	7.68115
5.41	29.2681	2.32594	7.35527	5.91	34.9281	2.43105	7.68765
5.42	29.3764	2.32809	7.36206	5.92	35.0464	2.43311	7.69415
5.43	29.4849	2.33024	7.36885	5.93	35.1649	2.43516	7.70065
5.44	29.5936	2.33238	7.37564	5.94	35.2836	2.43721	7.70714
5.45	29.7025	2.33452	7.38241	5.95	35.4025	2.43926	7.71362
5.46	29.8116	2.33666	7.38918	5.96	35.5216	2.44131	7.72010
5.47	29.9209	2.33880	7.39594	5.97	35.6409	2.44336	7.72658
5.48	30.0304	2.34094	7.40270	5.98	35.7604	2.44540	7.73305
5.49	30.1401	2.34307	7.40945	5.99	35.8801	2.44745	7.73951

TABLE A-9 (*Cont.*)

Squares and Square Roots

n	n^2	$\sqrt{n}$	$\sqrt{10n}$	n	n^2	$\sqrt{n}$	$\sqrt{10n}$
6.00	36.0000	2.44949	7.74597	6.50	42.2500	2.54951	8.06226
6.01	36.1201	2.45153	7.75242	6.51	42.3801	2.55147	8.06846
6.02	36.2404	2.45357	7.75887	6.52	42.5104	2.55343	8.07465
6.03	36.3609	2.45561	7.76531	6.53	42.6409	2.55539	8.08084
6.04	36.4816	2.45764	7.77174	6.54	42.7716	2.55734	8.08703
6.05	36.6025	2.45967	7.77817	6.55	42.9025	2.55930	8.09321
6.06	36.7236	2.46171	7.78460	6.56	43.0336	2.56125	8.09938
6.07	36.8449	2.46374	7.79102	6.57	43.1649	2.56320	8.10555
6.08	36.9664	2.46577	7.79744	6.58	43.2964	2.56515	8.11172
6.09	37.0881	2.46779	7.80385	6.59	43.4281	2.56710	8.11788
6.10	37.2100	2.46982	7.81025	6.60	43.5600	2.56905	8.12404
6.11	37.3321	2.47184	7.81665	6.61	43.6921	2.57099	8.13019
6.12	37.4544	2.47386	7.82304	6.62	43.8244	2.57294	8.13634
6.13	37.5769	2.47588	7.82943	6.63	43.9569	2.57488	8.14248
6.14	37.6996	2.47790	7.83582	6.64	44.0896	2.57682	8.14862
6.15	37.8225	2.47992	7.84219	6.65	44.2225	2.57876	8.15475
6.16	37.9456	2.48193	7.84857	6.66	44.3556	2.58070	8.16088
6.17	38.0689	2.48395	7.85493	6.67	44.4889	2.58263	8.16701
6.18	38.1924	2.48596	7.86130	6.68	44.6224	2.58457	8.17313
6.19	38.3161	2.48797	7.86766	6.69	44.7561	2.58650	8.17924
6.20	38.4400	2.48998	7.87401	6.70	44.8900	2.58844	8.18535
6.21	38.5641	2.49199	7.88036	6.71	45.0241	2.59037	8.19146
6.22	38.6884	2.49399	7.88670	6.72	45.1584	2.59230	8.19756
6.23	38.8129	2.49600	7.89303	6.73	45.2929	2.59422	8.20366
6.24	38.9376	2.49800	7.89937	6.74	45.4276	2.59615	8.20975
6.25	39.0625	2.50000	7.90569	6.75	45.5625	2.59808	8.21584
6.26	39.1876	2.50200	7.91202	6.76	45.6976	2.60000	8.22192
6.27	39.3129	2.50400	7.91833	6.77	45.8329	2.60192	8.22800
6.28	39.4384	2.50599	7.92465	6.78	45.9684	2.60384	8.23408
6.29	39.5641	2.50799	7.93095	6.79	46.1041	2.60576	8.24015
6.30	39.6900	2.50998	7.93725	6.80	46.2400	2.60768	8.24621
6.31	39.8161	2.51197	7.94355	6.81	46.3761	2.60960	8.25227
6.32	39.9424	2.51396	7.94984	6.82	46.5124	2.61151	8.25833
6.33	40.0689	2.51595	7.95613	6.83	46.6489	2.61343	8.26438
6.34	40.1956	2.51794	7.96241	6.84	46.7856	2.61534	8.27043
6.35	40.3225	2.51992	7.96869	6.85	46.9225	2.61725	8.27647
6.36	40.4496	2.52190	7.97496	6.86	47.0596	2.61916	8.28251
6.37	40.5769	2.52389	7.98123	6.87	47.1969	2.62107	8.28855
6.38	40.7044	2.52587	7.98749	6.88	47.3344	2.62298	8.29458
6.39	40.8321	2.52784	7.99375	6.89	47.4721	2.62488	8.30060
6.40	40.9600	2.52982	8.00000	6.90	47.6100	2.62679	8.30662
6.41	41.0881	2.53180	8.00625	6.91	47.7481	2.62869	8.31264
6.42	41.2164	2.53377	8.01249	6.92	47.8864	2.63059	8.31865
6.43	41.3449	2.53574	8.01873	6.93	48.0249	2.63249	8.32466
6.44	41.4736	2.53772	8.02496	6.94	48.1636	2.63439	8.33067
6.45	41.6025	2.53969	8.03119	6.95	48.3025	2.63629	8.33667
6.46	41.7316	2.54165	8.03741	6.96	48.4416	2.63818	8.34266
6.47	41.8609	2.54362	8.04363	6.97	48.5809	2.64008	8.34865
6.48	41.9904	2.54558	8.04984	6.98	48.7204	2.64197	8.35464
6.49	42.1201	2.54755	8.05605	6.99	48.8601	2.64386	8.36062

TABLE A-9   *(Cont.)*

Squares and Square Roots

n	n^2	$\sqrt{n}$	$\sqrt{10n}$	n	n^2	$\sqrt{n}$	$\sqrt{10n}$
7.00	49.0000	2.64575	8.36660	7.50	56.2500	2.73861	8.66025
7.01	49.1401	2.64764	8.37257	7.51	56.4001	2.74044	8.66603
7.02	49.2804	2.64953	8.37854	7.52	56.5504	2.74226	8.67179
7.03	49.4209	2.65141	8.38451	7.53	56.7009	2.74408	8.67756
7.04	49.5616	2.65330	8.39047	7.54	56.8516	2.74591	8.68332
7.05	49.7025	2.65518	8.39643	7.55	57.0025	2.74773	8.68907
7.06	49.8436	2.65707	8.40238	7.56	57.1536	2.74955	8.69483
7.07	49.9849	2.65895	8.40833	7.57	57.3049	2.75136	8.70057
7.08	50.1264	2.66083	8.41427	7.58	57.4564	2.75318	8.70632
7.09	50.2681	2.66271	8.42021	7.59	57.6081	2.75500	8.71206
7.10	50.4100	2.66458	8.42615	7.60	57.7600	2.75681	8.71780
7.11	50.5521	2.66646	8.43208	7.61	57.9121	2.75862	8.72353
7.12	50.6944	2.66833	8.43801	7.62	58.0644	2.76043	8.72926
7.13	50.8369	2.67021	8.44393	7.63	58.2169	2.76225	8.73499
7.14	50.9796	2.67208	8.44985	7.64	58.3696	2.76405	8.74071
7.15	51.1225	2.67395	8.45577	7.65	58.5225	2.76586	8.74643
7.16	51.2656	2.67582	8.46168	7.66	58.6756	2.76767	8.75214
7.17	51.4089	2.67769	8.46759	7.67	58.8289	2.76948	8.75785
7.18	51.5524	2.67955	8.47349	7.68	58.9824	2.77128	8.76356
7.19	51.6961	2.68142	8.47939	7.69	59.1361	2.77308	8.76926
7.20	51.8400	2.68328	8.48528	7.70	59.2900	2.77489	8.77496
7.21	51.9841	2.68514	8.49117	7.71	59.4441	2.77669	8.78066
7.22	52.1284	2.68701	8.49706	7.72	59.5984	2.77849	8.78635
7.23	52.2729	2.68887	8.50294	7.73	59.7529	2.78029	8.79204
7.24	52.4176	2.69072	8.50882	7.74	59.9076	2.78209	8.79773
7.25	52.5625	2.69258	8.51469	7.75	60.0625	2.78388	8.80341
7.26	52.7076	2.69444	8.52056	7.76	60.2176	2.78568	8.80909
7.27	52.8529	2.69629	8.52643	7.77	60.3729	2.78747	8.81476
7.28	52.9984	2.69815	8.53229	7.78	60.5284	2.78927	8.82043
7.29	53.1441	2.70000	8.53815	7.79	60.6841	2.79106	8.82610
7.30	53.2900	2.70185	8.54400	7.80	60.8400	2.79285	8.83176
7.31	53.4361	2.70370	8.54985	7.81	60.9961	2.79464	8.83742
7.32	53.5824	2.70555	8.55570	7.82	61.1524	2.79643	8.84308
7.33	53.7289	2.70740	8.56154	7.83	61.3089	2.79821	8.84873
7.34	53.8756	2.70924	8.56738	7.84	61.4656	2.80000	8.85438
7.35	54.0225	2.71109	8.57321	7.85	61.6225	2.80179	8.86002
7.36	54.1696	2.71293	8.57904	7.86	61.7796	2.80357	8.86566
7.37	54.3169	2.71477	8.58487	7.87	61.9369	2.80535	8.87130
7.38	54.4644	2.71662	8.59069	7.88	62.0944	2.80713	8.87694
7.39	54.6121	2.71846	8.59651	7.89	62.2521	2.80891	8.88257
7.40	54.7600	2.72029	8.60233	7.90	62.4100	2.81069	8.88819
7.41	54.9081	2.72213	8.60814	7.91	62.5681	2.81247	8.89382
7.42	55.0564	2.72397	8.61394	7.92	62.7264	2.81425	8.89944
7.43	55.2049	2.72580	8.61974	7.93	62.8849	2.81603	8.90505
7.44	55.3536	2.72764	8.62554	7.94	63.0436	2.81780	8.91067
7.45	55.5025	2.72947	8.63134	7.95	63.2025	2.81957	8.91628
7.46	55.6516	2.73130	8.63713	7.96	63.3616	2.82135	8.92188
7.47	55.8009	2.73313	8.64292	7.97	63.5209	2.82312	8.92749
7.48	55.9504	2.73496	8.64870	7.98	63.6804	2.82489	8.93308
7.49	56.1001	2.73679	8.65448	7.99	63.8401	2.82666	8.93868

TABLE A-9   (*Cont.*)

Squares and Square Roots

n	n^2	$\sqrt{n}$	$\sqrt{10n}$	n	n^2	$\sqrt{n}$	$\sqrt{10n}$
8.00	64.0000	2.82843	8.94427	8.50	72.2500	2.91548	9.21954
8.01	64.1601	2.83019	8.94986	8.51	72.4201	2.91719	9.22497
8.02	64.3204	2.83196	8.95545	8.52	72.5904	2.91890	9.23038
8.03	64.4809	2.83373	8.96103	8.53	72.7609	2.92062	9.23580
8.04	64.6416	2.83549	8.96660	8.54	72.9316	2.92233	9.24121
8.05	64.8025	2.83725	8.97218	8.55	73.1025	2.92404	9.24662
8.06	64.9636	2.83901	8.97775	8.56	73.2736	2.92575	9.25203
8.07	65.1249	2.84077	8.98332	8.57	73.4449	2.92746	9.25743
8.08	65.2864	2.84253	8.98888	8.58	73.6164	2.92916	9.26283
8.09	65.4481	2.84429	8.99444	8.59	73.7881	2.93087	9.26823
8.10	65.6100	2.84605	9.00000	8.60	73.9600	2.93258	9.27362
8.11	65.7721	2.84781	9.00555	8.61	74.1321	2.93428	9.27901
8.12	65.9344	2.84956	9.01110	8.62	74.3044	2.93598	9.28440
8.13	66.0969	2.85132	9.01665	8.63	74.4769	2.93769	9.28978
8.14	66.2596	2.85307	9.02219	8.64	74.6496	2.93939	9.29516
8.15	66.4225	2.85482	9.02774	8.65	74.8225	2.94109	9.30054
8.16	66.5856	2.85657	9.03327	8.66	74.9956	2.94279	9.30591
8.17	66.7489	2.85832	9.03881	8.67	75.1689	2.94449	9.31128
8.18	66.9124	2.86007	9.04434	8.68	75.3424	2.94618	9.31665
8.19	67.0761	2.86182	9.04986	8.69	75.5161	2.94788	9.32202
8.20	67.2400	2.86356	9.05539	8.70	75.6900	2.94958	9.32738
8.21	67.4041	2.86531	9.06091	8.71	75.8641	2.95127	9.33274
8.22	67.5684	2.86705	9.06642	8.72	76.0384	2.95296	9.33809
8.23	67.7329	2.86880	9.07193	8.73	76.2129	2.95466	9.34345
8.24	67.8976	2.87054	9.07744	8.74	76.3876	2.95635	9.34880
8.25	68.0625	2.87228	9.08295	8.75	76.5625	2.95804	9.35414
8.26	68.2276	2.87402	9.08845	8.76	76.7376	2.95973	9.35949
8.27	68.3929	2.87576	9.09395	8.77	76.9129	2.96142	9.36483
8.28	68.5584	2.87750	9.09945	8.78	77.0884	2.96311	9.37017
8.29	68.7241	2.87924	9.10494	8.79	77.2641	2.96479	9.37550
8.30	68.8900	2.88097	9.11043	8.80	77.4400	2.96648	9.38083
8.31	69.0561	2.88271	9.11592	8.81	77.6161	2.96816	9.38616
8.32	69.2224	2.88444	9.12140	8.82	77.7924	2.96985	9.39149
8.33	69.3889	2.88617	9.12688	8.83	77.9689	2.97153	9.39681
8.34	69.5556	2.88791	9.13236	8.84	78.1456	2.97321	9.40213
8.35	69.7225	2.88964	9.13783	8.85	78.3225	2.97489	9.40744
8.36	69.8896	2.89137	9.14330	8.86	78.4996	2.97658	9.41276
8.37	70.0569	2.89310	9.14877	8.87	78.6769	2.97825	9.41807
8.38	70.2244	2.89482	9.15423	8.88	78.8544	2.97993	9.42338
8.39	70.3921	2.89655	9.15969	8.89	79.0321	2.98161	9.42868
8.40	70.5600	2.89828	9.16515	8.90	79.2100	2.98329	9.43398
8.41	70.7281	2.90000	9.17061	8.91	79.3881	2.98496	9.43928
8.42	70.8964	2.90172	9.17606	8.92	79.5664	2.98664	9.44458
8.43	71.0649	2.90345	9.18150	8.93	79.7449	2.98831	9.44987
8.44	71.2336	2.90517	9.18695	8.94	79.9236	2.98998	9.45516
8.45	71.4025	2.90689	9.19239	8.95	80.1025	2.99166	9.46044
8.46	71.5716	2.90861	9.19783	8.96	80.2816	2.99333	9.46573
8.47	71.7409	2.91033	9.20326	8.97	80.4609	2.99500	9.47101
8.48	71.9104	2.91204	9.20869	8.98	80.6404	2.99666	9.47629
8.49	72.0801	2.91376	9.21412	8.99	80.8201	2.99833	9.48156

TABLE A-9 (*Cont.*)

Squares and Square Roots

n	n^2	$\sqrt{n}$	$\sqrt{10n}$	n	n^2	$\sqrt{n}$	$\sqrt{10n}$
9.00	81.0000	3.00000	9.48683	9.50	90.2500	3.08221	9.74679
9.01	81.1801	3.00167	9.49210	9.51	90.4401	3.08383	9.75192
9.02	81.3604	3.00333	9.49737	9.52	90.6304	3.08545	9.75705
9.03	81.5409	3.00500	9.50263	9.53	90.8209	3.08707	9.76217
9.04	81.7216	3.00666	9.50789	9.54	91.0116	3.08869	9.76729
9.05	81.9025	3.00832	9.51315	9.55	91.2025	3.09031	9.77241
9.06	82.0836	3.00998	9.51840	9.56	91.3936	3.09192	9.77753
9.07	82.2649	3.01164	9.52365	9.57	91.5849	3.09354	9.78264
9.08	82.4464	3.01330	9.52890	9.58	91.7764	3.09516	9.78775
9.09	82.6281	3.01496	9.53415	9.59	91.9681	3.09677	9.79285
9.10	82.8100	3.01662	9.53939	9.60	92.1600	3.09839	9.79796
9.11	82.9921	3.01828	9.54463	9.61	92.3521	3.10000	9.80306
9.12	83.1744	3.01993	9.54987	9.62	92.5444	3.10161	9.80816
9.13	83.3569	3.02159	9.55510	9.63	92.7369	3.10322	9.81326
9.14	83.5396	3.02324	9.56033	9.64	92.9296	3.10483	9.81835
9.15	83.7225	3.02490	9.56556	9.65	93.1225	3.10644	9.82344
9.16	83.9056	3.02655	9.57079	9.66	93.3156	3.10805	9.82853
9.17	84.0889	3.02820	9.57601	9.67	93.5089	3.10966	9.83362
9.18	84.2724	3.02985	9.58123	9.68	93.7024	3.11127	9.83870
9.19	84.4561	3.03150	9.58645	9.69	93.8961	3.11288	9.84378
9.20	84.6400	3.03315	9.59166	9.70	94.0900	3.11448	9.84886
9.21	84.8241	3.03480	9.59687	9.71	94.2841	3.11609	9.85393
9.22	85.0084	3.03645	9.60208	9.72	94.4784	3.11769	9.85901
9.23	85.1929	3.03809	9.60729	9.73	94.6729	3.11929	9.86408
9.24	85.3776	3.03974	9.61249	9.74	94.8676	3.12090	9.86914
9.25	85.5625	3.04138	9.61769	9.75	95.0625	3.12250	9.87421
9.26	85.7476	3.04302	9.62289	9.76	95.2576	3.12410	9.87927
9.27	85.9329	3.04467	9.62808	9.77	95.4529	3.12570	9.88433
9.28	86.1184	3.04631	9.63328	9.78	95.6484	3.12730	9.88939
9.29	86.3041	3.04795	9.63846	9.79	95.8441	3.12890	9.89444
9.30	86.4900	3.04959	9.64365	9.80	96.0400	3.13050	9.89949
9.31	86.6761	3.05123	9.64883	9.81	96.2361	3.13209	9.90454
9.32	86.8624	3.05287	9.65401	9.82	96.4324	3.13369	9.90959
9.33	87.0489	3.05450	9.65919	9.83	96.6289	3.13528	9.91464
9.34	87.2356	3.05614	9.66437	9.84	96.8256	3.13688	9.91968
9.35	87.4225	3.05778	9.66954	9.85	97.0225	3.13847	9.92472
9.36	87.6096	3.05941	9.67471	9.86	97.2196	3.14006	9.92975
9.37	87.7969	3.06105	9.67988	9.87	97.4169	3.14166	9.93479
9.38	87.9844	3.06268	9.68504	9.88	97.6144	3.14325	9.93982
9.39	88.1721	3.06431	9.69020	9.89	97.8121	3.14484	9.94485
9.40	88.3600	3.06594	9.69536	9.90	98.0100	3.14643	9.94987
9.41	88.5481	3.06757	9.70052	9.91	98.2081	3.14802	9.95490
9.42	88.7364	3.06920	9.70567	9.92	98.4064	3.14960	9.95992
9.43	88.9249	3.07083	9.71082	9.93	98.6049	3.15119	9.96494
9.44	89.1136	3.07246	9.71597	9.94	98.8036	3.15278	9.96995
9.45	89.3025	3.07409	9.72111	9.95	99.0025	3.15436	9.97497
9.46	89.4916	3.07571	9.72625	9.96	99.2016	3.15595	9.97998
9.47	89.6809	3.07734	9.73139	9.97	99.4009	3.15753	9.98499
9.48	89.8704	3.07896	9.73653	9.98	99.6004	3.15911	9.98999
9.49	90.0601	3.08058	9.74166	9.99	99.8001	3.16070	9.99500
				10.00	100.0000	3.16228	10.00000

appendix b:

the use of table A-9

(squares and square roots)

OBTAINING SQUARES OF NUMBERS

To find the square of a number between 1 and 10, simply locate the number in Table A-9 in the column headed n and read the square of the number in the column headed n^2. For example, locating 3.00 in the column headed n, we read 9.0000 (the square of 3.00) in the column headed n^2. Similarly, we find that $(3.18)^2 = 10.1124$.

To find the square of a number less than 1 or greater than 10 it is necessary first to adjust the location of the decimal point to the right or left in order to obtain a number between 1 and 10. For example, to obtain the square of 318 we first move the decimal point two places to the left, obtaining 3.18, a number between 1 and 10. We then read from the table that $(3.18)^2 = 10.1124$. Finally, in order to correct for the change made in the location of the decimal point, we must adjust the location of the decimal point in the value read from the table. The general rule for making the latter adjustment is this: *For every decimal place that the decimal point is moved in the number to be squared, the decimal point in the square read from the table must be moved two places in the opposite direction.* Applying this rule to the example presented above, we determine that $(318)^2 = 101,124$. Similarly, $(.318)^2 = .101124$, and $(.0318)^2 = .00101124$.

Alternatively, the location of the decimal point may be disregarded in reading the table and located in the final answer by means of a rough approximation. For example, suppose it is desired to determine the square of .52. Disregarding the location of decimal points temporarily, we read from the table that $(520)^2 = 270400$. To locate the decimal point we square a number that is close to .52 and selected for ease of squaring. In this instance, we may square .5, obtaining .25. This result enables us to locate the decimal point in the square of .52 as follows: $(.520)^2 = .270400$. A variation of this approach is illustrated in the following example: Suppose we wish to determine the value of $(.45)^2$. Disregarding the location of decimal points, we read from Table A-9 that $(450)^2 = 202500$. We could obtain a rough approximation of $(.45)^2$ by squaring either .4 or .5, which are equidistant from .45. However, a somewhat better approximation may be obtained by multiplying .4 (a number less than .45) by .5 (a number greater than .45). The result, $.4(.5) = .20$, indicates that the decimal in the square of .450 should be located as follows: $(.450)^2 = .202500$.

OBTAINING SQUARE ROOTS OF NUMBERS

SQUARE ROOTS OF NUMBERS BETWEEN 1 AND 10

Numbers between 1 and 10, varying in steps of .01, are listed in Table A-9 in the column headed n; the square roots of these numbers are listed in the column headed $\sqrt{n}$. Thus, for example, to obtain the square root of 9.00 we locate 9.00 in the column headed n and read 3.00000 (the square root of 9.00) in the column headed $\sqrt{n}$. Similarly, to obtain the square root of 9.15 we locate 9.15 in the column headed n and read 3.02490 in the column headed $\sqrt{n}$.

SQUARE ROOTS OF NUMBERS BETWEEN 10 AND 100

Square roots of numbers between 10 and 100 are given in the column headed $\sqrt{10n}$. For example, to obtain the square root of 25 locate 2.50 in the column headed n and read 5.00000 (the square root of 25) in the column headed $\sqrt{10n}$. Similarly, to obtain the square root of 40 locate 4.00 in the column headed n and read 6.32456 (the square root of 40) in the column headed $\sqrt{10n}$.

SQUARE ROOTS OF NUMBERS LESS THAN 1 OR GREATER THAN 100

When the number whose square root is required is less than 1 or greater than 100, the decimal point must be shifted an *even* number of places to the right or left so as to obtain a number between 1 and 100. The square root of the resulting number is then obtained in the manner explained in the preceding subsections—i.e., as explained in the first of the above subsections if the resulting number is between 1 and 10, or as explained in the second of the above subsections if the resulting number is between 10 and 100.   For example, to obtain the square root of 625 we move the decimal point two places (an even number) to the left, obtaining 6.25. We then locate 6.25 in the column headed n and read the square root, 2.50000, in the column headed $\sqrt{n}$.   Finally, to correct for the original change of the decimal place, it is necessary to adjust the location of the decimal point in the square root in the opposite direction, *one* decimal place for each *pair* of places in the original adjustment.   In the present example, the decimal point in the square root must be moved one place to the right, giving as our final result 25.0000 (the square root of 625).   Following a similar procedure, we find $\sqrt{.000625} = .025$, $\sqrt{.0625} = .25$, and $\sqrt{62,500} = 250$.   On the other hand, suppose we wish to find the square root of 6,250.   Moving the decimal point two places to the left, we obtain 62.5—a number between 10 and 100.   The square root of 62.5 is found in the column headed $\sqrt{10n}$ (opposite $n = 6.25$) and is seen to have a value of 7.90569.   Moving the decimal point in the latter value one place to the right (to adjust for the pair of places the decimal was moved in the original number), we obtain 79.0569 (the square root of 6,250).   In a similar manner, we find $\sqrt{.625} = .790569$.

A rough check of the results obtained by the above procedure is provided by squaring a number close to the square root and noting whether the resulting number approximates the original number of which the square root was taken.   In the last illustration given in the preceding paragraph, for example, a check is provided by squaring .8 (an approximation of the square root .790569); the result is .64, which closely approximates .625. This check will usually disclose an error in which the wrong column of the table is used to obtain a square root—i.e., an error in which a root is taken from the column headed $\sqrt{n}$ when the column headed $\sqrt{10n}$ should be used, or vice versa.

index